John Brockingto...

B.Sc., C.Chem, M.R...

Peter Stampe...

Ph.D., C.Chem, M.R.S...

Inorganic chemistry for higher education

Longman London and New York

Longman Group Limited
Longman House, Burnt Mill, Harlow
Essex CM20 2JE, England
Associated companies throughout the world

*Published in the United States of America
by Longman Inc., New York*

First published 1983

British Library Cataloguing in Publication Data

Brockington, J.
    Inorganic chemistry for higher education.—
    (Longman technician series: Maths and sciences sector)
    1. Chemistry, Inorganic
    I. Title   II. Series
    546   QD151.2

    ISBN 0-582-41232-3

Library of Congress Cataloging in Publication Data

Brockington, John.
    Inorganic chemistry for higher education.
    (Longman technician series. Mathematics and sciences sector)
    Includes index.
    1. Chemistry, Inorganic.   I. Stamper, Peter,
1944–   . II. Title.   III. Series.
QD151.2.B74 1983   546   82-17241
ISBN 0-582-41232-3 (pbk.)

Set in 10/11 Compugraphic English Times
Printed in Singapore by Huntsmen Offset Printing (Pte) Ltd

Longman Technician Series

Mathematics and Sciences

Sector Editor:

D.R. Browning, B.Sc., C.Chem., F.R.S.C., A.R.T.C.S.
Principal Lecturer and Head of Chemistry, Bristol Polytechnic

Books already published in this sector of the series:

Technician mathematics Level 1 Second edition   **J.O. Bird** and **A.J.C. May**
Technician mathematics Level 2 Second edition   **J.O. Bird** and **A.J.C. May**
Technician mathematics Level 3   **J.O. Bird** and **A.J.C. May**
Technician mathematics Levels 4 and 5   **J.O. Bird** and **A.J.C. May**
Mathematics for electrical and telecommunications technicians   **J.O. Bird** and
    A.J.C. May
Mathematics for science technicians Level 2   **J.O. Bird** and **A.J.C. May**
Mathematics for electrical technicians Level 3   **J.O. Bird** and **A.J.C. May**
Mathematics for electrical technicians Levels 4 and 5   **J.O. Bird** and
    A.J.C. May
Calculus for technicians   **J.O. Bird** and **A.J.C. May**
Statistics for technicians   **J.O. Bird** and **A.J.C. May**
Algebra for technicians   **J.O. Bird** and **A.J.C. May**
Physical sciences Level 1   **D.R. Browning** and **I. McKenzie Smith**
Engineering science for technicians Level 1   **D.R. Browning** and **I. McKenzie
    Smith**
Safety science for technicians   **W.J. Hackett** and **G.P. Robbins**
Fundamentals of chemistry   **J.H.J. Peet**
Further studies in chemistry   **J.H.J. Peet**
Technician chemistry Level 1   **J. Brockington** and **P.J. Stamper**
Technician physics Level 1   **E. Deeson**
Technician physics Level 2   **E. Deeson**
Cell biology for technicians   **N.A. Thorpe**
Mathematics for scientific and technical students   **H.G. Davies** and
    G.A. Hicks
Mathematical formulae for TEC courses   **J.O. Bird** and **A.J.C. May**
Science facts formulae for TEC courses   **D.R. Browning**
Microprocessor appreciation   **J.F.A. Thompson**
Organic chemistry for higher education   **J. Brockington** and **P.J. Stamper**

Contents

Contents

Preface

This is one of a series of three textbooks that we have prepared
primarily to meet the needs of students on the first year of TEC
courses leading to higher awards in physical science and technology.
Students on the first year of single or general honours degree courses
which include chemistry should also find it useful.

In the course of preparing this book we studied numerous Level IV
units from various colleges. Because of the wide disparity of topics that
they contained, it was clear that we could not hope to accommodate all
aspects of every syllabus in a book of modest length. We were
therefore obliged to concentrate on the principal units, namely the
TEC Level IV Standard Unit and that produced by the Committee of
Heads of Polytechnic Chemistry Departments. However, we have not
hesitated to extend these units wherever we felt that, by so doing, we
could provide a better understanding of the subject matter. It is for
this reason that we have introduced a chapter on chemical bonding,
based on a simplified molecular orbital approach and in which all
references to hybridisation have been omitted. We have also selected
some additional material, including a considerable amount of descriptive
chemistry, intended to give students a wider appreciation of inorganic
chemistry.

Throughout this book we have adhered to IUPAC nomenclature and
presented data in SI units. The former has been taken from
Nomenclature of Inorganic Chemistry (Butterworths), and the latter
from *Chemistry Data Book* by J.G. Stark and H.G. Wallace (John
Murray).

We are particularly grateful to David Browning of Bristol
Polytechnic who has edited the book and made many constructive
criticisms. Also, we should like to express our gratitude to Longman's
editorial staff and the typesetters for their painstaking assistance in
producing this book.

John Brockington and Peter Stamper
May 1983

Acknowledgements

We are indebted to the following for permission to reproduce copyright material:

The authors, C.F. Bell & K.A.K. Lott for our Fig. 4.16 from Fig. 3.7, p. 65 *Modern Approach to Inorganic Chemistry* 3rd ed. pub. Butterworths; the authors, E. Cartmell & G.W.A. Fowles for our Fig. 2.10 from Fig. 19, p. 45 *Valency & Molecular Structure* 2nd ed. pub. Butterworths; Longman Group Ltd for our Figs. 4.32, 4.34, 9.2 from Figs. 23, 20, 22 by G.I. Brown, pp. 38–39 *Introduction to Inorganic Chemistry* 1st ed. 1974 & our Figs. 14.10 (extract), 14.18 from Figs. 4.21, 5.12 by M. Hudson, pp. 102, 122 *Crystals & Crystal Structure*, Concepts in Chemistry Series; Prentice-Hall Inc., Englewood Cliffs, N.J. for our Fig. 2.7 from Fig. 14.3 by Walter J. Moore, p. 631 *Physical Chemistry* 4th ed. © 1972; John Wiley & Sons Inc. for our Fig. 14.7 from Fig. 26.12 by Cotton & Wilkinson, p. 674 *Advanced Inorganic Chemistry* 1966.

Chapter 1

Nomenclature

Chemical substances are named in accordance with the recommendations of the International Union of Pure and Applied Chemistry (IUPAC), which are subject to occasional revision. The most recent edition of *Nomenclature of Inorganic Chemistry* was published in 1970 by Butterworths. The underlying philosophy is that for many simple substances *trivial names* should be retained if they are well established and unambiguous; other substances are given *systematic names* based on a series of well defined rules.

1.1 Elements

All the isotopes of an element, except hydrogen, bear the same name. For allotropes, IUPAC allows trivial names but also gives systematic names based on the structure of the molecule. Examples are as follows.

Allotrope	Trivial name	Systematic name
O_2	oxygen	dioxygen
O_3	ozone	trioxygen
S_8	λ-sulphur	*cyclo*-octasulphur
P_4	white phosphorus	*tetrahedro*-tetraphosphorus

1.2 Binary compounds

There are two systematic ways of naming such compounds.

(i) By means of *stoicheiometric names*, in which the proportions of the constituent elements are indicated by prefixes of Greek origin, e.g. mono, di, tri, tetra, penta and hexa. In practice, the prefix 'mono' is usually omitted. Oxides, sulphides and halides of non-metals, together with certain metal oxides, are conveniently named in this way, e.g.

N_2O	dinitrogen oxide	S_2Cl_2	disulphur dichloride
NO_2	nitrogen dioxide	MnO_2	manganese dioxide
N_2O_4	dinitrogen tetraoxide	Fe_3O_4	triiron tetraoxide
N_4S_4	tetranitrogen tetrasulphide	Pb_3O_4	trilead tetraoxide

(ii) Alternatively, *Stock's system* may be used, in which the oxidation number of an element is shown by a roman numeral enclosed in parentheses immediately after the name. This system is becoming increasingly favoured. With only a few exceptions, all metallic oxides, sulphides and halides, together with the oxides of phosphorus, are now named in this way. Examples:

$SnCl_2$	tin(II) chloride	MnO_2	manganese(IV) oxide
$SnCl_4$	tin(IV) chloride	Fe_3O_4	iron(II) diiron(III) oxide
CrO	chromium(II) oxide	Pb_3O_4	dilead(II) lead(IV) oxide
Cr_2O_3	chromium(III) oxide	P_4O_6	phosphorus(III) oxide
CrO_3	chromium(VI) oxide	P_4O_{10}	phosphorus(V) oxide

Hydrides constitute a special case. They may be named in accordance with the above rules, e.g. sodium hydride for NaH, but many of them have well established trivial names whose continued use is recommended. Common examples are water and ammonia; others are as follows:

B_2H_6	diborane	N_2H_4	hydrazine
CH_4	methane	PH_3	phosphine
SiH_4	silane	P_2H_4	diphosphane
GeH_4	germane	AsH_3	arsine
SnH_4	stannane	SbH_3	stibine
PbH_4	plumbane	BiH_3	bismuthine

1.3 Cations

Monoatomic cations derived from elements of variable valency are given the name of the element with its appropriate oxidation number, e.g.

Fe^{2+} iron(II) ion Fe^{3+} iron(III) ion

In the naming of cations derived from elements of constant valency, IUPAC recommends that the oxidation number is omitted, e.g.

Na^+ sodium ion
Ca^{2+} calcium ion
Al^{3+} aluminium ion

The common polyatomic cations are named as follows:

H_3O^+	oxonium ion	PH_4^+	phosphonium ion
NH_4^+	ammonium ion	NO^+	nitrosyl cation
$HONH_3^+$	hydroxylammonium ion	NO_2^+	nitryl cation
$NH_2NH_3^+$	hydrazinium$(1+)$ ion		

1.4 Anions

The name of a monoatomic anion is derived from that of the element and has the termination '-ide', e.g.

H^-	hydride	N^{3-}	nitride
Cl^-	chloride	P^{3-}	phosphide
O^{2-}	oxide	C^{4-}	carbide
S^{2-}	sulphide	Si^{4-}	silicide

Polyatomic anions may have names that end in '-ide', '-ate' or '-ite'. The commonest ones which end in '-ide' are as follows:

HO^-	hydroxide	HF_2^-	hydrogendifluoride
O_2^{2-}	peroxide	N_3^-	azide
O_2^-	hyperoxide	NH_2^-	amide
HS^-	hydrogensulphide	$NHOH^-$	hydroxylamide
S_2^{2-}	disulphide	CN^-	cyanide
I_3^-	triiodide	C_2^{2-}	acetylide

The names of most oxoanions consist of the root of the name of the characteristic element, followed by the suffix '-ate', e.g. sulphate for SO_4^{2-}. Although it is permissible to name such anions systematically as though they were complex anions (§1.10), e.g. tetraoxosulphate(VI) for SO_4^{2-}, IUPAC does not advise this except for less well known and newly discovered ions. Other examples are as follows.

NO_3^-	nitrate	SiO_3^{2-}	metasilicate
CO_3^{2-}	carbonate	ClO_3^-	chlorate
PO_4^{3-}	phosphate or orthophosphate	OCN^-	cyanate
PHO_3^{2-}	phosphonate	CrO_4^{2-}	chromate
$PH_2O_2^-$	phosphinate	MnO_4^-	permanganate
BO_3^{3-}	borate or orthoborate		

Certain oxoanions, containing an element in a low oxidation state, have long-established trivial names that end in '-ite'. They are as follows.

NO_2^-	nitrite	SO_3^{2-}	sulphite	ClO_2^-	chlorite
$N_2O_2^{2-}$	hyponitrite	$S_2O_5^{2-}$	disulphite	ClO^-	hypochlorite
NOO_2^-	peroxonitrite	$S_2O_4^{2-}$	dithionite	BrO^-	hypobromite
AsO_3^{3-}	arsenite	$S_2O_2^{2-}$	thiosulphite	IO^-	hypoiodite
		SeO_3^{2-}	selenite		

The use of these, *but no other names ending in '-ite'*, is permitted by IUPAC. Note particularly that PHO_3^{2-}, formerly known as the phosphite ion, is now called the phosphonate ion.

1.5 Isopolyanions

IUPAC recommends two systems for naming isopolyanions, i.e. anions which contain more than one atom of the characteristic element.

(i) If structural information is unavailable, the ion is given a stoicheiometric name; e.g. $S_2O_7^{2-}$ could be named in this way as the heptaoxodisulphate ion.

(ii) If structural information is available, and if it is known that the characteristic element is in an oxidation state corresponding to the number of its group in the periodic table, the number of oxygen atoms can be omitted. The number of atoms of the characteristic element must still be indicated, by means of a numerical prefix, and the charge on the anion is placed in parentheses immediately after the name, e.g.

$S_2O_7^{2-}$	disulphate(2−)
$P_2O_7^{4-}$	diphosphate(4−)
$H_2P_2O_7^{2-}$	dihydrogendiphosphate(2−)

It is customary to omit the ionic charge from the name, a practice recognised by IUPAC in recommending the name dichromate ion for $Cr_2O_7^{2-}$. (The ionic charge must never be omitted from the formula.)

If the characteristic element is in a lower oxidation state than its periodic table group number, a Stock number must be included to show that oxidation state, e.g. disulphate(IV)(2−) ion for $S_2O_5^{2-}$.

Cyclic and chain structures are denoted by means of the prefixes *cyclo* and *catena* respectively, although the latter is usually omitted, e.g.

cyclo-triphosphate

(*catena*-)triphosphate

1.6 Radicals

For purposes of nomenclature, the term 'radical' is defined by IUPAC as a group of atoms that occurs repeatedly in a number of different compounds. The names of the commonest radicals are as follows. Note that the names bismuthyl and antimonyl, formerly used in naming such compounds as BiClO and SbClO, are no longer approved. (The naming of basic salts is described in §1.9.)

HO	hydroxyl	PO	phosphoryl
CO	carbonyl	SO	sulphinyl or thionyl
NO	nitrosyl	SO_2	sulphonyl or sulphuryl
NO_2	nitryl	CrO_2	chromyl

These radicals are always regarded as forming the positive part of any compound in which they occur. They are therefore written first in the formula, and referred to first in the name, e.g.

$COCl_2$	carbonyl chloride
$NOCl$	nitrosyl chloride
$SOCl_2$	sulphinyl chloride or thionyl chloride
SO_2Cl_2	sulphonyl chloride or sulphuryl chloride

1.7 Acids

Acids are named after the anions to which they give rise. If the name of the anion ends in '-ide', the acid is named as hydrogen -ide, e.g.

HCl	hydrogen chloride
H_2S	hydrogen sulphide
HCN	hydrogen cyanide

Note that HN_3 is named as hydrogen azide; not hydrazoic acid.

If the IUPAC name of the anion ends in '-ite' or '-ate', that of the acid ends in '-ous acid' or '-ic acid' respectively, e.g.

HNO_2	nitrous acid	HNO_3	nitric acid
H_2SO_3	sulphurous acid	H_2SO_4	sulphuric acid
$HClO_2$	chlorous acid	$HClO_3$	chloric acid

An '-ous acid' thus contains the characteristic element in a low oxidation state, while an '-ic acid' contains the element in a high oxidation state. A name of the kind 'hypo-ous acid' is used to show that the element is in a particularly low oxidation state, e.g.

$HClO$	hypochlorous acid	(oxidation state of Cl = +1)
$H_2N_2O_2$	hyponitrous acid	(oxidation state of N = +1)

It should be noted that HPH_2O_2, a compound formerly known as hypophosphorous acid, is now called phosphinic acid.

Until recently, the prefix 'per-' (not to be confused with 'peroxo-')

was used for naming certain acids containing an element in a particularly high oxidation state. This prefix is now used only for $HMnO_4$, permanganic acid, $HClO_4$, perchloric acid, and the corresponding acids of bromine and iodine.

Isopolyacids, i.e. oxoacids containing more than one atom of the characteristic element, are named, like simple acids, after the anions to which they give rise. For example, $H_4P_2O_7$ is called diphosphoric acid. The trivial name of pyrophosphoric acid is not recommended; indeed, the prefix 'pyro-' is no longer in common use. Nevertheless, the prefixes 'ortho-' and 'meta-' are permitted by IUPAC to distinguish between acids of differing water content, e.g.

H_3BO_3	orthoboric acid	$(HBO_2)_n$	metaboric acid
H_4SiO_4	orthosilicic acid	$(H_2SiO_3)_n$	metasilicic acid
H_3PO_4	orthophosphoric acid	$(HPO_3)_n$	metaphosphoric acid

The prefix 'peroxo-' is used to indicate the substitution of ——O—— by ——O——O——, e.g.

HNO_4	peroxonitric acid
H_2SO_5	peroxomonosulphuric acid
$H_2S_2O_8$	peroxodisulphuric acid

Acids in which an atom of oxygen has been substituted by one of sulphur are known as thioacids, e.g.

$H_2S_2O_3$ thiosulphuric acid   HSCN thiocyanic acid

1.8 Acid derivatives

Acid chlorides, i.e. those compounds in which the HO groups of the acid have been replaced by atoms of chlorine, are named by IUPAC in accordance with the acid radicals they contain, e.g. nitrosyl chloride for NOCl (see §1.6).

Amides, in which the HO groups of the acid have been replaced by NH_2 groups, may be named either by replacing the word 'acid' by 'amide', 'diamide', etc, or by utilising the name of the acid radical. For example, the compound $SO_2(NH_2)_2$, derived from sulphuric acid, may be called either sulphuric diamide or sulphonyl diamide.

If not all the HO groups have been replaced by NH_2 groups, the compound may be named as either an 'amido- acid' or an '-amidic acid', e.g.

NH_2SO_3H amidosulphuric acid or sulphamidic acid

(The abbreviated name, sulphamic acid, is not recommended.)

1.9 Salts

Simple salts are named according to Stock's system for binary compounds; see §1.2.

Acid salts, i.e. those containing acid hydrogen, are named by introducing the prefix 'hydrogen-', with di, tri, etc, if necessary, to the name of the anion, e.g.

$NaHCO_3$ sodium hydrogencarbonate
NaH_2PO_4 sodium dihydrogenphosphate

When naming double salts, the cations should be cited in alphabetical order in both formulae and names. (This may cause the cation order in a formula to differ from that in the name.) Acidic hydrogen is always placed last, e.g.

$KNaCO_3$ potassium sodium carbonate
$MgNH_4PO_4$ ammonium magnesium phosphate
$NaNH_4HPO_4$ ammonium sodium hydrogenphosphate

For salt hydrates, two systems may be followed.

(i)   In the absence of structural information, the extent of hydration may be indicated by writing 'monohydrate', 'dihydrate', etc, after the name, e.g.

   $AlCl_3 \cdot 6H_2O$ aluminium chloride hexahydrate

   Alternatively, the number of water molecules may be represented by an arabic numeral, e.g.

   $AlCl_3 \cdot 6H_2O$ aluminium chloride 6-water
   $AlK(SO_4)_2 \cdot 12H_2O$ aluminium potassium sulphate 12-water

(ii)   If the mode of hydration is known, both the formula and the name of the salt may be modified accordingly. For example, in aluminium chloride hexahydrate the six water molecules are coordinated to the aluminium ion. The compound is effectively a complex salt, $[Al(H_2O)_6]Cl_3$, and may be named as such, i.e. hexaaquaaluminium(III) chloride.

Basic salts, better known as oxide and hydroxide salts, are regarded as double salts containing two or more anions, one of which is O^{2-} or HO^-. When naming them, the anions should be cited in alphabetical order, e.g.

$MgCl(OH)$ magnesium chloride hydroxide
$BiClO$ bismuth chloride oxide
$VO(SO_4)$ vanadium(IV) oxide sulphate

1.10 Complex salts

The following IUPAC rules apply to the formulae and names of all complex ions and certain other complexes.

Formulae of complex ions

The symbol for the central atom is written first, followed by anionic ligands and neutral ligands in that order. Within each ligand class the order should be alphabetical in terms of the symbol for the donor atom of the ligand. Polyatomic ligands, but not monoatomic ligands, are enclosed in curved brackets, and the formula of the whole complex is enclosed in square brackets, e.g.

$[Cr(H_2O)_6]^{3+}$
$[Al(OH)(H_2O)_5]^{2+}$
$[CoCl(NH_3)_5]^{2+}$ NH_3 in parentheses, but not Cl
$[Cu(NH_3)_4(H_2O)_2]^{2+}$

Naming of complex ions

Ligands are cited first, followed by the metal.

Ligand names

Some common ligands, with the names used for complex nomenclature, are as follows.

Neutral ligands		Anionic ligands			
H_2O	aqua	F^-	fluoro	HO^-	hydroxo
NH_3	ammine	Cl^-	chloro	CN^-	cyano
CO	carbonyl	Br^-	bromo	NO_2^-	nitro
NO	nitrosyl	I^-	iodo	H^-	hydrido†

† The term 'hydro' is used in complexes of boron.

Ligand numbers

A Greek prefix: di, tri, tetra, penta or hexa, is used to denote the number of each type of ligand. 'Mono' is not normally used.

Order of citation of ligands

Ligands are listed in alphabetical order, the multiplying prefix being ignored. Thus, pentaaqua is cited before dicyano.

Central metal

For all complex ions, the name of the metal follows the names of the ligands. In the case of complex anions the metal name is modified to end in '-ate'. In general, for elements ending in '-ium', the anionic name is obtained by replacing this ending by '-ate', e.g. chrom*ium* to chrom*ate*. Other examples are as follows:

Element	Name in complex	Element	Name in complex
Ti	titanate	Ag	argentate†
V	vanadate	Au	aurate†
Mn	manganate	Hg	mercurate
Fe	ferrate†	B	borate
Co	cobaltate	Al	aluminate
Ni	niccolate†	Ge	germanate
Cu	cuprate†	Sn	stannate†
Zn	zincate	Pb	plumbate†

† Based on the Latin names of the elements.

Oxidation state of the central atom

In the Stock notation the oxidation state of the central atom, i.e. the formal charge on the central ion, is indicated by a roman numeral in parentheses after the name of the complex.

A few examples should help to clarify the above rules. Notice that complex names are written as one word, with no hyphens, and no spacing between the name and the oxidation state of the central atom.

$[Cr(H_2O)_6]^{3+}$	hexaaquachromium(III) ion
$[Al(OH)(H_2O)_5]^{2+}$	pentaaquahydroxoaluminium(III) ion
	penta*aqua* before *hydroxo*
$[CoCl(NH_3)_5]^{2+}$	pentaamminechlorocobalt(III) ion
$[Fe(CN)_6]^{4-}$	hexacyanoferrate(II) ion
$[Fe(CN)_5(NO)]^{2-}$	pentacyanonitrosylferrate(III) ion
$[AlH_4]^-$	tetrahydridoaluminate(III) ion
$[BH_4]^-$	tetrahydroborate(III) ion

The salts of these and other complex ions are named accordingly, e.g.

$[CoCl(NH_3)_5]Cl_2$	pentaamminechlorocobalt(III) chloride
$K_4[Fe(CN)_6]$	potassium hexacyanoferrate(II)

Metal carbonyls are named in a similar manner to complex ions, e.g.

$[Ni(CO)_4]$ tetracarbonylnickel(0)

The oxidation state of nickel in this complex is zero.

Chapter 2

Electronic structure of atoms

2.1 The hydrogen spectrum

Much of our knowledge concerning the electronic structure of atoms originates from atomic spectra, and of particular importance in this respect is the *hydrogen spectrum*. Before discussing this spectrum, let us see how spectra are obtained from radiation in general by considering a simple example.

If light comprising, say, three different wavelengths is passed through a slit and then a prism we observe three different lines of light on a suitably placed screen (Fig. 2.1). The prism separates the incident light by refracting (i.e. bending) radiation of different wavelengths unequally. The shorter the wavelength of the radiation the greater is the angle through which it is refracted. The wavelengths of radiation after refraction constitute the *spectrum* of the incident radiation. (Wavelength (λ) and frequency (ν) are both used in descriptions of spectra.) In Fig. 2.1 each line on the screen represents radiation of a single frequency, with wavelengths in the order A < B < C. The lines A, B and C can be photographed so as to provide a permanent record of the spectrum. Similar results are obtained if a diffraction grating is used in place of a prism.

When an electric discharge is passed through hydrogen gas at low pressure, many of the molecules absorb energy by collision with electrons (cathode rays) and break up into atoms which then absorb energy and emit radiation (§2.3). By means of a prism the emitted radiation

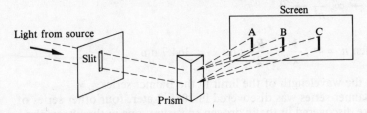

Fig. 2.1 Origin of spectral lines.

can be separated into its component wavelengths to produce the *emission spectrum of atomic hydrogen*, commonly called the 'hydrogen spectrum'. The spectrum comprises five series of lines, each line corresponding to radiation of one particular wavelength. Each series is named after its discoverer. In the *Balmer series*, which falls in the visible and ultraviolet parts of the spectrum, the lines become progressively closer together as the wavelength decreases until eventually they converge and stop at the *series limit* (Fig. 2.2). Beyond the series limit the spectrum is continuous, i.e. it does not consist of individual lines.

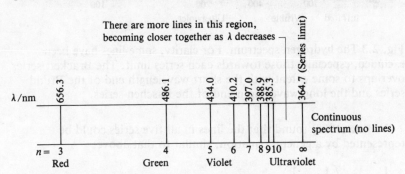

Fig. 2.2 The Balmer series. The lines labelled $n = 3, 4, 5$ and 6 are in the visible part of the spectrum. For clarity, lines in the series with an n value of greater than 10 have been omitted.

Despite the apparent complexity of this series, the wavelength of each line can be calculated from the simple equation

$$\frac{1}{\lambda} = R_H \left(\frac{1}{2^2} - \frac{1}{n^2} \right)$$

where λ is the wavelength of the emitted radiation and n is an integer greater than 2, i.e. $n = 3, 4, 5, 6$, etc. R_H is a constant, known as the *Rydberg constant*, equal to $1.096\,775\,8 \times 10^7$ m^{-1}. When $n = 3$ the equation gives the wavelength of the red line, when $n = 4$ that of the green line, and so on (Fig. 2.2).

12

As $n \rightarrow \infty, \dfrac{1}{n^2} \rightarrow 0$

$\therefore$ when $n = \infty$, $\dfrac{1}{\lambda} = \dfrac{R_H}{2^2}$ and $\lambda = 364.7$ nm

which is the wavelength of the limit in the Balmer series.

The Balmer series was discovered in 1885. Later, four other series of lines were discovered in the hydrogen spectrum, one in the ultraviolet region (the *Lyman* series) and three in the infrared (the *Paschen*, *Brackett* and *Pfund* series). Each series shows the same overall pattern as the Balmer series, i.e. lines which become closer together as the wavelength decreases until a series limit is reached (Fig. 2.3).

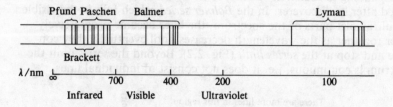

Fig. 2.3 The hydrogen spectrum. For clarity, some lines have been excluded, especially those towards each series limit. The Brackett series overlaps to some extent with the short wavelength end of the Pfund series and the long wavelength end of the Paschen series.

W. Ritz (1908) found that the lines in all five series could be represented by a general equation, similar to that above:

$$\frac{1}{\lambda} = R_H \left(\frac{1}{n_2^2} - \frac{1}{n_1^2} \right)$$

where n_1 and n_2 are integers and $n_1 > n_2$. For each particular series n_2 remains constant throughout and n_1 varies. The values for all five series in the hydrogen spectrum are as follows:

Series	n_2	n_1	Spectral region
Lyman	1	2, 3, 4, etc	ultraviolet
Balmer	2	3, 4, 5, etc	visible/ultraviolet
Paschen	3	4, 5, 6, etc	infrared
Brackett	4	5, 6, 7, etc	infrared
Pfund	5	6, 7, 8, etc	infrared

The Lyman series limit, where $n_1 = \infty$, is given by:

$$\frac{1}{\lambda} = R_H \left(\frac{1}{1^2} - \frac{1}{\infty^2} \right) = R_H \text{ or } \lambda = \frac{1}{R_H}$$

2.2 Electrons in atoms

Niels Bohr (1913) proposed a theory for the electronic structure of atoms based on classical mechanics, and offered the first explanation of the atomic spectrum of hydrogen. Nowadays, although the Bohr theory has been superseded, it is noteworthy because two of Bohr's original assumptions are still applicable and form the basis of modern theory. These assumptions are:

(i) an electron in an atom cannot have a continuously varying energy, but is constrained to one of a certain number of fixed energy values, called *energy levels*;

(ii) radiant energy (radiation) is emitted only when an electron moves from a level of relatively high energy to one of lower energy. Thus, if E_a and E_b each represent energy levels within an atom, and $E_a > E_b$, then radiant energy is emitted when an electron moves from level E_a to level E_b. The wavelength (λ) of the emitted radiation is given by:

$$\Delta E = \frac{hc}{\lambda} = h\nu \qquad \text{(Planck's equation)}$$

where $\Delta E = E_a - E_b$
h is Planck's constant, $6.625\,6 \times 10^{-34}$ J s
c is the velocity of light, 3.0×10^8 m s^{-1}.

Bohr's theory was applied to the electronic structure of atoms until about 1923. Serious problems, however, arose from its use. It worked well with the hydrogen atom but not with other atoms. We now know that in the submicroscopic world of the atom the rules of classical mechanics do not apply. At this submicroscopic level, particles and waves merge in nature and are governed by a new set of principles called *quantum mechanics*. Strictly, the laws of classical or Newtonian mechanics do not apply to the movement of everyday objects, or even to the motion of the planets around the sun. They are approximations, but for practical purposes they work well enough. Only at the submicroscopic level does the theory of Newtonian mechanics break down completely.

In 1923 Louis de Broglie suggested that an electron has a dual nature and may behave as a particle or as a wave. He surmised that an experiment to detect an electron as a wave will detect a wave, whereas one to detect an electron as a particle will do just that.

Light has a dual nature and may behave as a stream of particles, called *photons*, or as a wave. For a photon,

$$E = mc^2 \qquad \text{(Einstein's equation)}$$

$$\text{and } E = h\nu = \frac{hc}{\lambda} \qquad \text{(Planck's equation)}$$

$$\therefore \ mc^2 = h\nu = \frac{hc}{\lambda}$$

$$\therefore \ \lambda = \frac{h}{mc} = \frac{h}{p}$$

where m = mass, and $p = mc$ = momentum of the photon.

A photon thus has a wavelength which is dependent upon its momentum. de Broglie reasoned that an electron, similarly, should have an associated wavelength governed by its momentum, i.e.

$$\lambda = \frac{h}{m_e \upsilon} = \frac{h}{p_e}$$

where m_e = the mass of an electron, υ = its velocity and p_e = its momentum.

Prior to 1927 evidence existed only for the particulate (i.e. particle like) nature of electrons, but in that year evidence for their wave nature was obtained. C. Davisson and L.H. Germer showed that a beam of electrons could be diffracted by a thin metal foil. Since diffraction phenomena can occur only with waves, the dual wave and particulate nature of electrons was confirmed.

In 1927 W. Heisenberg introduced his *uncertainty principle*, which states essentially that the precise position and momentum of an electron cannot be determined simultaneously. Let us regard an electron as a very small moving particle of extremely low mass. If we attempt to establish its position, for example by shining a beam of radiation at it, the photons of the radiation on striking the electron will alter its velocity and hence its momentum. Similarly, the mass is so low that if we attempt to measure the momentum of an electron we alter its position. Thus, there is always uncertainty when determining the simultaneous position and momentum of an electron.

Wave mechanics

In wave mechanics, instead of using the particulate approach of Bohr, we treat the electron as a wave motion. An equation is set up which describes the motion of the electron as a three-dimensional *standing wave* or *stationary wave*. Examples of standing waves are commonplace. A vibrating string of a guitar, for example, describes a standing wave in one dimension. To produce such a wave the string must be fixed at both ends and then plucked. The extremes of the motion between fixed ends are shown in Fig. 2.4(a).

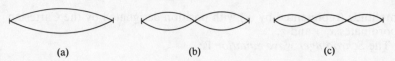

(a)   (b)   (c)

Fig. 2.4 Some possible extremes of motion of a vibrating string fixed at both ends.

If we pluck the string harder it is possible to obtain a standing wave of form 2.4(b); pluck it harder still and we get standing wave 2.4(c), and so on. In theory, there is no limit to the number of different standing waves that can be obtained. A general equation for such waves is:

$$2d = n\lambda$$

where d is the distance between the fixed points and λ is the wavelength of the wave. For a standing wave to exist n must be an integer, e.g. for Fig. 2.4(a) $n = 1$, for 2.4(b) $n = 2$, for 2.4(c) $n = 3$, and so forth.

Let us now consider an electron wave in one plane about the nucleus of an atom (Fig. 2.5(a)). A standing wave can exist only if the wavelength is an integral value of the circumference, i.e. if

$$n\lambda = 2\pi r_e$$

where n is again an integer. If this condition is not satisfied, a standing wave cannot exist because destructive interference occurs (Fig. 2.5(b)).

(a)   (b)

Fig. 2.5 Schematic diagram of an electron wave constrained to move in one plane around the central nucleus. Figure 2.5(a) represents a possible stationary wave where constructive interference occurs. Figure 2.5(b) shows how a wave of somewhat different wavelength would be destroyed by interference.

In the equations relating to all standing waves we find that integers occur naturally, as the above examples illustrate. Integers occur also in the equations relating to the three-dimensional standing waves that electrons describe in atoms. The mathematical complexities of such equations will not be dealt with here; only their outcome.

Schrödinger wave equation
In 1927 Erwin Schrödinger set up his famous wave equation, which treats the behaviour of an electron in an atom as a three-dimensional standing wave. Essentially, this equation expresses the variation of

amplitude (represented by ψ) with position designated by the Cartesian coordinates x, y and z.

The *Schrödinger wave equation* is:

$$\frac{\partial^2 \psi}{\partial x^2} + \frac{\partial^2 \psi}{\partial y^2} + \frac{\partial^2 \psi}{\partial z^2} + \frac{8\pi^2 m}{h^2} (E - V)\psi = 0$$

where h = Planck's constant,
     E = total energy,
     V = potential energy,
     m = mass of an electron.

This equation tells us that if we take the sum of the second differentials of ψ with respect to the Cartesian coordinates x, y and z and add this to the expression

$$\frac{8\pi^2 m}{h^2} (E - V)\psi$$

the result is zero provided that we find a correct function ψ. A function ψ which permits this is a solution of the wave equation and is known as a *wave function*. As in the case of many mathematical equations, e.g. quadratic and cubic equations, more than one solution exists. Each solution, i.e. each different wave function ψ_1, ψ_2, ψ_3, etc, corresponds to a different, and constant, total energy for the electron, E_1, E_2, E_3, etc. These are often referred to as *stationary states* of an atom.

What does ψ mean?

Let us start by considering the nucleus of an atom lying at the origin of a Cartesian coordinate system (Fig. 2.6): ψ is a function of the coordinates x, y and z. It has a particular value for any given combination of

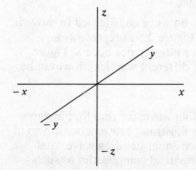

Fig. 2.6 Cartesian coordinate system. The three axes are mutually perpendicular to one another. In the above orientation the x and z axes lie in the plane of the paper, while the y axis is perpendicular to it; $-y$ above the plane and $+y$ below it ($-x$, $-y$ and $-z$ are not shown on subsequent figures).

these coordinates, i.e. at any given point in space the value of ψ is constant; ψ can be regarded as representing the amplitude of the electron wave as a function of the coordinates. However, the most useful aspect is that, if ψ describes the amplitude of the electron wave at point x, y and z, ψ^2 expresses the *probability* of locating the electron wave. To summarise,

ψ = amplitude of the electron wave at a given point, and
ψ^2 = probability of finding the electron at this point.

Probability provides us with the most useful interpretation of the behaviour of electrons in atoms.

Solutions of the wave equation

An exact solution of the wave equation is possible only for one-electron systems, e.g. the hydrogen atom. The task of solving the wave equation is simplified by changing from Cartesian coordinates to a set of spherical polar coordinates (Fig. 2.7): r represents the distance of the electron from the nucleus; θ represents the angle between r and the

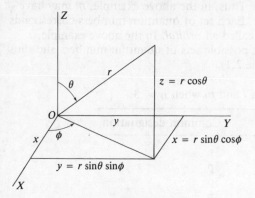

Fig. 2.7 Spherical polar coordinates.

z axis; and ϕ is the angle between the x axis and the projection of r on to the xy plane. Simple geometry enables us to interrelate these two types of coordinates, i.e.

$r^2 = x^2 + y^2 + z^2$
$x = r \sin \theta \cos \phi$
$y = r \sin \theta \sin \phi$
$z = r \cos \theta$

Polar coordinates can also be used to specify the exact position of an object on the earth's surface. To do this we quote its height, which is related to its distance from the centre of the earth (cf. r), its latitude (cf. θ) and longitude (cf. ϕ).

By changing to polar coordinates, ψ becomes a function of a radial coordinate, r, and the two angular coordinates θ and ϕ. This allows us to factorise the wave equation into simpler equations that depend upon r (radial wave function) and θ and ϕ (angular wave function). The mathematics of solving the wave equation is rather complicated and is discussed at a higher level. In the solution three integral constants appear; they are called *quantum numbers*. These quantum numbers, which are used to identify the various wave equations, are:

n, the principal quantum number,
l, the secondary (or azimuthal) quantum number, and
m, the magnetic quantum number.

For any realistic wave equation n, l and m have interconnected values. The value of n is always greater than 0, i.e. 1, 2, 3, 4, etc. For any given value of n, l has values given by:

$$n \geqslant l + 1$$

i.e. l values may be $n - 1$, $n - 2$, $n - 3$, etc. For example, a solution with $n = 3$ has l values of 2, 1 and 0. For each l value, m has values $\pm l$, $\pm l - 1$, $\pm l - 2 \ldots 0$. Thus, in the above example, m may have values $+2$, $+1$, 0, -1, -2. Each set of quantum numbers corresponds to a wave function which is called an *orbital*. In the above example, where $n = 3$, there are nine possible sets of quantum numbers and thus nine different orbitals (Table 2.1).

Table 2.1 Possible values of l and m when $n = 3$.

n	l	m	Common designation
3	0	0	3s
3	1	+1	3p
3	1	0	3p
3	1	−1	3p
3	2	+2	3d
3	2	+1	3d
3	2	0	3d
3	2	−1	3d
3	2	−2	3d

In the common s, p, d, f notation for representing orbitals we use only the principal quantum number. Instead of using the l value we substitute a letter, i.e.

$l = 0 \quad 1 \quad 2 \quad 3 \quad 4 \quad 5$, etc
 s $\quad$ p $\quad$ d $\quad$ f $\quad$ g $\quad$ h, etc, following alphabetically.

We do not use the m value at all. A complete designation of all orbitals up to and including $n = 4$ is given in Table 2.2.

Table 2.2 A complete designation of all orbitals where n = 1, 2, 3 or 4.

n	l	m	Label	Number of orbitals
1	0	0	1s	1
2	0	0	2s	1
2	1	0, ±1	2p	3
3	0	0	3s	1
3	1	0, ±1	3p	3
3	2	0, ±1, ±2	3d	5
4	0	0	4s	1
4	1	0, ±1	4p	3
4	2	0, ±1, ±2	4d	5
4	3	0, ±1, ±2, ±3	4f	7

The energy of orbitals (and hence electrons) increases with the n value. A given value of n corresponds to a fixed level of energy for the electron. Hence we often refer to an orbital as an *energy level*. The n value also gives us an indication of the average distance of an electron from the nucleus. The higher the n value the greater is the distance and the larger is the orbital.

For a single electron system (e.g. the hydrogen atom) the lowest energy state, called the *ground state*, is the 1s orbital (n = 1, l = 0). The next lowest states correspond to a value of n = 2. Here there are four orbitals: 2s (n = 2, l = 0), 2p (n = 2, l = 1, m = 1), 2p (n = 2, l = 1, m = 0) and 2p (n = 2, l = 1, m = −1). These four orbitals all possess the same energy and are said to be *degenerate*. Notice that the total number of orbitals associated with a given n value is equal to n^2. Thus, for the next lowest states, where n = 3, there are nine degenerate orbitals (Table 2.1). In this way the process continues for values of n = 4 (16 orbitals), n = 5 (25 orbitals), etc, up to infinity.

For a hydrogen atom, orbitals with n values greater than 1 correspond to *excited states*, i.e. states of excess energy. In its ground state the electron is in the 1s orbital. If the atom absorbs sufficient energy, the electron can be *promoted* to orbitals of higher n value and hence higher energy. To describe the properties of the electron in a hydrogen atom we therefore need the three quantum numbers n, l and m.

The representation of orbitals

As chemists, we need to be able to attach some physical significance to orbitals. One of the best ways of doing this is to use probability, ψ^2, instead of ψ. In this context it is common practice, although strictly incorrect, to refer to probability distributions as 'orbitals'. They can be represented either graphically or pictorially. We shall adopt the latter approach, since it is the more useful from the chemical and bonding standpoint, and we shall refer the probability diagrams to a Cartesian coordinate system.

20

s Orbitals

For an s orbital, at any given distance (r) from the nucleus, ψ and hence ψ^2 has the same value irrespective of the value of θ and ϕ. The charge cloud or probability distribution for an s orbital is thus spherically symmetrical about the nucleus (Fig. 2.8).

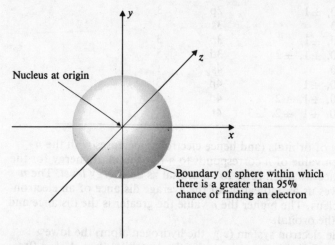

Fig. 2.8 The spherical shape of the boundary surface of a 1s orbital. The figure represents an envelope within which there is a high probability (greater than a 95 per cent chance) of finding an electron in the orbital.

The sphere is taken to represent a volume within which the probability of finding the electron is high; greater than 95 per cent. Similar charge clouds can be drawn for all s orbitals. The lower the n value the smaller is the sphere.

p Orbitals

p Orbitals are more complex than s orbitals. The angular probability distributions, i.e. the squares of the angular wave functions, are shown in Fig. 2.9.

Let us consider the orbital labelled $2p_x$ (Fig. 2.9(b)). The angular probability distribution of this orbital is concentrated around the x axis, for it comprises two balloon-type lobes situated to the left and right of the nucleus. Within these two lobes the probability of finding an electron is high. The $2p_y$ and $2p_z$ orbitals are similar to the $2p_x$ except that their lobes are concentrated along the y and z axes respectively. The three 2p orbitals are thus situated mutually at right angles.

The principal difference between the three 2p orbitals and p orbitals of higher n value, i.e. 3p, 4p, etc, is one of size and energy. As with s orbitals, the higher the n value the larger is the probability distribution and the higher is the energy.

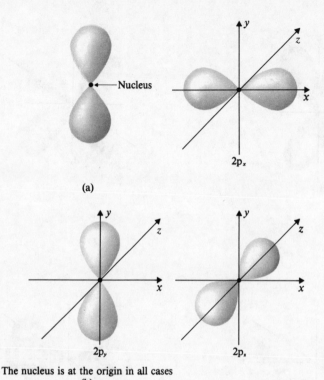

Nucleus

$2p_x$

(a)

$2p_y$

$2p_z$

The nucleus is at the origin in all cases

(b)

Fig. 2.9 Angular probability distributions for p orbitals.

d and f Orbitals

The probability distributions for 3d orbitals together with their labels
are shown in Fig. 2.10.

The lobes for the $d_{x^2-y^2}$ orbital are concentrated around the x and y
axes. Those for the d_{z^2} orbital are concentrated along the z axis; there is
also a peculiar collar-like lobe situated in the xy plane. The lobes for
the d_{xy} orbital lie in the xy plane and in between the x and y axes.
Similarly, the d_{xz} orbital has lobes that lie in between the x and z axes
in the xz plane. The lobes of the d_{yz} orbital are located in the yz plane
in between the y and z axes.

Probability distributions for f and other orbitals can also be obtained.
As the l values increase, the orbitals become more complex. An f orbital,
for example, comprises up to eight lobes.

Multielectron atoms

When there is more than one electron in an atom exact solutions of the
wave equation are impossible. This is because the presence of other
electrons introduces repulsion effects and modifies the attraction

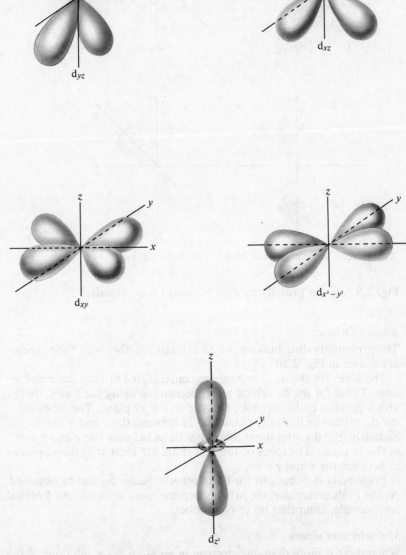

Fig. 2.10 Angular probability distributions for d orbitals.

between a given electron and the nucleus. By making approximations, however, solutions can be obtained, again involving the n, l and m quantum numbers. The orbitals are essentially similar in shape to those of a hydrogen atom, but their probability distributions and sizes differ.

Perhaps of more importance is that degeneracy is relieved. For a hydrogen atom all orbitals with the same n value have the same energy, e.g.

$$1s < 2s = 2p_x = 2p_y = 2p_z < 3s = 3p_x = 3p_y = 3p_z = 3d_{z^2}$$
$$= 3d_{x^2-y^2} = 3d_{xy} = 3d_{yz} = 3d_{xz}$$

However, for multielectron atoms:

$$1s < 2s < 2p_x = 2p_y = 2p_z < 3s < 3p_x = 3p_y = 3p_z < 3d_{z^2}$$
$$= 3d_{x^2-y^2} = 3d_{xy} = 3d_{yz} = 3d_{xz}$$

Pauli exclusion principle

In a multielectron atom it is possible for two electrons to occupy the same orbital, i.e. have the same values of n, l and m, provided that a certain condition is satisfied. This condition relates to *spin*. An electron in an atom behaves as a spinning particle, i.e. it has properties which we interpret as being due to its spinning about an axis. Only two directions of spin are possible about this axis. An electron may spin in one direction (e.g. clockwise) or in the opposite direction (e.g. anticlockwise). A spin quantum number, s, is used to distinguish between these two types of spin. Spin in one direction is designated by $s = +\frac{1}{2}$, and in the opposite direction by $s = -\frac{1}{2}$. The + and − signs are not intended to represent clockwise and anticlockwise spins, for such rotational directions are meaningless to an electron. The condition for two electrons to satisfy, for them both to occupy one orbital, is that they must have opposite spins, i.e. one must have an s value of $+\frac{1}{2}$ and the other $-\frac{1}{2}$. The electrons are then said to be *spin paired* or to have *antiparallel* spins. Four quantum numbers, i.e. n, l, m and s, are thus needed to specify each electron in an atom.

Pauli's exclusion principle states that no two electrons in an atom can have the same four quantum numbers. If, for example, two electrons in an atom have the same n, l and m values, i.e. if they are in the same orbital, they must be spin paired. In other words, s must equal $+\frac{1}{2}$ for one of the electrons and $-\frac{1}{2}$ for the other. Another expression of Pauli's principle is that if two electrons occupy one orbital they must have opposed (i.e. antiparallel) spins.

Shells

A *shell* is defined as a complete group of orbitals possessing the same principal quantum number. A shell is numbered by the n value of its constituent orbitals, although the letters K (for $n = 1$), L (for $n = 2$), M (for $n = 3$), etc, were formerly used. For example, the orbitals with a value of $n = 2$ constitute the second shell, and those with a value of

$n = 3$ the third shell. The first shell is unusual in that it consists of one orbital only.

For a given shell, the value of n is equal to the number of different types of orbital (i.e. l values) that exist within the shell, e.g.

first shell − s type;
second shell − s and p types.

The occupation of the first seven shells is shown in Table 2.3.

Table 2.3 The occupation of the first seven electron shells.

shell (n)	1	2	3	4	5	6	7
sub-shells†	1s (2)	2s (2)	3s (2)	4s (2)	5s (2)	6s (2)	7s (2)
		2p (6)	3p (6)	4p (6)	5p (6)	6p (6)	
			3d (10)	4d (10)	5d (10)	6d (10)	
				4f (14)	5f (14)		
total number of electrons per shell	2	8	18	32	32‡	18‡	2‡

† Figures in parentheses give the number of electrons per sub-shell.
‡ For higher shells, i.e. $n = 5$, 6 or 7, not all sub-shells are filled. For example, 5g, 6f and 7p orbitals are not occupied in the ground state of any known atom. The totals given for these shells represent their maximum occupation in known atoms.

2.3 The origin of the hydrogen spectrum

The hydrogen atom is unique in that all its orbitals with the same n value (i.e. all orbitals of the same shell) have the same energy. Consequently, a hydrogen atom has fewer energy levels than the atoms of other elements. They are conveniently represented by Fig. 2.11.

For a hydrogen atom in its ground state, i.e. state of lowest energy, the single electron occupies the $n = 1$ level (1s orbital). However, *electron transitions*, i.e. movements between different energy levels, can occur. By absorbing a sufficient quantity of energy, the electron can move or be *promoted* to higher energy levels ($n = 2$, 3, 4, etc) to produce an *excited* hydrogen atom. When an electron transition subsequently occurs from a higher level to the $n = 1$ level the excess energy is emitted in the form of radiation. The amount of energy emitted in such a transition (e.g. $n = 2$ to $n = 1$) is equal to the energy absorbed in promoting the electron to the higher energy level (e.g. $n = 1$ to $n = 2$). We shall now consider the relationship between some electron transitions in the hydrogen atom and the wavelength or frequency of the radiation that is emitted.

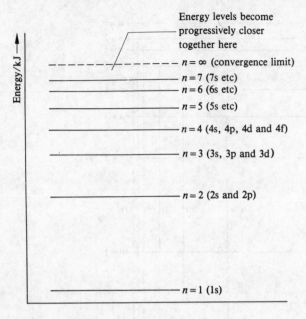

Fig. 2.11 The relative energy levels of a hydrogen atom.

Notes
(i)   A line represents the (relative) energy level of each shell according to its *n* value; e.g. the line labelled *n* = 2 gives the energy of orbitals of the second shell, i.e. 2s and 2p.
(ii) The energy of a shell increases as the value of *n* increases.
(iii) As *n* increases, the energy levels become closer together until eventually they converge at *n* = ∞. For clarity, energy levels with *n* values greater than 7 have been omitted.
(iv) An electron at the *n* = ∞ level is a free electron.

(i)   When an electron moves from $n = 2$ to $n = 1$ (arrow (a) in Fig. 2.12) the energy change (ΔE_a) is equal to the energy difference between the two levels. The wavelength (λ) or frequency (ν) of the emitted radiation and ΔE_a are related by Planck's equation:

$$E_2 - E_1 = \Delta E_a = \frac{hc}{\lambda_a} = h\nu_a$$

where E_2 represents the energy of the $n = 2$ level and E_1 the energy of the $n = 1$ level.

Thus, the $n = 2$ to $n = 1$ transition produces radiation of a single wavelength (i.e. one line in the spectrum). Since no other transition to the $n = 1$ level is accompanied by a lower energy change, the radiation corresponds to the line of longest wavelength (i.e. the first line) in the Lyman series of the hydrogen spectrum. This line is often labelled $n = 2$, to indicate the level from which the electron transition has occurred.

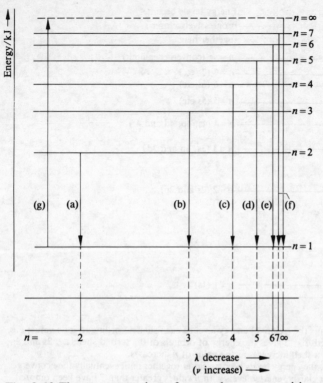

Fig. 2.12 The representation of some electron transitions in a hydrogen atom that give rise to lines in the Lyman series. Only the first six lines have been considered, i.e. those originating from the transitions represented by arrows (a) to (f). Dashed lines indicate which transitions produce which lines. Other transitions from levels higher than $n = 7$ to $n = 1$ also occur, to give lines in the spectrum between the lines labelled $n = 7$ and $n = \infty$. These have been omitted for the sake of clarity.

Arrow (g) represents the transition involved in ionising a ground state hydrogen atom.

(ii) Similarly, the transition from $n = 3$ to $n = 1$ (arrow (b) in Fig. 2.12) involves an energy change (ΔE_b):

$$E_3 - E_1 = \Delta E_b = \frac{hc}{\lambda_b} = h\nu_b$$

where $\Delta E_b > \Delta E_a$, since the $n = 3$ level is higher in energy than the $n = 2$ level. The emitted radiation again has a single wavelength, where $\lambda_b < \lambda_a$ (and $\nu_b > \nu_a$).

This transition is responsible for the second line of the Lyman series, and is labelled $n = 3$ for the same reason as above.

(iii) The transition from $n = 4$ to $n = 1$ produces the third line, labelled $n = 4$. A glance at the spectrum reveals a smaller difference in wavelength between the $n = 4$ and $n = 3$ lines than between the $n = 3$ and $n = 2$ lines. This is a consequence of the smaller difference in energy between successive levels as the value of n increases (Fig. 2.11, note (iii)).

(iv) The transition from $n = 5$ to $n = 1$ (arrow (d) in Fig. 2.12) produces the fourth line, labelled $n = 5$, in the spectrum, with a smaller difference between this line and $n = 4$ than between $n = 4$ and $n = 3$.

(v) For subsequent transitions (e.g. those represented by (e) and (f), and those from levels higher than $n = 7$ to $n = 1$, not shown in Fig. 2.12), the pattern continues as successive energy levels become closer together, until eventually the lines that they produce in the spectrum converge at the series limit. The series limit is labelled $n = \infty$, since it corresponds to an electron transition from $n = \infty$ to $n = 1$. This latter transition is, of course, the reverse of ionisation, for ionisation involves promoting an electron from its ground state, $n = 1$, to $n = \infty$ (arrow (g) in Fig. 2.12). By measuring the wavelength or frequency of the Lyman series limit, we can calculate the ionisation enthalpy of a hydrogen atom from the relationship:

$$\text{ionisation enthalpy} = \frac{hc}{\lambda_{SL}} = h\nu_{SL}$$

where λ_{SL} and ν_{SL} represent the wavelength and frequency respectively of the Lyman series limit.

Thus we see that transitions from higher levels to the $n = 1$ level give rise exclusively to the lines of the Lyman series. In practice, however, when an excited hydrogen atom sheds its excess energy, the electron does not always return to the lowest level ($n = 1$). Instead, it may return to one of the other levels, $n = 2, 3, 4, 5$, etc, before eventually returning to the ground state ($n = 1$) or being excited to a higher level. Transitions occurring to the $n = 2$ level give rise to the lines of the Balmer series (Fig. 2.13). The lines in the Balmer series are labelled, as before, according to the level from which the electron transition has occurred.

The origins of the other series are as follows:

Paschen series, from transitions to the $n = 3$ level;
Brackett series, from transitions to the $n = 4$ level;
Pfund series, from transitions to the $n = 5$ level.

We can now see the significance of the integers n_1 and n_2 in the Ritz equation (§2.1), i.e.

28

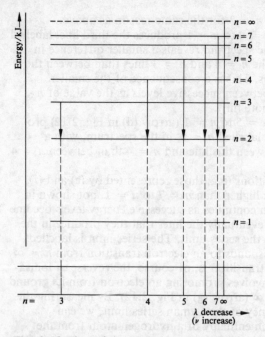

Fig. 2.13 The origin of the Balmer series. Arrows represent electron transitions, and dashed lines indicate which transitions produce which lines.

$$\frac{1}{\lambda} = R_H \left(\frac{1}{n_2^2} - \frac{1}{n_1^2} \right)$$

n_2 is the *lower* level, to which the transition occurs, and n_1 is the *higher* level, from which the electron transition originates.

2.4 The energy levels of multielectron atoms and the order in which atomic orbitals are filled (aufbau principle)

The *electronic configuration* of an atom, i.e. the way in which the electrons are arranged in the various orbitals in the ground state, is governed by several fundamental rules. We shall now study these rules, and afterwards see how they relate to some of the lower elements.

Aufbau principle For an atom to be in its ground state, i.e. to have the lowest possible energy, electrons must occupy the available orbitals in order of energy level. An orbital of lowest energy is always filled first, before orbitals of higher energy.

The energy levels of the lower orbitals increase with increasing n

value, except for the 4s orbital which is intermediate in energy between the 3p and 3d orbitals. The relative order of energy levels from 1s to 4p is thus as follows:

$$1s < 2s < 2p < 3s < 3p < 4s < 3d < 4p$$

and we shall see that the orbitals are filled in this order.

Pauli exclusion principle If two electrons occupy one orbital, they must have opposed or antiparallel spins.

We often represent an orbital by a box, e.g.

2s ☐ represents a 2s orbital.

An upward pointing half arrow, ↿, conveniently represents an electron spinning in one direction, while the same arrow, pointing downwards, ⇂, represents an electron of opposite spin. Two spin-paired electrons occupying the 2s orbital would be represented as:

2s ↿⇂

Notice that arrangements such as

2s ↿↾ or 2s ⇃⇂

in which the electrons have parallel spins, cannot occur.

Hund's rules When two or more electrons occupy a set of degenerate orbitals (e.g. a sub-shell), they occupy them: (i) singly, and (ii) with parallel spins, before spin pairing occurs in any one orbital.

Consider the set of three 2p orbitals represented as:

2p ☐☐☐

The only possible arrangements of electrons within these orbitals in harmony with Hund's rules and Pauli's principle are given in Fig. 2.14.

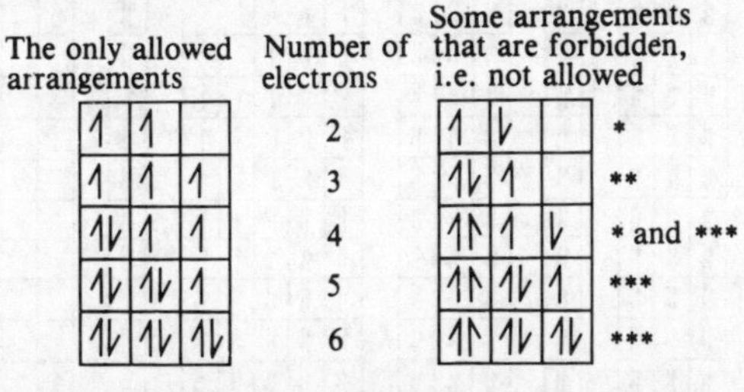

The only allowed arrangements	Number of electrons	Some arrangements that are forbidden, i.e. not allowed	
↿ ↿	2	↿ ⇂	*
↿ ↿ ↿	3	↿⇂ ↿	**
↿⇂ ↿ ↿	4	↿↾ ↿ ⇂	* and ***
↿⇂ ↿⇂ ↿	5	↿↾ ↿⇂ ↿	***
↿⇂ ↿⇂ ↿⇂	6	↿↾ ↿⇂ ↿⇂	***

Fig. 2.14 Arrangements of electrons in the three degenerate 2p orbitals. Objections to the forbidden arrangements are:
*violates Hund's rule (ii): the electrons have opposite spins;
**violates Hund's rule (i): the orbitals are not singly occupied;
***violates Pauli's principle: one orbital contains two electrons with parallel spins.

30

Table 2.4 shows that the electronic configurations of each of the elements from hydrogen ($Z = 1$) to krypton ($Z = 36$) conform to these principles. For elements beyond krypton see the periodic table (Fig. 3.1), which incorporates the complete aufbau principle.

Table 2.4 Electronic configurations of the elements from hydrogen to krypton.

Element	Atomic number	1s	2s	2p			3s	3p			3d					4s	4p		
hydrogen	1	↑																	
helium	2	⇅																	
lithium	3	⇅	↑																
beryllium	4	⇅	⇅																
boron	5	⇅	⇅	↑															
carbon	6	⇅	⇅	↑	↑														
nitrogen	7	⇅	⇅	↑	↑	↑													
oxygen	8	⇅	⇅	⇅	↑	↑													
fluorine	9	⇅	⇅	⇅	⇅	↑													
neon	10	⇅	⇅	⇅	⇅	⇅													
sodium	11	⇅	⇅	⇅	⇅	⇅	↑												
magnesium	12	⇅	⇅	⇅	⇅	⇅	⇅												
aluminium	13	⇅	⇅	⇅	⇅	⇅	⇅	↑											
silicon	14	⇅	⇅	⇅	⇅	⇅	⇅	↑	↑										
phosphorus	15	⇅	⇅	⇅	⇅	⇅	⇅	↑	↑	↑									
sulphur	16	⇅	⇅	⇅	⇅	⇅	⇅	⇅	↑	↑									
chlorine	17	⇅	⇅	⇅	⇅	⇅	⇅	⇅	⇅	↑									
argon	18	⇅	⇅	⇅	⇅	⇅	⇅	⇅	⇅	⇅									
potassium	19	⇅	⇅	⇅	⇅	⇅	⇅	⇅	⇅	⇅						↑			
calcium	20	⇅	⇅	⇅	⇅	⇅	⇅	⇅	⇅	⇅						⇅			
scandium	21	⇅	⇅	⇅	⇅	⇅	⇅	⇅	⇅	⇅	↑					⇅			
titanium	22	⇅	⇅	⇅	⇅	⇅	⇅	⇅	⇅	⇅	↑	↑				⇅			
vanadium	23	⇅	⇅	⇅	⇅	⇅	⇅	⇅	⇅	⇅	↑	↑	↑			⇅			
chromium	24	⇅	⇅	⇅	⇅	⇅	⇅	⇅	⇅	⇅	↑	↑	↑	↑	↑	↑			
manganese	25	⇅	⇅	⇅	⇅	⇅	⇅	⇅	⇅	⇅	↑	↑	↑	↑	↑	⇅			
iron	26	⇅	⇅	⇅	⇅	⇅	⇅	⇅	⇅	⇅	⇅	↑	↑	↑	↑	⇅			
cobalt	27	⇅	⇅	⇅	⇅	⇅	⇅	⇅	⇅	⇅	⇅	⇅	↑	↑	↑	⇅			
nickel	28	⇅	⇅	⇅	⇅	⇅	⇅	⇅	⇅	⇅	⇅	⇅	⇅	↑	↑	⇅			
copper	29	⇅	⇅	⇅	⇅	⇅	⇅	⇅	⇅	⇅	⇅	⇅	⇅	⇅	⇅	↑			
zinc	30	⇅	⇅	⇅	⇅	⇅	⇅	⇅	⇅	⇅	⇅	⇅	⇅	⇅	⇅	⇅			
gallium	31	⇅	⇅	⇅	⇅	⇅	⇅	⇅	⇅	⇅	⇅	⇅	⇅	⇅	⇅	⇅	↑		
germanium	32	⇅	⇅	⇅	⇅	⇅	⇅	⇅	⇅	⇅	⇅	⇅	⇅	⇅	⇅	⇅	↑	↑	
arsenic	33	⇅	⇅	⇅	⇅	⇅	⇅	⇅	⇅	⇅	⇅	⇅	⇅	⇅	⇅	⇅	↑	↑	↑
selenium	34	⇅	⇅	⇅	⇅	⇅	⇅	⇅	⇅	⇅	⇅	⇅	⇅	⇅	⇅	⇅	⇅	↑	↑
bromine	35	⇅	⇅	⇅	⇅	⇅	⇅	⇅	⇅	⇅	⇅	⇅	⇅	⇅	⇅	⇅	⇅	⇅	↑
krypton	36	⇅	⇅	⇅	⇅	⇅	⇅	⇅	⇅	⇅	⇅	⇅	⇅	⇅	⇅	⇅	⇅	⇅	⇅

Notes

(i) In writing the electronic configurations of atoms, orbitals of the same n value are usually written together, irrespective of their relative energy levels. Thus, nickel is written as:
$1s^2 \, 2s^2 \, 2p^6 \, 3s^2 \, 3p^6 \, 3d^8 \, 4s^2$ and *not*: $1s^2 \, 2s^2 \, 2p^6 \, 3s^2 \, 3p^6 \, 4s^2 \, 3d^8$.

(ii) To save time and space, noble gas cores are often utilised in writing electronic configurations, particularly of heavy atoms. For example:

    sodium [Ne] $3s^1$

    iron   [Ar] $3d^6 \, 4s^2$

where [Ne] represents a neon core configuration, i.e. $1s^2 \, 2s^2 \, 2p^6$, and [Ar] stands for $1s^2 \, 2s^2 \, 2p^6 \, 3s^2 \, 3p^6$. Mercury, in similar manner, would be [Xe] $5d^{10} \, 6s^2$. Occasionally, noble gas cores are written more explicitly, e.g. [Ar core].

(iii) Atoms of all the first series transition elements, except chromium and copper, have doubly filled 4s orbitals. Because of repulsion between the paired 4s electrons the $3d^4 \, 4s^2$ configuration is higher in energy than $3d^5 \, 4s^1$. Thus, chromium adopts the latter configuration. The 3d and 4s sub-shells do not differ greatly in energy, and towards the end of the series the 3d level appears to fill preferentially. Thus, copper adopts a $3d^{10} \, 4s^1$ configuration rather than $3d^9 \, 4s^2$.

(iv) The 4s and 3d electrons are very close in energy, but when ions are formed it is the 4s electrons that are lost first.

Chapter 3

The periodic table

3.1 Similarity of properties among the elements

The chemical and physical properties of an element are determined by the electronic configuration of its atoms. In particular, it is the electronic configuration in the *outermost shell* or *outermost orbitals* that is important. The electrons in the inner, often full, shells do not usually participate in chemical bonding and for many purposes can be disregarded. This is not surprising, for when two atoms approach each other prior to chemical bond formation, it is the electrons in the outermost orbitals that are most likely to interact. For this reason we often refer to them as *bonding electrons*, or perhaps as *valency electrons*, because they are responsible for the valency of the element.

We may therefore expect atoms with similar outer electronic configurations to resemble one another, both chemically and physically. For example, the strong resemblance between lithium and sodium arises because the atoms of both elements possess, in their outermost s orbitals, one electron that can be used in either chemical or metallic bonding (§4.7):

Li $1s^2 2s^1$ only the $2s^1$ electron is involved in bond formation
Na $1s^2 2s^2 2p^6 3s^1$ only the $3s^1$ electron is involved in bond formation

The resemblance between lithium and sodium extends to the other alkali metals (e.g. potassium) because of the similarity of their outer electronic configurations. Other elements which possess similar electronic configurations in their outermost shells are also comparable with one another in their chemical and physical properties.

3.2 Features of the periodic table of the elements

The modern 'long form' of the periodic table (Fig. 3.1) is a detailed statement of the aufbau principle (§2.4), in that it shows the order in which atomic orbitals are filled. For each element, the orbital occupied by the highest energy electron is shown at the left-hand side; see, for example, 1s by the side of hydrogen and helium, 2s by lithium and beryllium, and 2p by the elements boron to neon. Within the context of the periodic table, atomic orbitals increase in energy from top to bottom and from left to right, so that their order of ascending energy is as follows:

$$1s < 2s < 2p < 3s < 3p < 4s < 3d < 4p, \text{ etc}$$

The periodic table is essentially a list of the elements in increasing order of *atomic number*, arranged in such a way that elements with similar outer electronic configurations and therefore similar properties fall into a series of vertical columns called *groups*. Groups are indicated by means of arabic numerals, although roman numerals are sometimes used. The A and B sublabels have a historical significance, but are still in common use. For historical reasons, also, the noble gases have no group number, and the nine elements in the three groups headed by iron, cobalt and nickel are collectively known as group 8.

For the elements of groups 1A and 2A, and groups 1B to 7B inclusive, the group number is equal to the number of outermost electrons in the atoms concerned. Thus, the elements of group 1A have one outer electron (ns^1), those of group 2A have two such electrons (ns^2), and those of group 4B have four ($ns^2\,np^2$).

The following are exceptions to the rule that all elements in the same group have the same outer electronic configuration.

(i)   Helium ($1s^2$) is placed in the same group as the noble gases, which have $ns^2\,np^6$ configurations.

(ii) The elements of group 6A show slight differences in their outer configurations, i.e. Cr $3d^5\,4s^1$, Mo $4d^5\,5s^1$ and W $5d^4\,6s^2$.

(iii) Hydrogen ($1s^1$) is not placed in group 1A, even though the elements of this group all have ns^1 configurations (Table 7.1).

Despite these anomalies, the similarity in properties between the member elements of a group is so strong that inorganic chemistry is always studied on a group basis. The elements of some groups have collective names, as follows:

group 1A—the alkali metals;
group 2A—the alkaline earth metals (applies only to Ca, Sr, Ba
          and Ra);
group 6B—the chalcogens;
group 7B—the halogens;
no number—the noble gases (He, Ne, Ar, Kr, Xe and Rn).

A horizontal row of elements is called a *period*. Each one begins

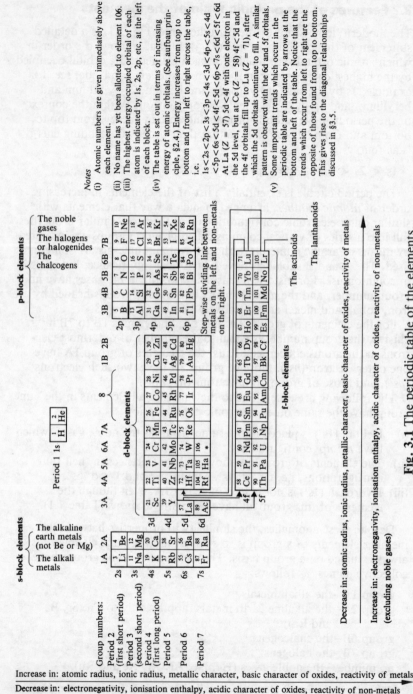

Notes

(i) Atomic numbers are given immediately above each element.

(ii) No name has yet been allotted to element 106.

(iii) The highest energy occupied orbital of each atom is indicated by 1s, 2s, 2p, etc, at the left of each block.

(iv) The table is set out in terms of increasing energy of atomic orbitals. (See aufbau principle, §2.4.) Energy increases from top to bottom and from left to right across the table, i.e.

$1s < 2s < 2p < 3s < 3p < 4s < 3d < 4p < 5s < 4d < 5p < 6s < 4f < 5d < 6p < 7s < 6d < 5f < 6d$

At La $(Z = 57)$ 5d < 4f with one electron in the 5d level, but at Ce $(Z = 58)$ 4f < 5d and the 4f orbitals fill up to Lu $(Z = 71)$, after which the 5d orbitals continue to fill. A similar pattern is observed with the 6d and 5f orbitals.

(v) Some important trends which occur in the periodic table are indicated by arrows at the bottom and left of the table. Notice that the trends which occur from left to right are the opposite of those found from top to bottom. This gives rise to the diagonal relationships discussed in §3.5.

Fig. 3.1 The periodic table of the elements.

Decrease in: atomic radius, ionic radius, metallic character, basic character of oxides, reactivity of metals

Increase in: electronegativity, ionisation enthalpy, acidic character of oxides, reactivity of non-metals (excluding noble gases)

Increase in: atomic radius, ionic radius, metallic character, basic character of oxides, reactivity of metals

Decrease in: electronegativity, ionisation enthalpy, acidic character of oxides, reactivity of non-metals with an element possessing one outermost electron (ns^1) and ends with a noble gas. The periods are numbered from the top of the periodic table, with hydrogen and helium comprising the *first period* (or period 1). The elements lithium to neon make up the *second period* and sodium to argon the *third period*.

The elements of groups 1A and 2A are collectively known as *s-block elements*, since their highest energy electrons occupy s orbitals. Correspondingly, the elements of groups 3B to 7B, which have their highest energy electrons in p orbitals, are known as *p-block elements*. The s- and p-block elements collectively are often referred to as the *representative, typical* or *main group elements*.

The *d-block elements* are formed by the filling of 3d, 4d and 5d orbitals. Included among these elements are the transition metals (Ch. 14). The two series of *f-block elements*, the *lanthanoids* and *actinoids*, result from outermost electrons occupying the 4f and 5f orbitals respectively. To avoid unnecessary sideways expansion of the periodic table, the f-block elements are usually placed at the bottom.

3.3 Periodicity and trends in the periodic table

When the elements are arranged in order of increasing atomic number, their physical and chemical properties show a *periodic variation* or *periodicity* which is embodied in the periodic table. Among the lighter elements (up to $Z = 20$), there is a periodic variation every eight elements, but this changes to every 18 elements up to $Z = 57$, and then to 32 for the heaviest elements. In group 1A, for example:

(i)   lithium ($Z = 3$) resembles sodium ($Z = 11$) and potassium ($Z = 19$), i.e. there is a periodic variation every eight elements;
(ii) potassium ($Z = 19$) resembles rubidium ($Z = 37$) and caesium ($Z = 55$), i.e. there is a periodic variation every 18 elements;
(iii) caesium ($Z = 55$) resembles francium ($Z = 87$), i.e. there is a variation after 32 elements.

The periodic variation is a direct result of the sequence in which the orbitals are occupied:

Li $1s^2\ 2s^1$ } difference = 8 (filling of 2s and 2p orbitals)

Na $1s^2\ 2s^2\ 2p^6\ 3s^1$ } difference = 8 (filling of 3s and 3p orbitals)

K $1s^2\ 2s^2\ 2p^6\ 3s^2\ 3p^6\ 4s^1$ } difference = 18 (filling of 3d, 4s and 4p)

Rb $1s^2\ 2s^2\ 2p^6\ 3s^2\ 3p^6\ 3d^{10}\ 4s^2\ 4p^6\ 5s^1$ } difference = 18

Cs $1s^2\ 2s^2\ 2p^6\ 3s^2\ 3p^6\ 3d^{10}\ 4s^2\ 4p^6\ 4d^{10}\ 5s^2\ 5p^6\ 6s^1$ } difference = 32

Fr $1s^2\ 2s^2\ 2p^6\ 3s^2\ 3p^6\ 3d^{10}\ 4s^2\ 4p^6\ 4d^{10}\ 4f^{14}\ 5s^2\ 5p^6$
$5d^{10}\ 6s^2\ 6p^6\ 7s^1$

Hence we see that the increasing number of elements in the periods results from the greater number of orbitals associated with the higher shells. Similar principles apply to the elements of other groups.

3.4 Some properties that show a periodic variation

Atomic volume

Lothar Meyer (1869–71) was among the first to demonstrate the periodicity of the elements. He did so by plotting atomic volume (i.e. the volume in cm³ of 1 mol of the element in the solid state) against relative atomic mass. An updated plot, using atomic numbers, is shown in Fig. 3.2.

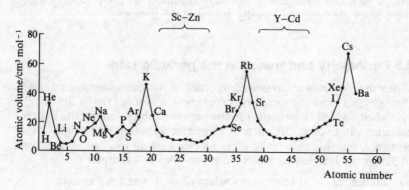

Fig. 3.2 Atomic volume curve.

The plot clearly shows a periodic variation in atomic volume, with many elements of similar properties (i.e. members of the same group) occurring at corresponding points on the curve. See, for example, the elements of groups 1A and 2A.

Atomic radius

An atom is spherical, with a radius that is dictated by the maximum distance of the outermost electron(s) from the nucleus. However, the boundary of an atom is not clearly defined: it is 'fuzzy' around the edge, in the sense that there is no definite boundary beyond which the probability of finding an electron is exactly zero. The direct determination of atomic radius is therefore impracticable, but by means of X-rays it is possible to locate the individual atoms in a crystalline solid and measure the distances between them. These distances enable atomic radius to be expressed in one of three ways, as follows:

(i)   *van der Waals' radius*, defined as half the shortest internuclear distance between two adjacent non-bonded atoms in a crystal of the element (Fig. 3.3(a) and (b));
(ii) *covalent bond radius*, defined as half the internuclear distance between two identical atoms joined by a single covalent bond (Fig. 3.3(b));
(iii) *metallic radius*, defined as half the shortest internuclear distance between two atoms in the metallic crystal.

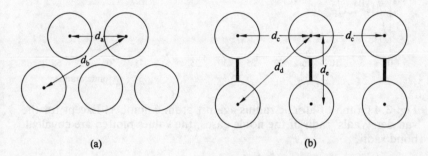

(a)   (b)

Heavy lines between atoms represent
covalent bonds

Fig. 3.3 (a) Representation of a noble gas crystal, where spheres indicate atoms. $d_a < d_b$; therefore d_a is the shortest internuclear distance, and van der Waals' radius $= d_a/2$. (b) Representation of a molecular crystal of a diatomic molecule. $d_c < d_d$; therefore d_c is the shortest internuclear distance between non-bonded atoms, and van der Waals' radius $= d_c/2$. Covalent bond radius $= d_e/2$.

van der Waals' radius gives the best estimate of the true size of an atom, since it provides a measure of how closely two atoms can approach each other without strong bonding forces becoming involved. Covalent bond radii are always shorter than van der Waals' radii, because covalent bond formation requires the overlap of orbitals in the outermost shells of adjacent atoms. Metallic radius depends on the crystal structure of the metal, but is always larger, by up to 20 per cent, than the corresponding covalent bond radius.

van der Waals' data are obtainable only for the noble gases and those non-metallic elements that form molecular crystals. No such data are available for metallic elements or for the non-metals carbon, silicon and boron, since the latter form atomic crystals with covalent bonds between the atoms. The covalent bond radius is known for most elements, and the term 'atomic radius' is generally taken to mean this quantity. A plot of atomic radius against atomic number clearly shows a periodic variation (Fig. 3.4).

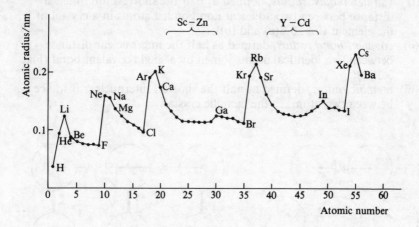

Fig. 3.4 Graph of atomic radius against atomic number. Except for the van der Waals' radii of the noble gases, the values plotted are covalent bond radii.

Two trends are apparent from Fig. 3.4.

(i) Atomic radius *increases* from top to bottom of a group, e.g. Li 0.123, Na 0.157, K 0.203, Rb 0.216, Cs 0.235 (all in nm). This is because, on progressing from lithium to caesium, the outermost electron occupies a successively higher shell, e.g. 2s for lithium but 3s for sodium.

(ii) Atomic radius *decreases* from left to right across a period, e.g. Li 0.123, Be 0.089, B 0.080, C 0.077, N 0.074, O 0.074, F 0.072 (nm). This stems from an increase in the *effective nuclear charge* as atomic number rises. Let us take lithium and beryllium as examples. In the former, the outermost 2s electron is shielded from the $+3$ nuclear charge by the two 1s electrons. Thus, the 2s electron experiences an effective nuclear charge of one proton, i.e. $+3 -2 = +1$. However, the two outer 2s electrons of beryllium are screened from the $+4$ nuclear charge by the two 1s electrons to give an effective nuclear charge of two protons, i.e. $+4 -2 = +2$. Therefore each outer electron of beryllium experiences a greater attraction to the nucleus, and is pulled closer towards it, than the outer electron of lithium. (The argument has been somewhat over-simplified, for the screening of one electron by another is not a 1 : 1 process.)

Ionisation enthalpy

A plot of first ionisation enthalpy against atomic number (Fig. 3.5) clearly shows a periodic variation.

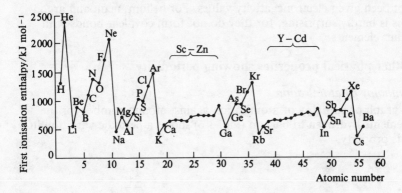

Fig. 3.5 Graph of first ionisation enthalpy against atomic number.

Four points are worthy of comment regarding this graph.

(i) The noble gases occur at maxima and the alkali metals at minima. The contraction of atomic radius within a period is at a maximum with the noble gases. Thus, for all periods, the outer electrons of noble gas atoms are closest to the nucleus, and these elements possess the highest first ionisation enthalpies. In alkali metal atoms, the outer electron is relatively distant from the nucleus and is well shielded from it by the inner shells (i.e. the noble gas core). Consequently, the outer electron is relatively easy to remove and the alkali metals have low ionisation enthalpies.

(ii) Within a period, there is a general increase in the ionisation enthalpy with increasing atomic number (§4.5 and §14.1).

(iii) Ionisation enthalpies decrease down a group (§4.5). Thus, in Fig. 3.5, the peaks and troughs become progressively lower with increasing atomic number.

(iv) Corresponding to the decrease in ionisation enthalpy down a group the elements become more metallic, and corresponding to the increase across a period they become less metallic (§4.5). Thus, the most metallic elements appear on the left-hand side of the periodic table and the least metallic, or non-metallic, on the right. There is a stepwise dividing line across the p-block of the periodic table (Fig. 3.1) which separates the metals from the non-metals, although many of the metals adjacent to this line possess both metallic and non-metallic characteristics. Such elements, e.g. germanium and arsenic, are termed *semi-metals* (formerly 'metalloids').

Electronegativity

Electronegativity (§4.4) increases from left to right across a period and from bottom to top of a group. Thus, the most electronegative elements are located at the top right-hand corner of the periodic table and the least electronegative at the bottom left. The noble gases have not been given electronegativity values. For helium, neon and argon this is hardly surprising, for they do not form covalent bonds with other elements.

Other physical properties showing periodicity

Enthalpy of atomisation
A graph of enthalpy of atomisation against atomic number for the elements hydrogen to barium (Fig. 3.6) shows a periodic variation in this property.

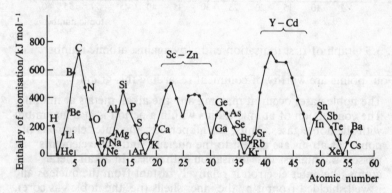

Fig. 3.6 Graph of enthalpy of atomisation against atomic number.

The reactivity of an element is very often related to its enthalpy of atomisation, since a chemical reaction can occur only after the element has been converted into free (i.e. isolated) atoms. In general, elements which possess high enthalpies of atomisation are unreactive, while those with low enthalpies of atomisation have a high reactivity. Noble gases are an exception to this rule. They exist in a monoatomic form and so have zero atomisation enthalpies, but display a lack of reactivity for the reasons given in Chapter 13.

Melting temperature and boiling temperature
Neighbouring elements in a period often have totally different structures, with the result that the changes in melting temperature and boiling temperature from left to right across a period are highly erratic. Some periodicity, however, is evident within the second and third periods (Fig. 3.7).

The noble gases and elements which form molecular crystals, e.g. oxygen and nitrogen, have low melting and boiling temperatures because of the weak van der Waals' forces that exist between the molecules. The elements carbon, silicon, boron and red phosphorus have very high melting and boiling temperatures because they form

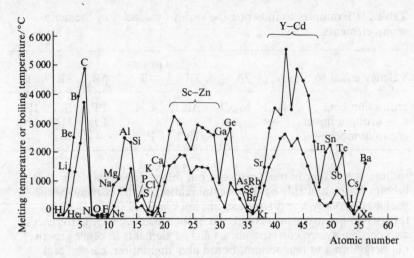

Fig. 3.7 Graphs of melting temperature (lower trace) and boiling temperature (upper trace) against atomic number.

atomic crystals in which strong covalent bonds exist between the atoms. Melting or boiling can occur only by breaking these bonds, and a large amount of thermal energy is necessary for this purpose. The melting and boiling temperatures of the metallic elements vary according to the strength of the metallic bonding.

Valency or oxidation state

The main group elements (For d-block elements see §14.1)

A valency or oxidation state numerically equal to the group number is displayed by all the elements of groups 1A, 2A, 3B and 4B. With the exception of the first or 'head' elements, the elements of groups 5B, 6B and 7B also achieve a valency or oxidation state equal to the group number, usually in combination with oxygen, fluorine or sometimes chlorine. With other reagents (e.g. hydrogen or sulphur) a valency of eight minus the group number is usually observed. Some p-block elements, particularly the heavier ones of groups 3B and 4B, also exhibit a valency equal to the group number minus two. This is due to their reluctance to utilise their outer s^2 electrons for bonding purposes, a phenomenon known as the *inert pair effect*. Some examples are given in Table 3.1.

The main group head elements

In many ways the head element of a group (i.e. the element in the second period), while resembling the second and subsequent members of the group (i.e. those elements of the third and higher periods), often exhibits significant differences from them. In group 1A lithium and

Table 3.1 Examples to illustrate the various valencies of the main group elements.

Valency equal to	1A	2A	3B	4B	5B	6B	7B
				Group			
group number	NaCl	$MgCl_2$	$AlCl_3$	CH_4	PF_5	SF_6	IF_7
8 − group number	—	—	—	—	PH_3	H_2S	HCl
group number − 2	—	—	TlCl	$PbCl_2$	—	—	—

sodium are similar in most respects, but differ, for example, in that lithium forms a nitride by direct combination of the elements while sodium does not. The differences are not confined to the elements themselves but are also encountered in their compounds. Differences also occur between corresponding pairs of elements in other groups, i.e. beryllium and magnesium, boron and aluminium, carbon and silicon, nitrogen and phosphorus, oxygen and sulphur, and fluorine and chlorine. Many of the differences will be explained later, but two important features are discussed here.

Maximum covalency The non-existence of 2d orbitals limits the maximum covalency or coordination number of the head element to four, i.e. the greatest number of electron pairs that can be accommodated in the 2s and 2p orbitals of the second shell is four. In contrast, the second and subsequent members of a group can achieve higher covalencies or coordination numbers by utilisation of the vacant d orbitals which exist in their outermost shells. Compare, for example, oxygen and sulphur (§11.3), and the reactivity towards water of CCl_4 and $SiCl_4$ (§9.6).

Multiple bonding The head elements have a much greater tendency than other group members to form multiple bonds. For example, carbon forms $C{=}O$, $C{\equiv}O$, $C{=}C$ and $C{\equiv}C$ bonds, whereas silicon seldom forms multiple bonds. A triple bond exists in the N_2 molecule, but phosphorus forms the P_4 molecule in which there are P——P single bonds (§10.2 and Fig. 10.1). Oxygen forms the $O{=}O$ molecule (§4.2), whereas sulphur is singly bonded in S_8 molecules (§11.2).

Chemical behaviour
The chemical properties of the elements also show a periodic variation. From left to right across a period the reactivity of metals decreases while that of non-metals increases and reaches a maximum at group 7B. The noble gases on the extreme right of the periodic table are noted for their chemical inertness.

From top to bottom of a group we usually observe an increasing reactivity for metals but a decreasing reactivity for non-metals. These and other changes are summarised in Fig. 3.1.

Properties of compounds

Trends and periodicity in properties are not confined to the elements themselves but are shared by many of their compounds. This is well illustrated by the oxides and halides.

Oxides

Corresponding to the decrease in metallic character, oxides become increasingly acidic (§11.5) from left to right across a period, e.g.

$$\underbrace{Na_2O \quad MgO}_{basic} \quad \underset{amphoteric}{Al_2O_3} \quad \underbrace{SiO_2 \quad P_4O_{10} \quad SO_3 \quad Cl_2O_7}_{acidic}$$

increasingly acidic $\longrightarrow$

decreasingly basic

Oxides become increasingly basic (§11.5) or decreasingly acidic from top to bottom of a group as the metallic character of the elements develops, e.g.

$$\underbrace{N_2O_3 \quad P_4O_6 \quad As_4O_6}_{acidic} \quad \underset{amphoteric}{Sb_4O_6} \quad \underset{basic}{Bi_2O_3}$$

decreasingly acidic $\longrightarrow$

increasingly basic

Halides

Many metals form ionic halides that are not hydrolysed by water. They possess high melting and boiling temperatures, and good electrical conductivity in solution or the fused state. The halides of non-metals, in contrast, are covalent and are generally hydrolysed by water. They have low melting and boiling temperatures, unless they are polymeric, and a low electrical conductivity. Some properties of period 3 chlorides are set out in Table 3.2.

Table 3.2, viewed from right to left, shows that halides become

Table 3.2 Some properties of the chlorides of period 3 elements.

	NaCl	MgCl$_2$	AlCl$_3$	SiCl$_4$	PCl$_3$	S$_2$Cl$_2$	Cl$_2$
bonding	ionic	ionic	polymeric covalent	covalent	covalent	covalent	covalent
melting temperature/°C	801	714	180 (sublimes)	-70	-112	-78	-102
conductivity	good	good	nil	nil	nil	nil	nil
whether hydrolysed by water	no	no	partially (§8.5)	yes	yes	yes	yes

increasingly ionic as the elements become more metallic. A similar trend is observed from top to bottom of a group, e.g.

$$\underbrace{NF_3 \quad PF_3 \quad AsF_3 \quad SbF_3}_{covalent} \quad \underset{ionic}{BiF_3}$$

3.5 Diagonal relationships

The trends that occur from left to right across the periodic table are always accompanied by the opposite trends from top to bottom of the groups (Fig. 3.1). For example, metallic character and ionic radius both *decrease* across a period, but *increase* down a group. As a result, a particular element often resembles the element which is in the period below it but one place to the right, especially in such properties as metallic character, electronegativity and atomic radius. There are thus *diagonal relationships* in the periodic table. The best examples are those at the left-hand side of periods 2 and 3, involving the following elements:

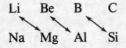

These similarities are discussed in §7.6 and §8.6.

Chapter 4

Chemical bonding and intermolecular attraction

Whenever two atoms approach each other, interactions may occur between their outer electrons resulting in the formation of a bond. In all cases the establishment of a bond between two isolated atoms leads to a lowering of energy. It is this lowering of energy which provides the necessary driving force or impetus for bond formation.

There are several types of bond, namely covalent, ionic, metallic and hydrogen. In addition, there are weak forces of attraction, called *van der Waals' forces*, between atoms that are not bonded together by any of these means. Since the properties of all substances, both elements and compounds, are governed by the nature of the bonding within them, an understanding of this subject must precede a detailed study of inorganic chemistry.

4.1 Single covalent bonds

A covalent bond cannot always be formed between two neighbouring atoms; certain conditions must be satisfied. Each atom must have one electron in one of its outermost atomic orbitals (AO), and these electrons must be spinning in opposite directions. Depending on the various forces of attraction and repulsion between them, two such atoms may approach each other sufficiently closely for their singly filled outer orbitals to overlap. The overlapping causes the two atomic orbitals to combine to form two *molecular orbitals*, known as a *bonding molecular orbital* (BMO) and an *antibonding molecular orbital*

46

(ABMO). The latter, which is relatively high in energy, remains unoccupied while the bonding molecular orbital, often called simply the 'molecular orbital' (MO), holds both the electrons. In a molecular orbital, as in a fully occupied atomic orbital, the two electrons have opposite spins.

Electron density is not uniform throughout a molecular orbital, but is greatest along the internuclear axis. The high concentration of (negative) electrons between the two (positive) atomic nuclei serves to bind the nuclei together. In this situation the atoms are said to be linked by a 'covalent bond'.

Three types of MO are recognised; in decreasing order of strength they are named as σ (sigma), π (pi) and δ (delta). σ MOs may result from the overlap of s, p or d atomic orbitals, π MOs from overlapping p or d orbitals, and δ MOs from d orbitals only. In this book we are concerned only with σ and π MOs.

Single covalent bonds consist of σ MOs, in contrast to multiple covalent bonds (i.e. double and triple bonds) which involve both σ and π MOs. σ MOs can be studied on the basis of the AOs from which they are constructed. Numerous combinations are possible, but we shall restrict discussion to σ MOs which result from the overlap of: (a) two s AOs; (b) two p AOs; and (c) one s and one p AO.

Overlap of two s AOs, as illustrated by the H_2 molecule

A hydrogen atom has the electronic configuration $1s^1$. As two such atoms join together to give a hydrogen molecule the 1s orbitals overlap to give a σ MO, designated as σ_{1s}. Because the hydrogen molecule has two such electrons in this MO, its configuration is given as σ_{1s}^2.

The 1s AO is spherically symmetrical, but when two such orbitals overlap the MO which is formed has a boundary surface that is ellipsoid in shape (Fig. 4.1). Thus, the shape of the MO is not derived just by partially superimposing the two AOs.

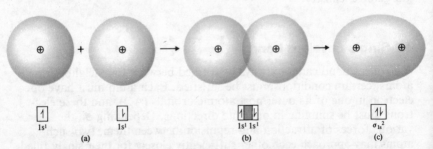

Fig. 4.1 Formation of the hydrogen molecule. (a) The approach of two hydrogen atoms, possessing electrons of opposite spins, (b) overlap of atomic orbitals, (c) the resultant molecular orbital.

A hydrogen molecule is more stable than two separate hydrogen atoms. Essentially, stability is due to the high electron density which exists between the two atomic nuclei (Fig. 4.2).

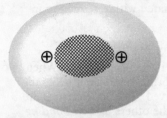

Fig. 4.2 The region of a hydrogen molecule where the probability of locating the two electrons is at a maximum.

The two electrons in this region reduce repulsion between the two nuclei. Furthermore, each positive nucleus is attracted to the cloud of two electrons. Thus, the two hydrogen atoms are firmly held in close proximity to each other.

Bonding is accompanied by a reduction in both potential and kinetic energy. That some sort of energy is lost is clear from the great amount of heat which is evolved during the combination. When two hydrogen atoms are remote from each other the electrical potential energy of the sytem is arbitrarily defined as zero. As the atoms attract and move towards each other there is a drop in potential energy according to the curve shown in Fig. 4.3. Clearly there must be a limit to the extent of such movement, for if the atoms were to get very close together their nuclei would strongly repel each other. There is, therefore, an optimum interatomic distance, represented by d in Fig. 4.3, at which there is minimum potential energy and thus maximum stability. At distances less than d the nuclei tend to move apart; at distances greater than d they tend to come together, but at d there is equilibrium.

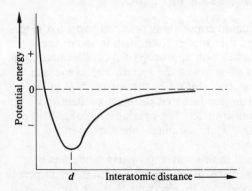

Fig. 4.3 The potential energy diagram for a hydrogen molecule.

The reduction in kinetic energy that accompanies bonding is due to the fact that hydrogen molecules travel more slowly than hydrogen atoms. The kinetic energy of a moving body depends on its mass and velocity (kinetic energy $= \frac{1}{2}mc^2$), and although bonding does not result in any change in the total mass it is associated with a reduction in velocity.

Overlap of two p AOs, as illustrated by the F_2 molecule

Fluorine has the electronic configuration $1s^2\, 2s^2\, 2p_x^2\, 2p_y^2\, 2p_z^1$. When two fluorine atoms join together to give a fluorine molecule it is the un-paired $2p_z$ electrons of each that are involved. The $2p_z$ electrons are referred to as *bonding electrons*, and all the others as *non-bonding electrons*.

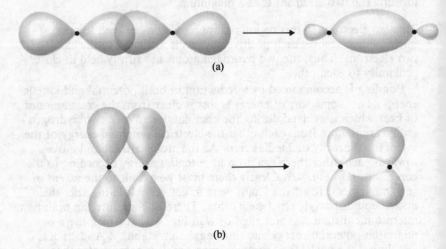

(a)

(b)

Fig. 4.4 (a) Head-on overlap of p orbitals, leading to a σ MO. (b) Sideways overlap of p orbitals, leading to a π MO.

The overlap of p orbitals could conceivably occur in two ways (Fig. 4.4). Wherever possible – and this applies to the formation of the fluorine molecule – there is a head-on approach of p orbitals because in this way there is the greatest overlap and the system attains maximum stability. The shape of the resultant MO, like that of the MO in the hydrogen molecule, stems from the fact that the electron density is greatest between the two atomic nuclei. The overlapping lobes of the AOs are thus increased in size, while the outer lobes are corres-pondingly decreased.

The F——F σ orbital formed in this way is properly written as σ_{2p_z}, but may be abbreviated to σ_z or $z\sigma$. Each fluorine atom in the molecule has two 1s, two 2s, two $2p_x$ and two $2p_y$ electrons that are not involved in bonding. Those in the outer shell, i.e. the 2s, $2p_x$ and $2p_y$ electrons, are said to constitute *lone pairs* of electrons, while those which belong to the inner shell, i.e. the 1s electrons, are referred to as *core electrons*. Lone pairs of electrons are important for two reasons: first, they affect the shapes of many molecules in which they occur, and second, they can be utilised in forming coordinate bonds.

In certain molecules with multiple bonds, e.g. $CH_2{=}CH_2$ and $N{\equiv}N$, p orbitals can overlap in a sideways manner to give rather weak π MOs (§4.2).

Overlap of one s and one p AO, as illustrated by the HF, H_2O and NH_3 molecules

If the AOs contributing to the MO are of different types, the MO is not symmetrical but has a shape that is derived from those of the constituent AOs. Thus, in the hydrogen fluoride molecule, where the overlapping AOs are 1s (from H) and $2p_z$ (from F), the shape is as shown in Fig. 4.5.

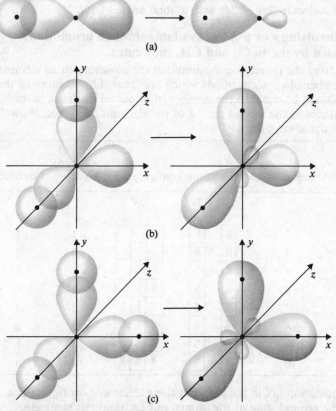

(a)

(b)

(c)

Fig. 4.5 Formation of (a) the HF molecule, (b) the H_2O molecule, and (c) the NH_3 molecule.

The situation in the water molecule is similar, the only difference being that there are two bonds of this kind. Oxygen has the electronic configuration $1s^2\ 2s^2\ 2p_x^2\ 2p_y^1\ 2p_z^1$, and when a water molecule is formed the unpaired $2p_y$ and $2p_z$ AOs overlap the 1s AOs of two hydrogen atoms (Fig. 4.5(b)). (In Fig. 4.5(b) and (c), for the sake of clarity, only one lobe of the $2p_x$, $2p_y$ and $2p_z$ AOs have been shown. For the same reason, the 1s and 2s AOs have been omitted.) The 2s and $2p_x$ electrons are unused in bonding, and are thus lone pairs. From this theory of bonding we might expect an H—O—H bond angle of 90°: experiment, however, indicates an angle of 104.5°. The greater bond angle stems from repulsion between the shared pairs of electrons (§4.6).

Figure 4.5(c) represents the formation of the ammonia molecule. Nitrogen has the electronic configuration $1s^2\ 2s^2\ 2p_x^1\ 2p_y^1\ 2p_z^1$, and in the formation of ammonia each of the unpaired 2p AOs overlaps the 1s AO of a hydrogen atom. The 2s electrons constitute a lone pair. Again, the bond angle (H—N—H) is greater than the expected 90° because of repulsion between electron pairs. Experiment indicates a pyramidal molecule (Fig. 4.24) with a bond angle of 106.7°.

Overlap involving s or p AOs, available through promotion, as illustrated by the BeCl₂ and CH₄ molecules.

It follows from the previous discussion that the *covalency* of an element, i.e. the number of covalent bonds which are formed by an atom of that element, should be equal to the number of unpaired electrons in the atom. A glance at the second period of the elements, however, shows that this is not always so.

Element	Atomic number	Electronic configuration					No. of unpaired electrons	Covalency
		1s	2s	2p x	y	z		
lithium	3	⇅	↑				1	1
beryllium	4	⇅	⇅				0	2
boron	5	⇅	⇅	↑			1	3
carbon	6	⇅	⇅	↑	↑		2	4
nitrogen	7	⇅	⇅	↑	↑	↑	3	3
oxygen	8	⇅	⇅	⇅	↑	↑	2	2
fluorine	9	⇅	⇅	⇅	⇅	↑	1	1
neon	10	⇅	⇅	⇅	⇅	⇅	0	0

The explanation lies in the fact that these electronic configurations relate to the ground state of the atoms, but excitation of some electrons can occur in atoms of beryllium, boron and carbon (and certain other elements, not shown here) as other atoms approach for combination, with the result that these electrons are *promoted* to other AOs at slightly higher energy levels:

	1s	2s	2p x	y	z	No. of unpaired electrons
beryllium	↑↓	↑	↑			2
boron	↑↓	↑	↑	↑		3
carbon	↑↓	↑	↑	↑	↑	4

The number of unpaired electrons now corresponds to the number of covalent bonds that are actually formed. There is, however, a limit to the extent to which electrons can be promoted: it is impossible, for instance, for the 1s electron of lithium to be promoted to a 2p orbital because the energy requirement is greater than that available in a chemical reaction.

In any compound of beryllium, boron or carbon we may therefore expect more than one type of MO to be formed, one involving the singly filled s orbital and one involving singly filled p orbital(s). This is indeed the case, as the following examples illustrate.

The beryllium chloride molecule

In a $BeCl_2$ molecule the chlorine atoms are attached to the beryllium atom partly by:

(i) a σ MO formed by the overlap of the 3p AOs of the chlorine atoms with the $2p_x$ AO of the beryllium atom (Fig. 4.6(a)); and

(ii) a σ MO formed by the overlap of the same AOs of the chlorine atoms with the 2s AO of beryllium (Fig. 4.6(b)).

These two MOs accommodate the four bonding electrons of the molecule – two from the beryllium atom and one from each chlorine atom.

Thus in a beryllium chloride molecule, *there is no single MO which is responsible for a complete Be——Cl bond*. Each Be——Cl bond consists of a combination of two MOs formed by the interactions shown in Fig. 4.6. The combination of orbitals is the same for both bonds. For this reason the bonds are identical with each other, as indicated by their equal lengths.

Although the Be——Cl bonds consist of a combination of MOs, they must not be regarded as multiple bonds. With four electrons involved in bonding, each bond comprises only two electrons and is therefore a single covalent bond.

52

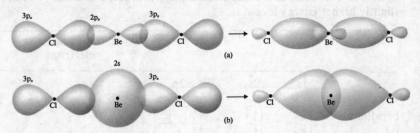

Fig. 4.6 Formation of the $BeCl_2$ molecule.

The methane molecule

In a molecule of methane the four hydrogen atoms, labelled H_a, H_b, H_c and H_d in Fig. 4.7, are distributed tetrahedrally around the carbon atom. This serves to minimise repulsion between them.

In this position the 2s AO of the carbon atom overlaps the 1s AO of each hydrogen atom to form a σ MO (Fig. 4.7(a)). Three other MOs are formed by the interaction of the three singly filled 2p orbitals with the 1s AOs of the hydrogen atoms (Fig. 4.7(b)). A total of four MOs is thus formed to accommodate eight bonding electrons, four from carbon and one from each of the four hydrogen atoms. Thus, in a methane molecule, each of the four C——H bonds consists of a combination of four MOs formed by the interactions shown in Fig. 4.7. There is no single orbital in this description to which the C——H bond can be attributed but, as in beryllium chloride, each bond is a single bond.

4.2 Multiple covalent bonds

Multiple bonds, such as the carbon–carbon double bond in ethene and the carbon–carbon triple bond in ethyne, involve both σ and π MOs. σ MOs have been discussed above; π MOs may result from overlapping p or d AOs, but we shall consider only those which arise from the sideways overlap of p orbitals (Fig. 4.4).

The ethene molecule

The two carbon atoms in a molecule of ethene cannot be held together merely by a σ bond; there must be a π bond as well. This is suggested by a number of experimental facts, e.g.

(i)   the high strength of the bond. The C==C bond has a bond dissociation enthalpy of 612 kJ mol⁻¹, whereas that of the C——C bond is only 348 kJ mol⁻¹;

2s (carbon) and 1s (hydrogen) overlap

(a)

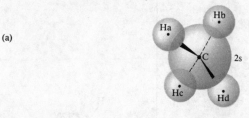

Equal overlap involving
Ha, Hb, Hc and Hd

2p (carbon) and 1s (hydrogen) overlap

(b)

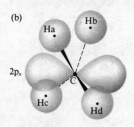 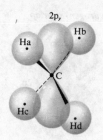 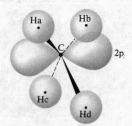

Overlap involving
Hc and Hd
No overlap of Ha and Hb

Equal overlap involving
Ha, Hb, Hc and Hd

Overlap involving
Ha and Hb
No overlap of Hc and Hd

Fig. 4.7 Formation of the CH_4 molecule.

(ii) the shortness of the bond: 0.134 nm, compared with 0.154 nm for the C—C bond;

(iii) restricted rotation about a C≡C bond. Compounds such as 1,2-dichloroethene exist in two isomeric forms, designated *cis* and *trans*. The carbon–carbon double bond locks the molecule in position, and prevents one isomer from changing into the other.

The ethene molecule possesses a planar *σ-framework* (Fig. 4.8) in which the carbon and hydrogen atoms are held together by σ bonds, rather like the carbon and hydrogen atoms in a molecule of methane. Thus, the C—C single bond is due partly to the overlap of 2s AOs and partly to the overlap of, let us say, $2p_x$ AOs. Each C—H bond is due partly to the 2s AO of the carbon atom overlapping the 1s AO of the hydrogen atom, and partly to the $2p_x$ and $2p_y$ AOs of the carbon atom overlapping the same 1s AO of the hydrogen atom.

Each of the carbon atoms still has a $2p_z$ AO available for bonding. These p_z orbitals lie at right angles to the plane of the σ-framework (Fig. 4.9) and are sufficiently close together to overlap in a sideways manner to give a π MO which is located partly above and partly below the plane of the σ-framework (Fig. 4.10).

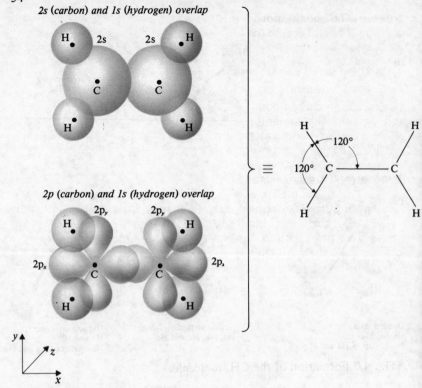

2s (carbon) and 1s (hydrogen) overlap

2p (carbon) and 1s (hydrogen) overlap

Fig. 4.8 The σ-framework of the ethene molecule.

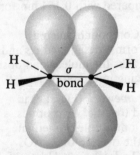

Fig. 4.9 Sideways overlap of $2p_z$ AOs in the ethene molecule.

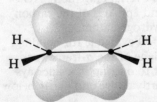

Fig. 4.10 The π MO in the ethene molecule.

There is no equalisation of the σ and π bonds. The π bond is weaker than the σ bond because the $2p_z$ AOs of carbon overlap to a relatively small extent. Furthermore, π electrons, unlike σ electrons, are not concentrated between the atomic nuclei.

The ethyne molecule

The carbon—carbon bond in ethyne is exceptionally short (0.120 nm) and exceptionally strong (bond dissociation enthalpy = 837 kJ mol⁻¹), because the two carbon atoms are held together by a triple bond, consisting of one σ and two π bonds.

The molecule has a linear σ-framework H—C—C—H, the formation of which involves the 2s and, say, the $2p_x$ AOs of the carbon atoms. This leaves the $2p_y$ and $2p_z$ AOs of each carbon atom free for further bonding. They remain directed at right angles to each other and to the line of the C—C bond (Fig. 4.11), and are close enough together for them both to overlap. In this way two π MOs are formed, stronger than the π MO in ethene.

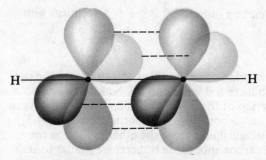

Fig. 4.11 Sideways overlap of 2p AOs in the ethyne molecule. (For the sake of clarity, the distance between the carbon atoms has been exaggerated. Dotted lines indicate where overlap occurs.)

The nitrogen molecule

In many respects the nitrogen molecule resembles that of ethyne, for in both molecules there is a triple bond consisting of one σ and two π MOs. Nitrogen has the electronic configuration $1s^2\ 2s^2\ 2p_x^1\ 2p_y^1\ 2p_z^1$. If we suppose that there is a head-on overlap of $2p_z$ AOs from two approaching nitrogen atoms, to give a σ MO, then sideways overlap of the remaining $2p_x$ and $2p_y$ AOs gives two π MOs.

The carbon monoxide molecule

The bonding in the carbon monoxide molecule (Fig. 4.12) may be represented as C≦O or C≡O, which symbolises one σ bond and two identical π bonds. The electronic configurations of carbon and oxygen are:

C $1s^2\ 2s^2\ 2p_x^1\ 2p_y^1$ O $1s^2\ 2s^2\ 2p_x^2\ 2p_y^1\ 2p_z^1$

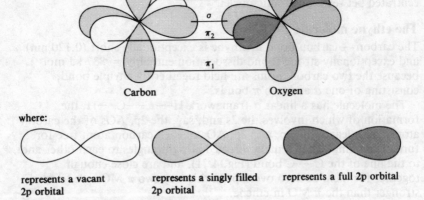

where:

represents a vacant
2p orbital

represents a singly filled
2p orbital

represents a full 2p orbital

Fig. 4.12 The bonding in carbon monoxide. Bond π_1 is identical with bond π_2.

The end-on and sideways overlap of singly filled 2p orbitals on the carbon and oxygen atoms produces a σ bond and a π bond. The second π bond is formed by the overlap of the doubly filled 2p orbital on oxygen and the vacant 2p orbital on carbon. This is a coordinate bond (§4.3), but once formed it is indistinguishable from the other π bond in the molecule. The bonding in carbon monoxide is therefore similar to that in nitrogen, since both molecules have the same number of electrons.

The oxygen molecule

The bonding in the oxygen molecule is commonly represented as O=O, which suggests the existence of a double bond similar to the carbon–carbon double bond in ethene, and at first sight this makes sense. Oxygen has the electronic configuration $1s^2\,2s^2\,2p_x^2\,2p_y^1\,2p_z^1$. When two such atoms approach each other there could be head-on overlap of, say, the $2p_z$ AOs to give a σ_{2p} MO. At the same time, there could be sideways overlap of the $2p_y$ AOs to give a π_y MO.

If this were the complete story, all electrons in the oxygen molecule would be paired and oxygen would be diamagnetic, i.e. unaffected by a magnetic field (§14.1). However, experiment shows that oxygen is paramagnetic, i.e. attracted by a magnetic field, and measurements of this property indicate the existence of two unpaired electrons.

The phenomenon is easily explained on the molecular orbital theory. A glance at Fig. 4.11, which illustrates the sideways overlap of 2p AOs, shows that any overlap of the $2p_y$ AOs is bound to be accompanied by overlap of the $2p_x$ AOs, *which, in the case of oxygen, are fully occupied*. Thus, the four $2p_x$ electrons (two from each atom) are forced to participate in bonding. Two of them enter a π_x MO; which leaves the interesting question of what happens to the other two. It was mentioned at the start of this chapter that the merging of two AOs gives two MOs; a bonding molecular orbital (BMO) and an antibonding molecular orbital (ABMO). The latter usually remains unoccupied because it is at a higher energy level than the former. In the present situation, however, the π_x ABMO, represented by π_x^*, must be occupied. It could conceivably hold both the electrons that require accommodation. However, the π_x^* ABMO is similar in every respect (except direction) to the π_y^* ABMO. The two are degenerate, i.e. at the same energy level. The electrons which must enter an ABMO are therefore divided, one into the π_x^* and the other, in accordance with Hund's rules (§2.4), into the π_y^* ABMO. To summarise, there are eight electrons involved in the bonding of an oxygen molecule. They occupy orbitals in the following manner:

σ_{2p}	π_x	π_y	π_x^*	π_y^*
2	2	2	1	1

The oxygen molecule is said to be a *diradical*, since it is, in effect, two free radicals joined together. (A 'free radical' is defined as an atom or group of atoms which possesses an unpaired electron.) In terms of energy, however, the two unpaired electrons in antibonding orbitals cancel out the contribution to bonding of two electrons in a π bonding orbital. Thus, instead of writing the formula of oxygen as O≡O, which would imply the existence of a triple bond similar to that in the nitrogen molecule, we write O=O. If we wish to emphasise the presence of two unpaired electrons, we can write Ȯ=Ȯ.

The nitrogen oxide molecule

A molecule of nitrogen oxide possesses one electron less than an oxygen molecule. The bonding in the two molecules is very similar, except that in nitrogen oxide only one electron occupies a π antibonding orbital. Let us consider the interactions between atoms of nitrogen and oxygen. The electronic configurations are:

N $1s^2\ 2s^2\ 2p_x^1\ 2p_y^1\ 2p_z^1$ O $1s^2\ 2s^2\ 2p_x^2\ 2p_y^1\ 2p_z^1$

As in the case of the oxygen molecule, end-on overlap of the $2p_z$ AOs produces a σ_{2p} MO, and sideways overlap of the $2p_y$ AOs forms a π_y MO. A π_x MO is produced by the sideways interaction of the $2p_x$ AOs. There are, however, *three* electrons originating from the $2p_x$ orbitals. Two of them enter a bonding π_x MO, leaving the remaining electron to occupy an antibonding π MO, either π_x^* or π_y^*. The nitrogen oxide molecule is therefore paramagnetic because it possesses one unpaired electron.

The unpaired electron in a π antibonding orbital cancels out the bonding contribution of one electron in a π bonding orbital. As a result, there are effectively $2\frac{1}{2}$ bonds between the atoms in a molecule of nitrogen oxide.

4.3 The coordinate bond

A *coordinate* or *dative covalent* bond is merely a special type of covalent bond. If two atoms A and B are joined together by a covalent bond, one electron of the bond comes from A and the other from B, but if the atoms are linked by a coordinate bond *both* the electrons originate from one atom. The atom (or ion) which provides the electrons is known as the *donor*, while the receiving atom (or ion) is termed the *acceptor*. The coordinate bond is represented by an arrow from donor to acceptor, thus:

$$A:\longrightarrow B \qquad\qquad A\dot{\times}B$$

Donor Acceptor   Covalent bond

Coordinate bond

A coordinate bond, once formed, is indistinguishable from a covalent bond. The only difference between them lies in the origin of the electrons.

If an atom or ion is to act as a donor it must have at least one lone pair of electrons in its outer shell, and for an atom or ion to act as an acceptor there must be at least one vacant orbital in its outer shell. Coordination, like covalent bond formation, takes place because there is a lowering of energy as the bonds are formed. Within limits, which are dictated by the available space and the number of vacant orbitals, an acceptor forms as many coordinate bonds as it can.

As a simple example, consider the formation of an oxonium ion, H_3O^+, by the coordination of a water molecule to a proton:

$$\begin{array}{c}H\\ \diagdown\\ \qquad O: \; + \; H^+ \; \rightarrow \\ \diagup\\ H\end{array} \quad \begin{array}{c}H\\ \diagdown\\ \qquad O \rightarrow H^+ \; \rightarrow\\ \diagup\\ H\end{array} \quad \left[\begin{array}{c}H\\ \diagdown\\ \qquad O\!-\!H\\ \diagup\\ H\end{array}\right]^+$$

The oxygen atom of the water molecule has two lone pairs of electrons in its outer shell, but usually only one participates in coordination. The proton (from an acid) has a vacant 1s orbital. Coordination, as shown, enables the proton to achieve the configuration of the noble gas helium, without unduly disturbing the stable electronic arrangement of the oxygen atom. The structural formula on the right shows that no attempt is made, in the oxonium ion, to distinguish among the three O—H bonds, and that the positive charge, which belonged originally to the proton, is now distributed over the ion as a whole. Note also that coordination does not affect the oxidation number (§5.1) of the atoms concerned. In H_2O and H^+, and in H_3O^+, oxygen has an oxidation number of -2 and hydrogen $+1$.

In the oxonium ion oxygen has a covalency of three, although it is more usual to state that the *coordination number* of oxygen is three. The 'coordination number' of an atom in a chemical species is defined as the number of nearest neighbours to the given atom.

The formation of H_3O^+ provides an example of *stabilisation by coordination*, for while a proton can exist in the form of H_3O^+ it cannot do so by itself. (Its minute radius, coupled with its full positive charge, gives it an extremely high density of charge on its surface and makes it very reactive.) The effect is sometimes referred to as *stabilisation by complexing*, because a species which is formed by coordination is called a *complex*.

A proton can also be stabilised by the coordination of a molecule of an alcohol or ammonia. In the latter case the product is the tetrahedral ammonium ion, NH_4^+:

Nitrogen, in the ammonium ion, still has an oxidation number of -3, but a coordination number of 4.

Other well known examples of stabilisation by coordination include the following.

Cations of metals in a high valency state Ions such as Sn^{4+} and Pb^{4+} seldom exist except in the form of complex ions. Many pure compounds of tin(IV) and lead(IV) are essentially covalent; tin(IV) chloride, for example, is a liquid (not a crystalline solid) and has a low electrical conductivity. In alkaline solution, however, complex ions are formed; e.g. $[Sn(OH)_6]^{2-}$, by the coordination of six hydroxide ions to a hypothetical Sn^{4+} ion. In this and other complex ions, such as $[SnCl_6]^{2-}$, the Sn^{4+} ion is 'stabilised by coordination'.

Grignard reagents (alkylmagnesium halides, RMgX) Grignard reagents are prepared in the presence of an ether, e.g. ethoxyethane, which stabilises the reagent by coordination to the magnesium atom.

Donor atoms

The most effective donors of lone pairs are small atoms of the non-metallic elements located at the top right-hand corner of the periodic table. (If an atom has a low atomic radius, the electrons in the outer shell are close together and there is a relatively strong repulsion between them.) In the following extract from the periodic table the principal donor atoms have been printed in bold type: lesser donors appear in medium type:

Group	1A	2A	3B	4B	5B	6B	7B
				C	**N**	**O**	**F**
					P	**S**	**Cl**
					As	Se	**Br**
							I

Donor atoms may be encountered in molecules or anions known as *ligands*. Examples of molecular ligands are H_2O, NH_3 and CO, which donate lone pairs of electrons from the oxygen, nitrogen and carbon atoms respectively. Well known examples of anionic ligands are F^-, Cl^-, HO^- and CN^-. The HO^- ion donates a lone pair of electrons from the oxygen atom. The CN^- ion can donate from either the carbon or the nitrogen atom, but usually does so from the carbon atom.

Acceptor atoms and ions

The acceptor of a lone pair of electrons is usually a metal cation. In certain other cases it may be an atom belonging to a molecule, or an atom of a transition element.

Cations

Cations of the transition elements, e.g. Fe^{2+}, Fe^{3+}, Ni^{2+} and Co^{3+}, with their vacant d orbitals and relatively high surface charge density (§4.5), exert a strong attraction for ligands and enter very readily into complex ion formation. For example, when anhydrous iron(II) sulphate is dissolved in water, six water molecules, acting as ligands, coordinate to the iron(II) ion to give the hydrated iron(II) ion, $[Fe(H_2O)_6]^{2+}$. The water molecule is a relatively weak ligand, and can be displaced by other ligands with a readiness that depends on their strength and concentration. Thus, the treatment of an aqueous solution of an iron(II) salt with a cyanide (e.g. NaCN) leads to the substitution of water molecules by cyanide ions. Eventually, all six water molecules are replaced:

$$[Fe(H_2O)_6]^{2+} + 6CN^- = [Fe(CN)_6]^{4-} + 6H_2O$$

Cations of the p-block elements, e.g. Sn^{2+} and Pb^{2+}, also enter into complex formation, but the phenomenon is seldom encountered with cations of the s-block elements. Such ions are relatively large (Fig. 4.17) and, in the case of the group 1A elements, have only a single positive charge. They therefore have a low surface charge density and exert only a feeble attraction for lone pairs of electrons. In addition, certain of these ions, e.g. Li^+, Na^+ and Mg^{2+}, have completed shells and can coordinate only into a higher shell, which is energetically unfavourable.

Molecules

Many molecular substances act as electron acceptors in coordinate bond formation, because in this way more stable species are formed. The role of Grignard reagents in this respect has already been mentioned. Compounds of group 3B elements form a wide range of complexes, e.g. ammonia—boron trifluoride(1/1), $BF_3 \cdot NH_3$, and aluminium chloride—ethoxyethane(1/1), $AlCl_3 \cdot (C_2H_5)_2O$. Aluminium chloride, besides reacting with ethers, also dimerises in such a way that a lone pair of electrons from a chlorine atom of one $AlCl_3$ molecule is donated to the aluminium atom of another (§8.5).

Covalent compounds of group 4B elements, e.g. SiF_4, also behave as electron acceptors. Compounds of carbon, however, are an important exception. There are no vacant orbitals in the outer shell of a combined carbon atom, and coordination to carbon cannot occur unless another atom or group is displaced from the carbon atom at the same time. There is a comparable situation in group 5B, in that compounds of phosphorus (e.g. PCl_3 and PCl_5) can serve as acceptors, while those of nitrogen cannot do so because of a completed outer shell. Covalent compounds of the transition elements also act as electron acceptors, and iron(III) chloride and gold(III) chloride have dimeric structures which are similar to that of aluminium chloride.

The coordination of water to a covalent halide causes its hydrolysis, e.g.

$$BCl_3 + 3H_2O = H_3BO_3 + 3HCl \qquad (\S8.5)$$

Other examples include $SiCl_4$ ($\S9.6$) and PCl_3 ($\S10.5$). Where coordination of water cannot occur, as with CCl_4, there can be no hydrolysis.

Transition metal atoms

Metal carbonyl compounds are formed by the coordination of carbon monoxide, through a lone pair of electrons in the outer shell of carbon, to an *atom* of a transition element. Probably the best known example is tetracarbonylnickel(0), $[Ni(CO)_4]$.

4.4 The polar covalent bond

Although the bonding in some diatomic molecules (e.g. H_2) is purely covalent, pure electrovalency does not exist. Even in potassium chloride, in many respects a typical electrovalent compound, Hannay and Smyth (p. 67) have calculated that the ionic character of the bond is only 52 per cent. In some compounds, e.g. aluminium chloride, tin(IV) chloride and lithium iodide, the bonding is so far removed from pure electrovalency that the compounds have low melting temperatures, low electrical conductivities in the molten state and high solubilities in organic solvents. Such substances are described as *polar covalent*.

Fajans' rules

Kasimir Fajans in 1924 published a set of rules which stated that the electrovalent bond in a compound $A^+ B^-$ tends towards covalency where any of the following conditions apply.

The charge on A^+ or B^- is high

Although unipositive and bipositive cations are commonplace (e.g. Na^+ and Ca^{2+}), simple cations with a triple or quadruple charge are rare. The Al^{3+} ion, for instance, exists in only a few compounds, e.g.

aluminium fluoride and aluminium oxide; most non-complexed compounds of aluminium are polar covalent. The reason is that as electrons are removed from an atom the remainder are held ever more strongly by a constant positive charge on the nucleus. The removal of one or two electrons from an atom requires relatively little energy, but the loss of further electrons requires more energy than is normally available in a chemical reaction.

A similar argument applies to anions. Although uni- and binegative anions are well known, simple anions with a triple or quadruple charge (e.g. N^{3-} and C^{4-}) are uncommon. The reason is that although the introduction of an electron into a neutral atom of a non-metal is a spontaneous process in which energy is released, the corresponding process in which an electron is introduced into an anion is difficult because of repulsion between the negatively charged ion and the negatively charged electron. The greater the charge on the anion, the greater is the repulsion and the more difficult it is to accomplish the change.

A^+ is small

Cations of metals at the top of the periodic table (e.g. Li^+, Be^{2+} and Al^{3+}) have a low ionic radius (Fig. 4.17). Most salts which contain these ions have a marked degree of covalent character, for two reasons.

(i) The electrons of the outer shell are close to the nucleus and therefore strongly attracted to it. As a result, small atoms tend not to ionise but to use their electrons in covalent bond formation.

(ii) A small cation, especially if it possesses more than a single positive charge, has a high surface charge density (§4.5) and can therefore distort or *polarise* the outer orbitals of the anion B^-. Electrons are attracted from B^- to A^+, i.e. covalency is encouraged.

B^- is large

Most metal iodides are polar covalent. Even sodium iodide is very soluble in ethanol and propanone. There are two reasons for this, both of which stem from the high ionic radius of the I^- ion.

(i) For a large atom, relatively little energy is released during the process:

$$X(g) + e^- \rightarrow X^-(g)$$

In other words, a large anion has relatively little tendency to be formed. Formation involves the entry of one or more electrons to the outer shell, where they are retained by nuclear attraction, but if the outer shell is remote from the nucleus, and in addition shielded from it by underlying electron shells, the force of attraction is relatively weak.

(ii) A large anion, because its electrons are so far away from the nucleus, is easily polarised, especially by a small cation.

Electronegativity

Between the extremes of pure covalency, where the molecular orbital is symmetrical, and hypothetical pure electrovalency, where the electron pair is located entirely at one atom, an infinite range of bonding is possible (Fig. 4.13).

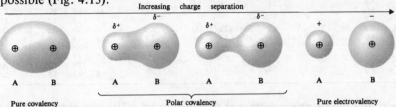

Fig. 4.13 The gradation of bonding from pure covalency to pure electrovalency.

The degree of charge separation depends on the *electronegativity* difference between the atoms A and B: the greater the difference, the greater is the polarity. The electronegativity of an atom is a measure of its tendency *in a molecule* to attract electrons and hence acquire a negative charge, but it is not a fundamental concept and is difficult to define precisely.

R.S. Mulliken argued that the electronegativity (x) of an element is equally related to its ionisation enthalpy (I) and its electron affinity (A). (The former is a measure of the tendency of its atoms to *lose* electrons, and the latter is a measure of the tendency to *gain* electrons.) He suggested that electronegativity be defined as the average of these two quantities, i.e.

$$x = \tfrac{1}{2}(I + A)$$

L. Pauling proposed a different basis for the definition. He observed that if two atoms A and B of similar electronegativity are joined together, the bond dissociation enthalpy ($DH^{\ominus}$) of the A——B covalent bond is approximately equal to the geometric mean of the A——A and B——B bond dissociation enthalpies, i.e.

$$DH^{\ominus}(\text{A——B}) \approx \sqrt{DH^{\ominus}(\text{A——A}) \times DH^{\ominus}(\text{B——B})}$$

If, however, A and B possess different electronegativities, the bond dissociation enthalpy of the A——B bond is greater than the geometric mean by an amount that is proportional to the electronegativity difference. Thus, by arbitrarily allocating an electronegativity value to one element (Pauling put $x = 4.0$ for fluorine), values for other elements can be calculated from data on bond dissociation enthalpies. Table 4.1 shows the principal elements of the periodic table together with their Pauling electronegativity values.

Electronegativity generally increases from left to right across the periodic table, and decreases from top to bottom. The most electronegative elements are thus concentrated in the top right-hand corner,

Table 4.1 Pauling electronegativity values of important elements

1A	2A	3A	4A	5A	6A	7A	←	8	→	1B	2B	3B	4B	5B	6B	7B
H 2.1																
Li 1.0	Be 1.5											B 2.0	C 2.5	N 3.0	O 3.5	F 4.0
Na 0.9	Mg 1.2											Al 1.5	Si 1.8	P 2.1	S 2.5	Cl 3.0
K 0.8	Ca 1.0	Sc 1.3	Ti 1.5	V 1.6	Cr 1.6	Mn 1.5	Fe 1.8	Co 1.8	Ni 1.8	Cu 1.9	Zn 1.6	Ga 1.6	Ge 1.8	As 2.0	Se 2.4	Br 2.8
Rb 0.8	Sr 1.0											In 1.7	Sn 1.8	Sb 1.9	Te 2.1	I 2.5
Cs 0.7	Ba 0.9											Tl 1.8	Pb 1.8	Bi 1.9	Po 2.0	At 2.2

with the least electronegative at the bottom left. The variation in electronegativity is related to variation in atomic radius. Electronegativity develops from left to right across a period because, as atomic radius decreases, there is an increase in the attractive force between the nucleus and the bonding electrons in the outer shell. Electronegativity declines from the top of a group to the bottom because the atoms become larger and the attraction between the nucleus and the peripheral electrons decreases.

The electronegativity concept is valuable throughout the whole of chemistry, and some of its principal uses are as follows:

(i) prediction of the degree of ionic character of a covalent bond (p. 67);
(ii) understanding the shapes of molecules (§4.6);
(iii) assignment of oxidation numbers (§5.1);
(iv) prediction of inductive effects in organic chemistry.

Dipole moment

A measure of the polarity of a molecule is provided by its *dipole moment* (μ), i.e. the turning moment which the molecule possesses, by virtue of its charge separation, when introduced into an electrical field (Fig. 4.14).

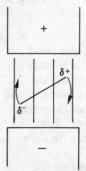

Fig. 4.14 The tendency of a polar diatomic molecule to orientate itself in an electric field.

The dipole moment of a diatomic molecule, in which the atoms carry charges of $+z$ and $-z$ respectively, and are a distance d apart, is defined by the equation:

$$\mu = z \times d$$

($+z$ and $-z$ correspond to δ^+ and δ^- respectively in Fig. 4.14.) A dipole moment is thus a vector quantity, since it has both magnitude and direction.

In a polyatomic molecule, the presence of polar covalent bonds does not necessarily result in an overall dipole moment; the geometry of the molecule also plays a part. Thus, although the electrons which constitute the C$=$O bond are displaced towards the oxygen atom, the carbon dioxide molecule has no dipole moment because the electron shifts cancel each other out:

$$\overset{\delta^-}{O}\!=\!\!=\!\!\overset{\delta^+\delta^+}{C}\!=\!\!=\!\!\overset{\delta^-}{O}$$

If, however, a molecule of the type AB_2 is angular instead of linear, electron displacements reinforce each other to give a dipole moment. This is the situation with water and sulphur dioxide:

$$\underset{\delta^-\;O\;\delta^-}{\overset{\delta^+}{H}\;\underset{104.5°}{\diagdown\diagup}\;\overset{\delta^+}{H}} \qquad \underset{\delta^+\;S\;\delta^+}{\overset{\delta^-}{O}\;\underset{119.5°}{\diagdown\diagup}\;\overset{\delta^-}{O}}$$

In any polyatomic molecule each covalent bond has its own dipole moment, known as a *bond moment* (m), which is proportional to the electronegativity difference between the two atoms that are bonded together. The dipole moment of the molecule as a whole is the sum of the vectors (i.e. directed quantities) of the various bond moments. Consider the water molecule shown in Fig. 4.15, in which the H—O—H bond angle is represented as 2θ.

Vectors along each O—H bond (Fig. 4.15(a)) can be broken down into two components mutually at right angles (Fig. 4.15(b)). Components q and s are equal and opposite and therefore cancel out. Vectors p and r reinforce each other to give a resultant along the line

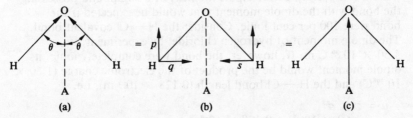

Fig. 4.15 The direction of the dipole moment of a water molecule.

AO (Fig. 4.15(c)). The magnitude of the vector along AO is $m \cos \theta$ for each O——H bond moment. Thus, the sum of the vectors of the bond moments, and hence the dipole moment of the compound, is $2m \cos \theta$.

The dipole moment of a compound can be determined experimentally from its behaviour when it is placed between oppositely charged electrodes. The SI unit for expressing dipole moments is the coulomb metre (C m), although a non-SI unit, the debye (D), is often used instead. (1 D = 3.335 640 × 10^{-30} C m.) The dipole moments of some typical covalent compounds are quoted in Table 4.2.

Table 4.2 Dipole moments of some compounds.

| Compound | Dipole moment | |
	(C m)	(D)
CH_4	0	0
CO	0.33 × 10^{-30}	0.10
CO_2	0	0
NH_3	4.94 × 10^{-30}	1.48
NF_3	0.73 × 10^{-30}	0.22
H_2O	6.14 × 10^{-30}	1.84
SO_2	5.44 × 10^{-30}	1.63
HCl	3.50 × 10^{-30}	1.05

The dipole moment of a molecule is often represented by an arrow drawn in the direction of the resultant, with the head pointing towards the negative end of the molecule and the tail lying near the positive end. The magnitude of the dipole moment is represented by the length of the arrow. Examples are as follows:

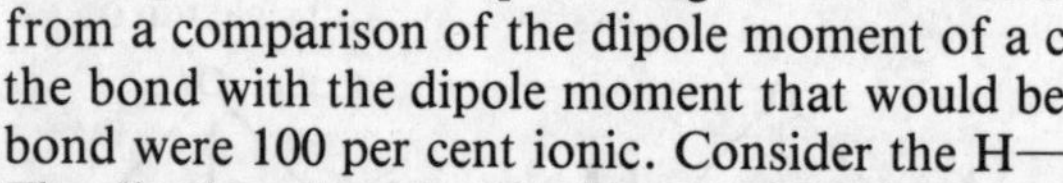

Percentage ionic character of a single bond

Pauling estimated the percentage ionic character of a covalent bond from a comparison of the dipole moment of a compound possessing the bond with the dipole moment that would be expected if the bond were 100 per cent ionic. Consider the H——Cl covalent bond. The dipole moment of hydrogen chloride, by experiment, is 3.50 × 10^{-30} C m. If, however, the bond were completely ionic, its dipole moment would be the product of the electronic charge (1.60 × 10^{-19} C) and the H——Cl bond length (0.128 × 10^{-9} m), i.e.

$$\mu = z \times d$$
$$= 1.60 \times 10^{-19} \times 0.128 \times 10^{-9}$$
$$= 20.48 \times 10^{-30} \text{ C m}$$

$$\therefore \text{ percentage ionic character} = \frac{\text{observed dipole moment}}{\text{calculated dipole moment}} \times 100$$

$$= \frac{3.50 \times 10^{-30}}{20.48 \times 10^{-30}} \times 100$$

$$= 17.1 \text{ per cent}$$

N.B.   Hannay and C.P. Smyth obtained results similar to Pauling's from a consideration of the electronegativity difference between the two atoms that are bonded together. If the two atoms A and B have electronegativities of x_A and x_B respectively, it can be shown empirically that:

$$\text{percentage ionic character} = 16(x_A - x_B) + 3.5(x_A - x_B)^2$$

From this formula a graph can be plotted (Fig. 4.16) relating the percentage ionic character of a bond to the electronegativity difference $x_A - x_B$.

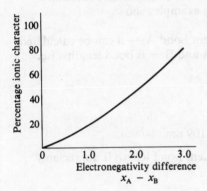

Fig. 4.16 The relationship between the percentage ionic character of a single bond and the electronegativity difference between the two atoms that are bonded together.

Figure 4.16 (or tables derived from it) can be used with Pauling electronegativity values to estimate the percentage ionic character of any covalent bond, e.g.

Bond A—B	x_A	x_B	$x_A - x_B$	Per cent ionic character (from graph)
F—H	4.0	2.1	1.9	43
Cl—H	3.0	2.1	0.9	17
Br—H	2.8	2.1	0.7	13
I—H	2.5	2.1	0.4	7

A qualitative assessment of the nature of a bond, often all that is necessary, can be made simply by comparing the difference of electronegativity values with 2.1. Figure 4.16 shows that a difference of 2.1 corresponds to approximately 50 per cent ionic character. A difference greater than 2.1 represents a bond which is effectively ionic, since one atom effectively gains control of the electron pair. To summarise:

$$A \overset{}{\underset{x}{\text{--}}} B \qquad \overset{\delta^-}{A} \overset{\delta^+}{\underset{x}{\text{--}}} B \qquad A^- \quad B^+$$

$$x_A = x_B \qquad x_A - x_B < 2.1 \qquad x_A - x_B > 2.1$$

non-polar bond $\qquad$ polar covalent bond $\qquad$ ionic bond

For example: $\quad$ F—Al $\quad x_F - x_{Al} = 2.5 \quad$ ionic bond

$\qquad\qquad\quad$ Cl—Al $\quad x_{Cl} - x_{Al} = 1.5 \quad$ polar covalent bond

A polar covalent bond is both shorter and stronger than a non-polar bond, owing to the attraction that exists between the oppositely charged atoms. For a non-polar bond the measured value for bond length or bond dissociation enthalpy is approximately equal to the calculated value, but for a polar bond the observed and calculated values do not agree, as the following examples show.

Bond length $\quad$ The length of a covalent bond A—B can be calculated as the arithmetic mean of the A—A and B—B bond lengths, i.e.

$$l_{A-B} = \tfrac{1}{2}(l_{A-A} + l_{B-B})$$

e.g.

$$l_{F-H} = \tfrac{1}{2}(l_{F-F} + l_{H-H})$$
$$= \tfrac{1}{2}(0.144 + 0.074) = 0.109 \text{ nm}$$

However, the *measured* F—H covalent bond length is appreciably shorter than this, being 0.092 nm.

Bond dissociation enthalpy $\quad$ In a similar manner the bond dissociation enthalpy of a covalent bond A—B can be calculated as the arithmetic mean of the A—A and B—B bond dissociation enthalpies, e.g.

$$DH^{\ominus}(F-H) = \tfrac{1}{2}[DH^{\ominus}(F-F) + DH^{\ominus}(H-H)]$$
$$= \tfrac{1}{2}(158 + 436) = 297 \text{ kJ mol}^{-1}$$

But the measured F—H bond dissociation enthalpy is 562 kJ mol^{-1}, indicating that the bond is much stronger than the calculation suggests. The difference is related to the electronegativity difference between the atoms although, as Pauling suggested, it is preferable to use geometric rather than arithmetic means in calculations of this sort.

4.5 The ionic bond

Compounds which are composed of ions (as opposed to molecules) are described as *ionic* or *electrovalent*. They are invariably crystalline solids of high melting temperature, in which oppositely charged ions are held together by electrostatic attraction.

In this section we are concerned first with the sizes of atoms and the ions to which they give rise. This subject is of paramount importance, for all trends associated with the periodic table, both down the groups and across the periods, can be attributed essentially to changing atomic or ionic radii. We shall continue with a study of the enthalpy changes accompanying the formation of ions, namely *ionisation enthalpy*, which is the enthalpy required to produce cations, and *electron affinity*, which is the enthalpy change accompanying the formation of anions. Afterwards we shall turn to *lattice enthalpy*, i.e. the enthalpy which is released when isolated cations and anions join together to give a crystal lattice, and we shall conclude by considering the formulae of ionic compounds; why, for example, sodium chloride has the formula $NaCl$ and not, say, $NaCl_2$.

Ionic radii

It can be seen from Fig. 4.17 that atomic radius increases down any group of the periodic table, as more electron shells are occupied, but decreases from left to right across a period (§3.4).

Ionic radius, like atomic radius, increases down a group and for the same reason. Movement across a period is marked by a decrease in both cationic and anionic radii. We must keep these concepts separate, for whereas any cation is *smaller* than its parent atom (compare Na^+ with Na), an anion is *larger* than its parent atom (compare Cl^- with Cl). The radius of a cation depends very much on its charge. As successive electrons are removed from an atom, ionic radius becomes smaller and smaller, e.g. $Na > Na^+ > Na^{2+}$, etc. Thus, for a series of isoelectronic ions, i.e. ions with the same number of electrons, such as we encounter when moving from left to right across a period, radius decreases as charge increases, e.g. $Na^+ > Mg^{2+} > Al^{3+}$.

For anions the reverse is true, in that a repulsion between the electrons of a negative ion causes an increase in size, and the more electrons that are introduced the larger it is, e.g. $N^{3-} > O^{2-} > F^-$.

For a sequence of isoelectronic ions, therefore, ionic radius decreases *in order of anions followed by cations*. The ions of a complete period are not all isoelectronic, for the anions have one more occupied shell than the cations, but the same rule applies, e.g. $N^{3-} > O^{2-} > F^- > Li^+ > Be^{2+} > B^{3+}$.

Ionisation enthalpy (ionisation energy)

The *first ionisation enthalpy* (ΔH_1) of an element is defined as the enthalpy required for the removal of 1 mol of electrons from 1 mol of

70

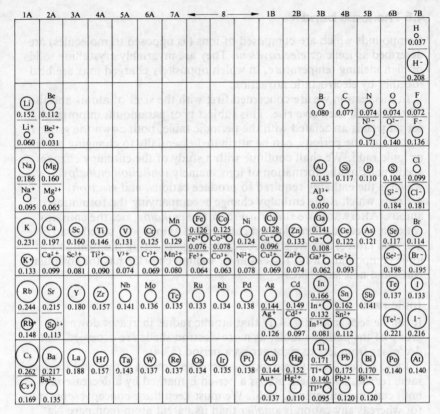

Fig. 4.17 Atomic and ionic radii in nanometres. The values quoted for metals are metallic bond radii, while those for non-metals are single covalent bond radii.

isolated atoms of the element, i.e.

$$M(g) \rightarrow M^+(g) + e^-$$

The *second ionisation enthalpy* (ΔH_2) is defined as the enthalpy needed for the removal of a second mole of electrons from 1 mol of isolated unipositive ions, i.e.

$$M^+(g) \rightarrow M^{2+}(g) + e^-$$

Higher ionisation enthalpies can be defined in a similar fashion. Thus, the nth ionisation enthalpy is the enthalpy required for the process:

$$M^{(n-1)+}(g) \rightarrow M^{n+}(g) + e^-$$

The second ionisation enthalpy of an element is always greater than the first; the third is greater still, and so on. For example:

	ΔH_1	ΔH_2	ΔH_3	/kJ mol^{-1} at 298 K
sodium	500	4 560	6 940	
magnesium	742	1 450	7 740	
aluminium	583	1 820	2 740	

There are several reasons for this, as follows.

(i)   As electrons are removed from an atom (or an ion) the remainder are more firmly held by the constant positive charge on the nucleus.

(ii) As the charge on a cation increases, its radius decreases (see above). Consequently, as we progress from M to M$^+$ to M^{2+}, etc, we are removing electrons which are ever closer to the nucleus (even if they belong to the same shell) and which are increasingly influenced by it. We can relate this idea to Fig. 2.12, which shows that ionisation enthalpy is the enthalpy required to remove completely an electron from an atomic orbital. As an orbital is pulled towards the nucleus its energy is lowered, and the ionisation enthalpy for the removal of an electron from it must increase, e.g. for magnesium:

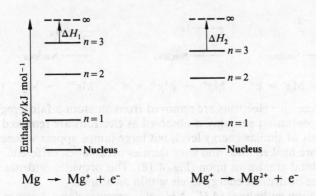

$$Mg \rightarrow Mg^+ + e^-$$

$$Mg^+ \rightarrow Mg^{2+} + e^-$$

(iii) For the alkali metals (group 1A), the jump from ΔH_1 to ΔH_2 is particularly large because the second electron to be removed originates from a lower shell. Thus, the first ionisation enthalpy of sodium relates to the removal of an electron from the third shell, while the second ionisation enthalpy relates to an electron leaving the second shell:

72

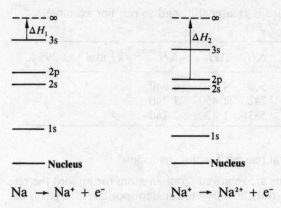

$$Na \rightarrow Na^+ + e^- \qquad\qquad Na^+ \rightarrow Na^{2+} + e^-$$

Similar effects are observed with elements of other groups wherever we start to draw electrons from a new shell. For example, this happens with group 2A elements as we move from the second to the third ionisation enthalpy:

$$Mg \rightarrow Mg^+ + e^- \qquad Mg^+ \rightarrow Mg^{2+} + e^- \qquad Mg^{2+} \rightarrow Mg^{3+} + e^-$$

When successive electrons are removed from an atom a fairly regular increase in ionisation enthalpy is observed as electrons are removed from orbitals of similar energy level, but large jumps appear whenever new shells are broken into, and irregularities occur when different types of orbital are drawn upon (Fig. 4.18). This provides evidence for the existence of distinct energy levels within an atom.

All ionisation enthalpies (ΔH_1, ΔH_2, etc) decrease down a group of the periodic table. The fall in first ionisation enthalpy corresponds to an increase in atomic radius, and is well illustrated by group 1A:

	Li	Na	K	Rb	Cs
ΔH_1/kJ mol^{-1} at 298 K	525	500	424	408	382

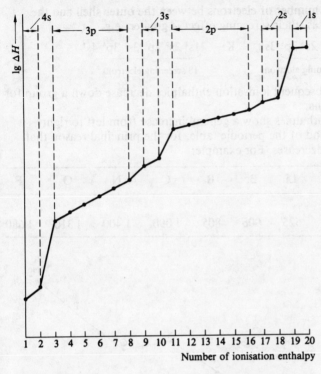

Fig. 4.18 Successive ionisation enthalpies of calcium.

As atoms become larger, the outer electron occupies a higher energy orbital so that less energy is required for its removal; compare sodium with potassium:

$$Na \rightarrow Na^+ + e^- \qquad K \rightarrow K^+ + e^-$$

Also, as the number of electrons between the outer shell and the nucleus increases, their screening effect is greater, e.g.

Na: $\underbrace{1s^2\ 2s^2\ 2p^6}\ 3s^1$ K: $\underbrace{1s^2\ 2s^2\ 2p^6\ 3s^2\ 3p^6}\ 4s^1$

     10 screening electrons   18 screening electrons

Second and subsequent ionisation enthalpies decrease down a group for the same reasons.

Ionisation enthalpies show a general increase from left to right across any period of the periodic table, for the principal reason that atomic radius decreases. For example:

	Li	Be	B	C	N	O	F
$\Delta H_1/\text{kJ mol}^{-1}$ at 298 K	525	906	805	1 090	1 400	1 310	1 680

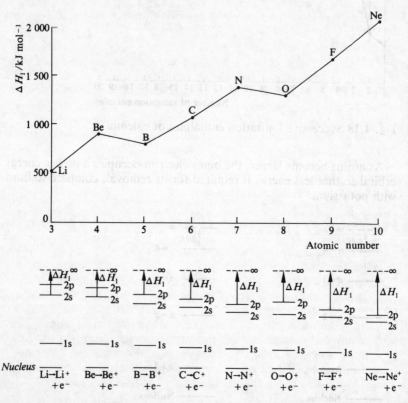

Fig. 4.19 First ionisation enthalpies of the elements of the second period.

As before, we can argue that the attraction between the outer electron and the nucleus increases as the distance between them decreases. The energy level of the outer atomic orbital therefore falls from left to right across a period, and the ionisation enthalpy must increase. Figure 4.19 illustrates graphically the first ionisation enthalpies of the elements of the second period (Li – Ne), with a diagrammatic explanation in terms of energy levels. There are two discontinuities to be explained, namely the decrease from beryllium to boron, and from nitrogen to oxygen.

(i)   The first ionisation enthalpy of boron is lower than that of beryllium because the electron is removed from a 2p orbital which is higher in energy than the 2s orbital of beryllium.

(ii) Whenever two electrons occupy a particular orbital they repel each other. As a result it is easier to remove one of the paired 2p electrons from an oxygen atom (Table 2.4) than it is to remove an unpaired 2p electron from a nitrogen atom.

Similar graphs are observed for the main group elements of other periods. They all show that ionisation enthalpies decrease on passing from an element with an ns^2 to an $ns^2 np^1$ configuration, and from one with an $ns^2 np^3$ to an $ns^2 np^4$ configuration.

Because it indicates quantitatively the ease of ion formation, ionisation enthalpy is a guide to the metallic character of an element. Thus, as ionisation enthalpy decreases down a group of the periodic table the elements become more metallic, and as ionisation enthalpy increases across a period the elements become less metallic. For this purpose ionisation enthalpy is to be preferred to standard electrode potential (§5.2). The latter comprises at least three separate enthalpy changes, only one of which is directly related to metallic character.

Electron affinity

All monoatomic anions have noble gas configurations. The ions are formed from atoms of non-metals in groups 5B, 6B and 7B of the periodic table by the gain of one or more electrons to the outer shell. As an electron is accepted by an atom or anion there is an enthalpy change known as the *electron affinity*.

Electron affinity is a net enthalpy change made up of two components. One component is the enthalpy required to move an isolated electron to the negatively charged outer shell of the atom. We shall call this the 'repulsion component'. The other is the enthalpy which is released when the electron, having reached the outer shell, enters it to give an anion. We shall call this the 'attraction component'.

The *first electron affinity* of an element is defined as the enthalpy released during the addition of 1 mol of electrons to 1 mol of isolated atoms of the element in the gaseous state, i.e.

$$A(g) + e^- \rightarrow A^-(g)$$

First electron affinity is always an exothermic change, because the attraction component is greater than the repulsion component. The values usually decrease down a group of the periodic table as the atomic radii of the elements increase, e.g.

	F	Cl	Br	I
ΔH_1/kJ mol^{-1} at 298 K	-342	-358	-336	-308

The reason is that the smaller the atom the closer is the outer shell to the nucleus and the more strongly are electrons attracted into it. This is in accordance with the inverse square law.

The value for fluorine is anomalous because it includes a high repulsion component. This is a consequence of a low atomic radius and a compact outer shell. Despite its relatively low electron affinity, fluorine is a better oxidant than chlorine because the bond dissociation enthalpy of the F——F bond is considerably below that of the Cl——Cl bond, i.e. a molecule of fluorine is dissociated into atoms more easily than a molecule of chlorine (§12.5).

The *second electron affinity* of an element relates to the uptake of a second electron, and is defined as the enthalpy *required* to add 1 mol of electrons to 1 mol of isolated uninegative ions, i.e.

$$A^-(g) + e^- \longrightarrow A^{2-}(g)$$

The change is endothermic because the repulsion component is greater than the attraction component. Among the few values that are known are those for oxygen and sulphur:

	O	S
ΔH_1/kJ mol^{-1} at 298 K	-136	-194
ΔH_2	$+850$	$+538$
Total electron affinity	$+714$	$+344$

It will be seen that the overall changes for the formation of O^{2-} and S^{2-} ions are endothermic.

Lattice enthalpy (lattice energy)

The strength of an ionic bond is denoted by *lattice enthalpy*; not by bond dissociation enthalpy, for this term applies only to a covalent bond. The lattice enthalpy of an ionic compound is defined as the enthalpy required for the separation of the ions in 1 mol of the crystal to an infinite distance from one another, i.e.

$$MX(s) \longrightarrow M^+(g) + X^-(g)$$

Lattice enthalpy can also be expressed as the *stabilisation energy* which is released when isolated gaseous ions join together so as to give 1 mol of the crystal. There is a decrease of both kinetic and potential energy during this process. Kinetic energy decreases because ions in the solid state have very little movement. (Only a certain amount of vibration is possible, whereas gaseous ions move about rapidly.) Electrical potential energy decreases as it always does when oppositely charged bodies are brought together.

Determination of lattice enthalpy

Lattice enthalpies are difficult to measure directly, but can readily be calculated from Born−Haber cycles. Consider the formation of 1 mol of an ionic compound M^+X^- from 1 mol of a metal, M, and 0.5 mol of a non-metal, X_2, i.e.

$$M(s) + \tfrac{1}{2}X_2(g, l \text{ or } s) = M^+X^-(s)$$

This reaction comprises the following steps.

(i) $M(s) = M(g)$ ΔH_1 = enthalpy of atomisation of the metal (endothermic).

(ii) $\tfrac{1}{2}X_2 (g, l \text{ or } s) = X(g)$ ΔH_2 = enthalpy of atomisation of the non-metal (endothermic). (For liquid or solid non-metals this term also includes the molar enthalpies of vaporisation or sublimation respectively.)

(iii) $M(g) = M^+(g) + e^-$ ΔH_3 = first ionisation enthalpy of the metal (endothermic).

(iv) $X(g) + e^- = X^-(g)$ ΔH_4 = first electron affinity of the non-metal (exothermic).

(v) $M^+(g) + X^-(g) = M^+X^-(s)$ ΔH_5 = lattice enthalpy of the compound (exothermic).

The information can be summarised by an enthalpy cycle known as a *Born−Haber cycle.*

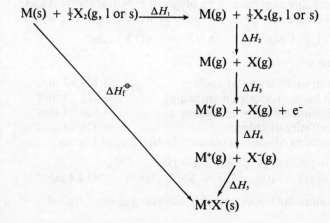

By Hess's law,

$$\Delta H_f^{\ominus} = \Delta H_1 + \Delta H_2 + \Delta H_3 + \Delta H_4 + \Delta H_5$$

Alternatively, we can draw the following enthalpy diagram.

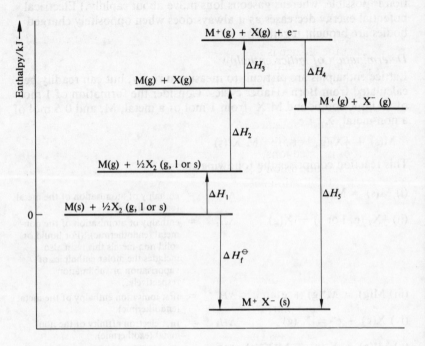

From the diagram,

$$\Delta H_f^{\ominus} = \Delta H_1 + \Delta H_2 + \Delta H_3 + \Delta H_4 + \Delta H_5$$

In either case lattice enthalpy (ΔH_5) can readily be calculated, since all the other enthalpy changes can be obtained experimentally. As an example, consider the formation of sodium chloride from its elements:

$$Na(s) + \tfrac{1}{2}Cl_2(g) = NaCl(s) \qquad \Delta H_f^{\ominus} = -411 \text{ kJ mol}^{-1}$$

$\Delta H_f^{\ominus}$ is the sum of:

(i)	enthalpy of atomisation of sodium	+109 kJ mol⁻¹
(ii)	$\tfrac{1}{2}$Cl—Cl bond dissociation enthalpy	+121 kJ mol⁻¹
(iii)	first ionisation enthalpy of sodium	+500 kJ mol⁻¹
(iv)	electron affinity of chlorine	−358 kJ mol⁻¹
(v)	lattice enthalpy of sodium chloride (ΔH_{LE})	unknown

$$\therefore -411 = +109 + 121 + 500 + (-358) + \Delta H_{LE}$$
$$\therefore \Delta H_{LE} = -411 - 109 - 121 - 500 + 358 = -783 \text{ kJ mol}^{-1}$$

If we wish to quote the lattice enthalpy according to our original definition, which concerns the *separation* of ions, we must write $+783$ kJ mol^{-1}.

For the formation of *gaseous* sodium chloride, i.e.

$$Na(s) + \tfrac{1}{2}Cl_2(g) = Na^+(g) + Cl^-(g)$$
$$\Delta H = +109 + 121 + 500 + (-358) = +372 \text{ kJ mol}^{-1}$$

This change is thus endothermic and unlikely to occur. (We cannot be *certain* that the change is impossible unless we consider free energy changes rather than enthalpy changes.) However, when sodium ions and chloride ions come together to form solid sodium chloride sufficient lattice enthalpy is released to turn this endothermic change into an exothermic one which is much more likely to take place.

Lattice enthalpy obtained from a Born–Haber cycle can be confirmed by calculating the stabilisation energy which is released in the approach of isolated ions, which we can regard as point charges. When one cation and one anion come together to give an *ion pair*, the electrostatic stabilisation energy (E_{ip}) is given by:

$$E_{ip} = \frac{(z_c e)(z_a e)}{4\pi\varepsilon d}$$

where e = electron charge, z_c and z_a = charge numbers of cation and anion respectively, d = distance between the ions and ε (epsilon) = permittivity (formerly 'dielectric constant') of the medium: $e = 1.60 \times 10^{-19}$ C, and for a vacuum $\varepsilon = 8.85 \times 10^{-12}$ farads per metre.

For a Na^+ Cl^- ion pair, $d = 0.281\,4 \times 10^{-9}$ m,

$$\therefore E_{ip} = \frac{(+1)(-1)(1.60 \times 10^{-19})^2}{4 \times 3.142 \times 8.85 \times 10^{-12} \times 0.281\,4 \times 10^{-9}} \text{ J}$$

$$= -8.18 \times 10^{-19} \text{ J} = -8.18 \times 10^{-22} \text{ kJ}$$

For the formation of 1 mol of ion pairs,

stabilisation energy = $E_{ip} \times L$,

where L = the Avogadro constant, 6.023×10^{23} mol^{-1}.

When the ion pairs join together in three dimensions to form a crystal, E_{ip} is increased by a factor which depends on the lattice geometry. This factor is known as the *Madelung constant*, A_M. Its value varies from one type of crystal lattice to another, but for the face centred cubic type of lattice, characteristic of sodium chloride, the value is 1.748.

Thus, for the formation of 1 mol of crystalline solid,

stabilisation energy = lattice enthalpy = $E_{ip} \times L \times A_M$
$\therefore$ lattice enthalpy (NaCl) = $-8.18 \times 10^{-22} \times 6.023 \times 10^{23} \times 1.748$
$\qquad\qquad\qquad\qquad = -861$ kJ mol^{-1}

This value is higher than that obtained by means of the Born–Haber cycle (-783 kJ mol^{-1}) because we have neglected the energy which is required to overcome repulsion between ions of similar charge as the ion pairs join together to form the crystal. The energy needed for this purpose has been calculated to be $+95$ kJ mol^{-1} for sodium chloride

$$\therefore \text{ lattice enthalpy (NaCl)} = -861 + 95 = -766 \text{ kJ mol}^{-1}$$

The value now corresponds very closely to that derived from the Born–Haber cycle.

Neglecting the repulsion effects, which are obviously much smaller than the attractive forces, we can argue from this theory that the lattice enthalpy of a compound depends mainly on the charge numbers (z) and radii (r) of its ions.

$$\Delta H_{LE} \propto \frac{z_c \times z_a}{d} \propto \frac{z_c \times z_a}{r_c + r_a}$$

where d represents the shortest interionic distance, and the subscripts 'c' and 'a' relate to the cation and anion respectively.

Lattice enthalpies therefore increase with ionic charge, but decrease with ionic radius. Thus, for a particular series of salts, the values decrease from top to bottom of any group of the periodic table as r_c or r_a increases, e.g.

	Group 1A					Group 7B		
	LiF	NaF	KF	RbF	CsF	NaF	NaCl	NaBr	NaI
ΔH_{LE}/kJ mol^{-1} at 298 K	1 035	915	814	780	729	915	783	745	696

Movement from left to right across a period is accompanied at first by an increase in lattice enthalpy as z_c increases (e.g. Na$^+$, Mg^{2+}, Al^{3+}), but finally by a decrease in lattice enthalpy as z_a decreases (e.g. N^{3-}, O^{2-}, F$^-$).

Surface charge density

A useful concept in connection with lattice enthalpy is *surface charge density*. The surface charge density of an ion is an indication of how densely the charge is distributed over its surface: it is directly related to the charge number (z), but inversely related to the surface area of the ion. Small ions with a high charge, e.g. Al^{3+}, have a high surface charge density, while large ions with a low charge, e.g. Cs$^+$, have a low surface charge density. For a compound in which both cation and anion have a high surface charge density, e.g. Al$_2$O$_3$, lattice enthalpy is high, while for one in which both ions have a low surface charge density, e.g. CsI, lattice enthalpy is low.

The effect of lattice enthalpy on the physical properties of ionic compounds

Lattice enthalpies have a major bearing on the ease or difficulty of any physical change in which the ions of a compound become separated from one another. This applies to melting, boiling and dissolving; thus lattice enthalpies influence the melting temperatures, boiling temperatures and solubilities of ionic compounds. The following statements are generalisations which will be discussed in more detail below.

(i)   High lattice enthalpy results in high melting temperature and boiling temperature, while low lattice enthalpy has the opposite effect. A low melting temperature may, however, be associated with a partially covalent bond.

(ii) High lattice enthalpy is responsible for low water solubility, while low lattice enthalpy leads to high solubility. Exceptions can occur because water solubility is governed by two factors, namely lattice enthalpy and hydration enthalpy, and while the former is usually dominant this is not invariably so.

Melting and boiling temperatures

The processes of melting and boiling require the overcoming of electrostatic attraction between ions. Consequently, the melting and boiling temperatures of a compound are related to its lattice enthalpy, which in turn is related to the charge numbers of its ions (see above). Thus, as we progress from group 1A to group 2A of the periodic table, with an increase in z_c from $+1$ to $+2$, the lattice enthalpies of compounds increase and their melting and boiling temperatures increase, e.g.

	$\Delta H_{LE}/kJ\ mol^{-1}$	$\theta_{C,m}/°C\ (T_m/K)$	$\theta_{C,b}/°C\ (T_b/K)$
caesium chloride	657	645 (918)	1 287 (1 560)
barium chloride	2 042	957 (1 230)	1 557 (1 830)

Clearly, if we double z_c and double z_a lattice enthalpy increases fourfold, provided that all else remains constant. That is why magnesium oxide has the very high melting temperature of 2 800 °C (3 073 K), while sodium chloride, with an identical structure, melts at 801 °C (1 074 K).

Within a particular group of the periodic table, and for a particular series of ionic compounds, lattice enthalpies and hence melting temperatures decrease down the group, e.g.

	LiCl	NaCl	KCl	RbCl	CsCl
lattice enthalpy/ kJ mol^{-1}	858	783	713	688	657
$\theta_{C, m}/°C$ (T_m/K)	607 (880)	801 (1 074)	767 (1 040)	715 (988)	645 (918)

The relatively low melting temperature of lithium chloride suggests that the bonding in this compound has a certain amount of covalent character.

Solubility

Ionic compounds vary considerably in their solubility in water, from extremely soluble compounds such as calcium iodide to almost totally insoluble compounds such as barium sulphate. To understand this variation we must begin by visualising the dissolving process.

Ions in solution are separated by a considerable distance and are able to move about in a random manner. To achieve this state, the crystal structure must be completely broken down. The lattice enthalpy must be overcome, and the energy which is required for this purpose originates from the hydration of ions.

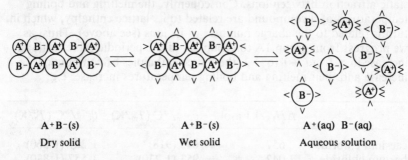

$A^+B^-(s)$	$A^+B^-(s)$	$A^+(aq)$ $B^-(aq)$
Dry solid	Wet solid	Aqueous solution

Fig. 4.20 The dissolving of an electrovalent compound A^+B^- in water. represents a water molecule, i.e.

$$\overset{\delta^+}{H} \overset{\times}{\underset{\delta^-}{\times}} \overset{\delta^+}{H} \\ O$$

When an ionic solid is placed in water, some of the water molecules, because of their charge separation, orientate themselves towards the cations and anions (Fig. 4.20). The process is entirely spontaneous, because unlike charges attract each other, and energy is released which may be sufficient to overcome the lattice enthalpy of the compound. Every ion has its own *hydration enthalpy*, which is defined as the enthalpy released during the hydration of 1 mol of isolated ions in the gaseous state by an infinitely large quantity of water, i.e.

$$X^{n\pm}(g) + aq \rightarrow X^{n\pm}(aq)$$

Let the sum of the hydration enthalpies of cation and anion be represented by ΔH_{hyd}. Then in general:

if $|\Delta H_{LE}| \gg |\Delta H_{hyd}|$, AB is insoluble;

if $|\Delta H_{hyd}| \gg |\Delta H_{LE}|$, AB is soluble;

and if $|\Delta H_{hyd}| \approx |\Delta H_{LE}|$, AB is likely to be soluble.

(Vertical lines denote numerical values irrespective of sign.)

Although water solubility is controlled primarily by lattice enthalpy and hydration enthalpy, certain other factors, notably the entropy change, also play a part. In all cases, when dissolution occurs, entropy increases.

The dissolution of AB is exothermic if $|\Delta H_{hyd}| > |\Delta H_{LE}|$, and endothermic if $|\Delta H_{LE}| > |\Delta H_{hyd}|$. The difference between ΔH_{LE} and ΔH_{hyd} gives the *enthalpy of solution* (ΔH_s) of the compound. This is defined as the enthalpy change when 1 mol of the solid is dissolved in a large quantity of water, such that the addition of more water produces no further enthalpy change.

Figure 4.21(a) represents the dissolving of a salt for which $|\Delta H_{LE}| > |\Delta H_{hyd}|$. The process is endothermic and ΔH_s is positive. The salt XY (Fig. 4.21(b)) dissolves in water exothermically. $|\Delta H_{hyd}| > |\Delta H_{LE}|$ and ΔH_s is negative.

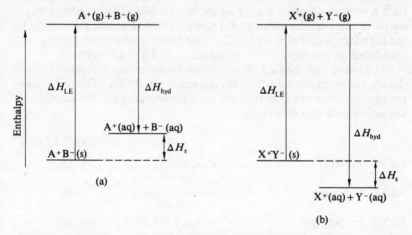

Fig. 4.21 Enthalpy changes on dissolving salts A^+B^- and X^+Y^- in water.

The hydration of ions is essentially an electrostatic process, but in the case of transition metal cations, the beryllium ion, and cations derived from metals in groups 3B, 4B and 5B of the periodic table, the ion−dipole attraction is reinforced by coordination. Hydration is always an exothermic process because it leads to a reduction of both potential energy and kinetic energy. Potential energy is lowered because the shells of water molecules effectively shield oppositely charged ions from one another, and kinetic energy is reduced because hydrated ions are bulky and move more slowly than the free ions.

The more water molecules an ion can attract, the greater is the loss of both potential and kinetic energy and the greater is the hydration enthalpy. Hydration enthalpy is therefore directly related to the charge number of an ion and inversely related to its size. We can combine these factors and argue that the hydration enthalpy of an ion is directly related to its surface charge density. Thus, hydration enthalpy decreases down any group of the periodic table (e.g. from the small Li^+ ion to the large Cs^+ ion) as the surface charge density decreases, but increases from left to right across a period (e.g. from Na^+ to Mg^{2+} to Al^{3+}) as the surface charge density increases.

Stoicheiometry of ionic compounds

Ionic compounds, like all natural substances, are electrically neutral. For sodium chloride this condition is satisfied by the formula NaCl, but could equally well be satisfied by the formula $NaCl_2$, i.e. $Na^{2+} (Cl^-)_2$. Admittedly, the ion Na^{2+} would not possess a noble gas configuration, but ions do not *necessarily* possess such structures. (Consider, for example, Sn^{2+}, Pb^{2+} and most ions of the transition elements.)

The formula $NaCl_2$ is by no means absurd, for in the formation of such a compound extra energy would be released. This would be due partly to the electron affinity of a second chlorine atom, but mainly to the high lattice enthalpy of $NaCl_2$. (The lattice enthalpy of $NaCl_2$, calculated on the basis of electrostatics, is $-2\,539$ kJ mol^{-1}; cf. -783 kJ mol^{-1} for NaCl.) However, as the following calculation shows, the extra energy which is released is totally insufficient to compensate for the extra energy requirement, especially for the second ionisation enthalpy of sodium.

$$\Delta H^{\ominus}/\text{kJ mol}^{-1}$$

$Na(s) \rightarrow Na(g)$	= enthalpy of atomisation	$+109$
$Na(g) \rightarrow Na^+(g)$	= first ionisation enthalpy	$+500$
$Na^+(g) \rightarrow Na^{2+}(g)$	= second ionisation enthalpy	$+4560$
$Cl_2(g) \rightarrow 2Cl(g)$	= bond dissociation enthalpy	$+242$
$2Cl(g) \rightarrow 2Cl^-(g)$	= 2 × electron affinity	-716
$Na^{2+}(g) + 2Cl^-(g) \rightarrow NaCl_2(s)$	= negative lattice enthalpy	-2539

$\therefore$ for $Na(s) + Cl_2(g) = NaCl_2(s)$, $\qquad \Delta H_f^{\ominus} = \qquad +2\,156$ kJ mol^{-1}

The positive enthalpy change is so large that the possibility of $NaCl_2$ being formed is very remote. The formulae of other compounds can be justified in a similar manner.

4.6 Shapes of molecules and ions

Although the structural formula of methane is commonly written as

H
|
H——C——H, it has been known for many years that the molecule is
|
H

not planar. As long ago as 1874 J. van't Hoff and J. Le Bel proposed that the four covalent bonds of the carbon atom were directed towards the four corners of a regular tetrahedron (Fig. 4.22).

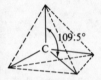

Fig. 4.22 A carbon atom located in the centre of a tetrahedron.

More recently, electron diffraction experiments, which are used to measure bond angles and bond lengths, have confirmed this view.

According to N.V. Sidgwick and H.M. Powell (*Sidgwick–Powell theory*, 1940), the shape of the methane molecule is due to electrostatic repulsion between the four pairs of electrons which constitute the C——H covalent bonds. The observed H——C——H bond angle of 109.5° is the maximum that is possible, and is due to the four bond pairs arranging themselves so as to minimise their mutual repulsions. A simple test of the theory can be conducted by tying together four balloons, each representing a bond pair of electrons. It will be found that the balloons repel one another equally, and in doing so arrange themselves so that they point towards the corners of a regular tetrahedron.

It is important to realise that *on this theory* the shape of the molecule is due primarily to repulsion between bond pairs of electrons, and not to repulsion between the hydrogen atoms.

The linear structure of beryllium chloride, the trigonal planar structure of boron trifluoride, and the symmetrical structures of many other simple molecules and ions can all be explained on the Sidgwick–Powell theory in terms of repulsion between bond pairs of electrons (Fig. 4.23).

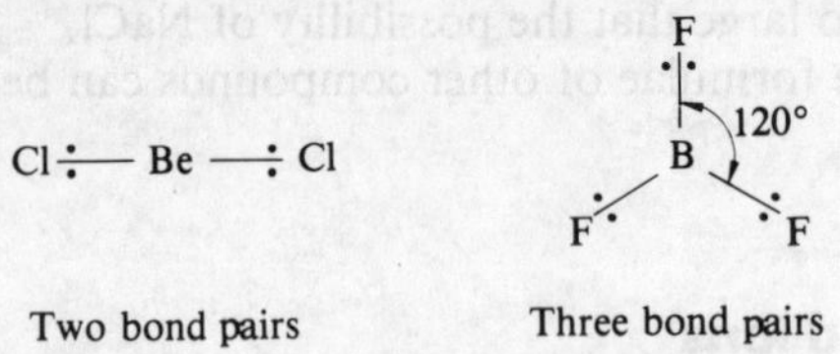

$$Cl \overset{\cdot}{\cdot} Be \longrightarrow \overset{\cdot}{\cdot} Cl$$

Two bond pairs   Three bond pairs

Fig. 4.23 The shapes of the beryllium chloride and boron trifluoride molecules.

Because ammonia and boron trifluoride have similar formulae we might expect the molecules to have similar shapes, but experiment shows that the ammonia molecule (Fig. 4.24(a)) is not planar: the plane of the hydrogen atoms is depressed below the nitrogen atom, and the H——N——H bond angle is 106.7°.

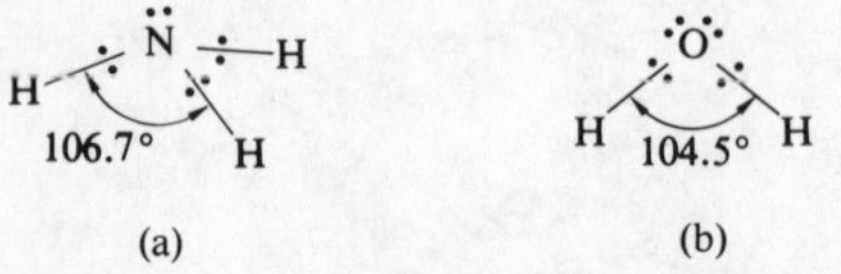

(a)   (b)

Fig. 4.24 (a) The trigonal pyramidal shape of the ammonia molecule. (b) The angular shape of the water molecule.

The difference between the BF_3 and NH_3 molecules stems from the fact that in the latter the central atom possesses a lone pair of electrons, which repels the three bond pairs. Consequently, the shape of the molecule is governed by repulsion between *four* pairs of electrons, cf. methane, and we might reasonably expect a bond angle of 109.5°. The fact that the observed bond angle is less than this must mean that the repulsion between lone pair and bond pair is greater than that between two bond pairs. There are two reasons for this. First, the lone pair of electrons is closer to the bond pairs than the bond pairs are to one another, and second, the lone pair is able to spread sideways, whereas each bond pair is strongly orientated along the line between the nitrogen and hydrogen atoms.

The angular shape of the water molecule (Fig. 4.24(b)) can be explained in the same way. Again, the shape is due to repulsion between four pairs of electrons, but in this molecule they comprise two bond pairs and two lone pairs. The relatively small bond angle of 104.5° reflects the high repulsion which exists between two lone pairs of electrons.

The order of repulsion between electron pairs is thus as follows:

two lone pairs > lone pair and bond pair > two bond pairs.

The hydrogen sulphide molecule is structurally similar to the water molecule, and we might perhaps expect it to possess an identical shape, but experiment shows that while it is bent, like the water molecule, the bond angle is only 92.5°. Because sulphur is less electronegative than oxygen, the location of the bond pairs of electrons in the two molecules is different (Fig. 4.25). The relative remoteness of the bond pairs from the sulphur atom allows the H_2S molecule to 'close up' rather more than the water molecule.

Fig. 4.25 A comparison of the shapes of the water and hydrogen sulphide molecules.

In their influence on molecular or ionic shape, multiple bonds, because they occupy only one position in space, act as single bonds. Thus, the carbon dioxide molecule is linear, and in ethene the distribution of bonds about each carbon atom is trigonal planar (Fig. 4.26).

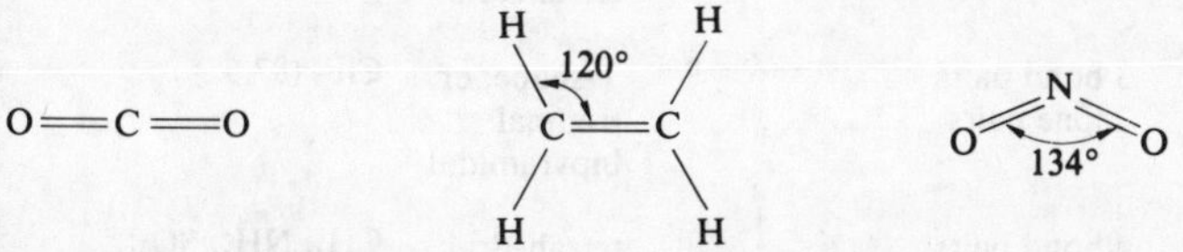

Fig. 4.26 The shapes of the carbon dioxide, ethene and nitrogen dioxide molecules.

An unpaired electron, such as exists in NO_2, ClO_2 and other stable free radicals, may be treated as half a lone pair. Thus, in the nitrogen dioxide molecule (Fig. 4.26) the O—N—O bond angle is 134°. If the unpaired electron were absent the bond angle would be 180° (cf. CO_2), and if it were a lone pair the bond angle would be 115.4°, as in the nitrite ion, NO_2^-.

Table 4.3 shows the shapes of many simple molecules and ions. Regular shapes are obtained only when all the electron pairs are used in bonding to identical atoms. If some of the atoms are different, departures from the ideal shapes occur in accordance with the electronegativities of the elements concerned.

Because the shape of a molecule or ion is based merely on an electron count, without reference to the origin of the electrons or the orbitals to which they belong, the following simple procedure can be used to predict the shape of a species.

Table 4.3 The shapes of simple molecules and ions.

Stoicheiometry	Electron pairs	Shape	Description	Examples, with bond angle
AB_2	2 bond pairs	B—A—B	linear	$BeCl_2$, CO_2, $CH \equiv CH$
AB_2	2 bond pairs ½ lone pair		angular (wide angle)	NO_2 (134°)
AB_2	2 bond pairs 1 lone pair		angular, cf. trigonal planar	SO_2 (119.5°), O_3 (116.8°), NO_2^- (115.4°)
AB_2	2 bond pairs 1½ lone pairs		angular	ClO_2 (117°)
AB_2	2 bond pairs 2 lone pairs		angular, cf. tetrahedral	H_2O (104.5°), H_2S (92°), ClO_2^- (110°)
AB_3	3 bond pairs		trigonal planar	BF_3, SO_3, NO_3^-, CO_3^{2-} (all 120°)
AB_3	3 bond pairs 1 lone pair		trigonal pyramidal, cf. tetrahedral	NH_3 (106.7°), PH_3 (93°), SO_3^{2-} ($\angle$ not known)
AB_3	3 bond pairs 2 lone pairs	B—A—B	T-shape, cf. trigonal bipyramidal	ClF_3 (87.5°)
AB_4	4 bond pairs		tetrahedral	CH_4, NH_4^+, SO_4^{2-}, PO_4^{3-}, ClO_4^- (all 109.5°)
AB_4	4 bond pairs 2 lone pairs		square planar, cf. octahedral	XeF_4, $[ICl_4]^-$ (all 90°)
AB_5	5 bond pairs		trigonal bipyramidal $\angle B_1AB_2$ 90° $\angle B_2AB_2$ 120°	PF_5, PCl_5 (g)
AB_6	6 bond pairs		octahedral	SF_6, $[PF_6]^-$, $[AlF_6]^{3-}$ and many other complex ions (all 90°)

(i) Count the number of outer electrons on the central atom. (This is equal to the group number of the element in the periodic table.)

(ii) To this add the number of electrons contributed by the atoms bonded to the central atom.

(iii) Divide the total by two to obtain the number of electron pairs.

(iv) Determine how many are bond pairs and how many are lone pairs.
(v) Apply the shapes listed in Table 4.3.

The Sidgwick–Powell theory does not apply to complexes of the transition elements.

4.7 The metallic bond

Although there is no clear dividing line between metals and non-metals, metals can generally be characterised by the following properties: metallic lustre, high ductility and malleability, high electrical and thermal conductivity, and high electropositive nature. These properties can be satisfactorily explained by the modes of packing of metal atoms and by the type of bonding which holds them together.

Metallic structure

Most metals have a coordination number of 12 (i.e. each atom is surrounded by 12 other atoms) and pack together very tightly in the face centred cubic (Fig. 4.27(a)) or hexagonal systems (Fig. 4.27(b)). This type of packing is very efficient and is known as *close packing*.

A comparison of the two modes of packing in Fig. 4.28 shows the much greater efficiency of close packing. Some metals display a slightly less efficient method of packing, namely body centred cubic. In this case the coordination number is 8, i.e. each metal atom is surrounded by eight others.

face centred cubic:	copper, silver, gold, aluminium, γ-iron
hexagonal:	magnesium, beryllium, zinc
body centred cubic:	sodium, potassium, α-iron, tungsten

These results have been confirmed by X-ray diffraction studies.

Metallic bonding

The structures and properties of metallic elements suggest that the force of attraction between atoms is too strong to be due solely to van der Waals' forces (§4.8). On the other hand, the presence of ionic or covalent bonds does not provide a satisfactory explanation for these properties either. Ionic bonds are unlikely because only one type of atom is present and electron transfer cannot take place. Covalent bonds are equally unlikely, because not enough electrons are present in the valence shells of the atoms to allow electron-pair formation with 8 or 12 nearest neighbours. In addition, some free movement of electrons is necessary to explain the high electrical conductivity of metals. The only conclusion to be drawn from this discussion is that we have a type

90

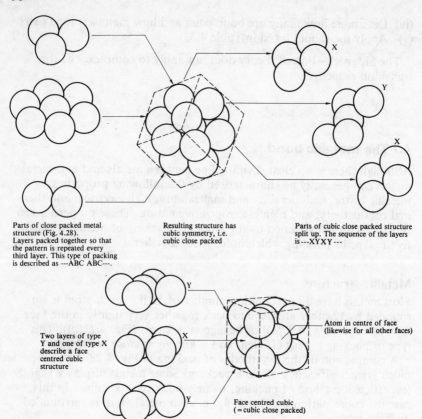

Parts of close packed metal structure (Fig. 4.28). Layers packed together so that the pattern is repeated every third layer. This type of packing is described as ---ABC ABC---.

Resulting structure has cubic symmetry, i.e. cubic close packed

Parts of cubic close packed structure split up. The sequence of the layers is ---XYXY---

Two layers of type Y and one of type X describe a face centred cubic structure

Atom in centre of face (likewise for all other faces)

Face centred cubic (= cubic close packed)

Fig. 4.27(a) Cubic close packing (face centred cubic).

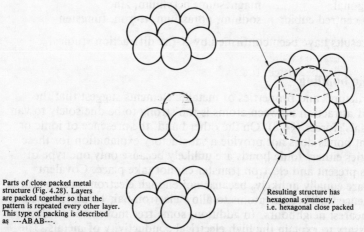

Parts of close packed metal structure (Fig. 4.28). Layers are packed together so that the pattern is repeated every other layer. This type of packing is described as ---ABAB---.

Resulting structure has hexagonal symmetry, i.e. hexagonal close packed

Fig. 4.27(b) Hexagonal close packing

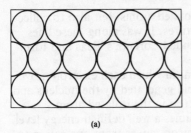 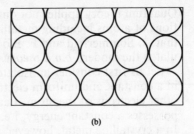

(a)   (b)

Fig. 4.28 (a) Close packing, and (b) non-close packing, of metal atoms in one layer.

of bonding different from anything we have considered before; it is called a *metallic bond*.

The first theory of metallic bonding was proposed by H.A. Lorentz in 1923. He suggested that a crystalline metal comprises a lattice of metal cations, which are formed from metal atoms by the loss of the outer or 'valency' electrons. The electrons which are lost in this way do not remain in one place but are *delocalised*, i.e. they move freely throughout the lattice. To summarise, Lorentz envisaged a metal as a collection of metal ions embedded in a 'sea' or a 'cloud' of delocalised electrons. On this simple theory, the cohesion or electrostatic attraction that exists between the metal ions and the sea of electrons constitutes the metallic bond.

Many of the properties of metals can be explained on this simple theory. Of particular note is electrical conductivity. In the absence of a potential difference across the metal the electron motion is random, but when a potential difference is applied delocalised electrons move in one direction and a current flows.

Physical properties, such as melting temperature and boiling temperature, generally increase with the strength of the metallic bond. This in turn depends upon two factors.

(i)   The structure of the crystalline metal. The closer the packing of cations in the lattice, the stronger is the metallic bond.

(ii) The surface charge density of the metal ions. This is to be expected, since the attraction between the sea of electrons and the cations depends upon the density of charge on the latter. Good examples of the effect of surface charge density are to be seen in the physical properties of the s-block elements (Table 7.1). Another example concerns the melting temperatures of sodium, magnesium and aluminium. The values increase with atomic number as the surface charge densities of the cations increase, i.e. $Na^+ < Mg^{2+} < Al^{3+}$.

Because this theory accounts for some of the properties of metals, we must not think that it represents the complete and correct picture.

92

Quantum theory applies not only to isolated atoms, but also to collections of atoms including metallic structures. It was along these lines that A. Sommerfeld and F. Bloch extended Lorentz's ideas and formulated the modern *band theory*.

Let us first consider an isolated atom, in which each electron moves in a constant and uniform electrical field generated by the nucleus and other electrons of the atom. Each electron in the isolated atom possesses a constant energy, i.e. it occupies a well defined energy level. In a crystalline metal, however, an electron moves from one cation to another, and the electrical field that it experiences varies. All the delocalised electrons move in an electrical field which varies periodically throughout the whole of the crystal. In this situation, energy levels are no longer precisely defined as they are in an isolated atom. Consider, for example, the outer s levels of atoms comprising a metal lattice. In the isolated atoms these outer s electrons are degenerate, but in the metal lattice this degeneracy is lost because the s electrons move through an electrical field which varies periodically. As a result, there is a *band* of closely spaced energy levels, derived from the s levels of the isolated atoms. Each of the s orbitals contributes one energy level to the band, and each level of the band (like each s orbital) can accommodate two spin-paired electrons. To summarise, n isolated atoms give a band of n energy levels, and the complete band can hold $2n$ electrons.

Energy — n isolated atoms — Band comprising n energy levels closely spaced in the crystal

The complete band model includes all the energy levels of an atom. However, electrons derived from the lower and full levels of an atom remain essentially localised, and for simplicity only the outer or 'valency' electrons are considered here.

Let us now consider a few examples in more detail. In a crystal of sodium, formed by the accumulation of n atoms, each atom provides one electron to the 3s band, i.e. the band derived from the 3s levels. Since the 3s band can hold $2n$ electrons it is only half full in the case of sodium. Electrons at or near the top of the band can move relatively easily into the unfilled higher levels of the band. In this way the electrons can move randomly through the crystal. The application of a potential difference causes the electrons to move in one direction only, but again electron movement is via the unfilled levels of the band. Electron movement can occur only if the band derived from the outer level is not completely filled. Put simply, if the electrons are to move, they must have somewhere to go. If a band is full, there is nowhere for them to go; they are therefore unable to move and the electrical conductivity is zero.

In magnesium the 3s band is full, because the *n* magnesium atoms contribute 2*n* 3s electrons to the 3s band. We should therefore expect magnesium to be a non-conductor. In fact, however, it is a conductor, because there is another band which overlaps the 3s one. This is the 3p band, which is formed from the (vacant) 3p levels of the magnesium atom.

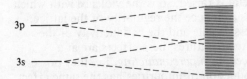

Because of this overlap, electrons at or near the top of the full 3s band can move easily into the vacant 3p band; magnesium is therefore able to conduct electricity. In aluminium, likewise, the full 3s band overlaps the partly filled 3p band and so, again, electron movement occurs from the 3s to the 3p band. A similar overlap occurs also in the case of sodium.

To summarise, electrical conductivity is associated with:

(i)   partially filled bands; or
(ii) overlapping of filled with either partially filled or vacant bands.
      With the transition elements d bands are also involved.

One of the advantages of the band theory is that it can be expanded to encompass non-conductors and semi-conductors.

Properties of metals

Metallic lustre

Lustre is the result of metals reflecting light very strongly. This is partly because of the highly efficient close packing of atoms in metals; the resulting high density of atoms gives a correspondingly high opacity. Also, since electrons are mobile, energy transitions can occur with great ease, so that light of all frequencies can be absorbed and re-emitted shortly afterwards. Both effects lead to high reflectivity.

High ductility and malleability

Metal atoms lie in layers one on top of another (Fig. 4.27). The layers are not held rigidly in position because there are no rigid bonds between the atoms. They can therefore move (or slip) over one another on the application of mild stress. Slippage over a distance of one atom restores the original structure. If the slippage is less than one inter-atomic distance the atoms move back to their original positions on the removal of the stress. (They are said to be *elastic*.) This ease of movement of one layer of atoms over another causes the metal to be malleable. The ductility of metals is also a direct consequence of the ease of slippage.

High electrical conductivity

We have already seen that electrons can flow through a metal by making use of vacant higher energy levels. Under an applied electrical potential electrons pass from the cationic lattice to the positive pole, and more electrons flow in from the negative pole to take their place. There is therefore a high electrical conductivity through the metal.

As the temperature of a metal is raised, so is the violence with which the cations vibrate. This tends to reduce the regularity of the lattice; hence the electrons become less mobile and the conductivity of the metal decreases. At very low temperatures these effects are at a minimum and metals often become *superconducting*, i.e. they possess very low resistance. The introduction of impurities has the same effect as raising the temperature, in that it destroys regularity in the crystal and increases the resistance.

High thermal conductivity

The atoms in a metal are relatively free to vibrate, and can transfer kinetic energy readily by their movement and by collision. This is responsible for high thermal conductivity.

4.8 van der Waals' forces (intermolecular forces)

We discussed earlier (§4.4) the existence of permanent dipoles in

molecules such as HCl ($\overset{\delta^+}{\text{H}}$——$\overset{\delta^-}{\text{Cl}}$), but this does not explain the fact that many molecules like H_2 or even atoms like helium have no permanent dipoles and yet are capable of liquefaction. They must therefore form strong enough intermolecular attractions to overcome thermal excitation, at least at low temperatures where liquefaction occurs. An explanation was postulated by F. London. He suggested that the electrons in, say, H_2 are not always midway between the atoms but are in constant motion and can for a fraction of a microsecond be nearer one atom than the other, giving rise to a dipole with one atom slightly positive and the other slightly negative. These 'temporary dipoles' abound, and the positive end of one H_2 molecule will attract the negative end of another. As the molecules get closer together the forces of attraction increase until the molecules are so close that their electron clouds repel each other. Eventually equilibrium is reached, where the forces of attraction and repulsion are equal. At this stage the distance between them is known as the *collision diameter* (σ) (Fig. 4.29). The type of temporary dipole arising in atoms is shown in Fig. 4.30.

The forces of attraction due to the presence of temporary and permanent dipole moments are known as *van der Waals' forces* and are independent of normal bonding forces. When these forces are strong

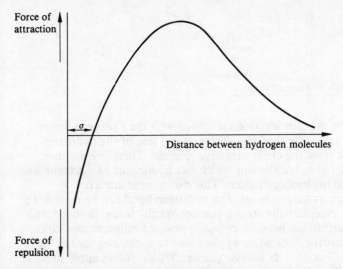

Fig. 4.29 Forces of attraction and repulsion between two hydrogen molecules at varying distances from each other.

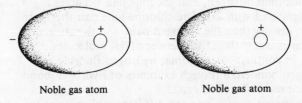

Noble gas atom   Noble gas atom

Fig. 4.30 Temporary dipoles in atoms of a noble gas.

enough to overcome thermal agitation (i.e. when the molecules are close enough together), they increase rapidly and cause liquefaction. This increase is represented by the peak in Fig. 4.29. It can be shown that a and b in the van der Waals' equation are related to the forces of attraction and repulsion; a to the forces of attraction and b to both.

4.9 Hydrogen bonding

Intermolecular forces of attraction, very much stronger than van der Waals' forces, exist wherever hydrogen is covalently bonded to strongly electronegative elements such as fluorine, oxygen or nitrogen. In this situation the bond pair of electrons is attracted closer to these elements than to hydrogen, and dipoles are formed (§4.4).

$$\overset{\delta^+}{H}\!\!-\!\!\overset{\delta^-}{F} \qquad \overset{\delta^-}{O}\!\!\begin{matrix}\overset{\delta^+}{H}\\ \\ \underset{\delta^+}{H}\end{matrix} \qquad \overset{\delta^-}{N}\!\!\begin{matrix}\overset{\delta^+}{H}\\ \overset{\delta^+}{H}\\ \underset{\delta^+}{H}\end{matrix}$$

decreasing strength of dipole moments
————————————————————————→

Since these are the only electrons involved with the hydrogen atom, there will be very little shielding effect on the side of the hydrogen atom furthest from the electronegative element. Therefore another strongly electronegative element which has a lone pair of electrons will be attracted to the hydrogen atom. This electrostatic attraction is referred to as a *hydrogen bond*. The hydrogen bond can be regarded as a special and exceptionally strong van der Waals' force. Both involve electrostatic attraction between opposite poles of adjacent molecules, but whereas hydrogen bonding applies only to molecules containing H—F, H—O or H—N bonds, van der Waals' forces apply to all other molecules and also to atoms of the noble gases.

On this basis we might expect chlorine, which has a similar electronegativity to nitrogen, to form hydrogen bonds. However, chlorine has a larger atomic radius than nitrogen, and the lone pair occupies a larger orbital (3p compared with 2s). The chlorine lone pair therefore has a lower electron density than the nitrogen pair, and the attraction between HCl molecules is less than that between NH_3 molecules. Hydrogen chloride, in contrast to ammonia, hydrogen fluoride and water, is not hydrogen bonded, although examples of hydrogen bonding involving chlorine are believed to exist.

When hydrogen bonding occurs between different molecules of the same compound, as in HF and H_2O (see below), it is referred to as *intermolecular hydrogen bonding*. Hydrogen bonding may also occur within a single molecule, as in the case of 2-nitrophenol:

This is known as *intramolecular hydrogen bonding*.

Although the forces of attraction giving rise to hydrogen bonds are several orders of magnitude weaker than for either ionic or covalent bonds, they are still strong enough to give compounds much higher boiling temperatures than might be anticipated. For example, we would expect water ($M_r = 18$) to have a lower boiling temperature than hydrogen sulphide ($M_r = 34$), but this is not so. Intermolecular hydrogen bonding between H_2O molecules is stronger than the van der Waals' forces between H_2S molecules; hence the melting temperature and boiling temperature of water are *higher* than those of hydrogen sulphide. Similar situations arise with hydrogen fluoride and ammonia, but not with methane (Fig. 4.31). These effects provide us with some of the best evidence for hydrogen bonding.

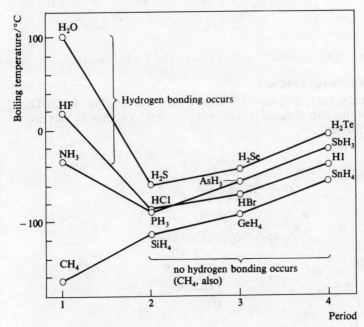

Fig. 4.31 Boiling temperatures of various hydrides.

When hydrogen bonding does not occur, as for example in H_2S, H_2Se and H_2Te, boiling temperatures increase almost linearly with relative molecular mass. Other physical properties, such as melting temperatures and enthalpies of vaporisation, show similar trends to boiling temperatures.

Structures involving hydrogen bonding

In the solid state and to a lesser extent in the liquid state hydrogen bonding often leads to the formation of one-, two- and three-dimensional structures.

One-dimensional structures

The relative molecular mass of hydrogen fluoride in the solid or liquid phase, or in the gaseous phase just above the boiling temperature, is found to be higher than the expected value of 20. This is because the molecules are hydrogen bonded together to form chains. The chains possess a zigzag structure, with is attributed to the fact that hydrogen bonding occurs through a lone pair of p electrons on the fluorine atom, thus:

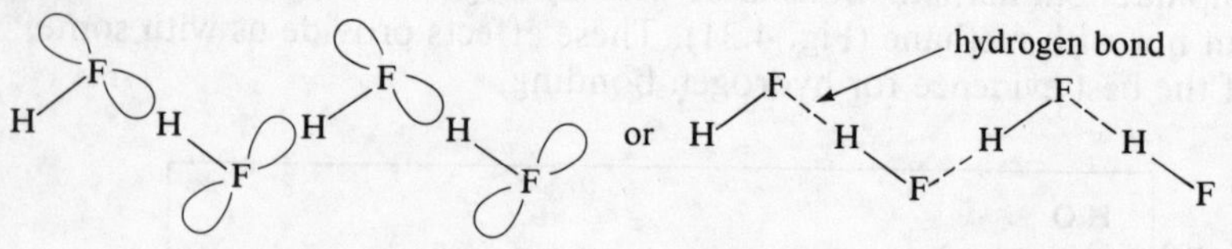

Adjacent chains are held together by van der Waals' forces.

Two-dimensional structures

This occurs, for example, in orthoboric acid, H_3BO_3 (Fig. 4.32). The layers of this two-dimensional network are held together by van der Waals' forces.

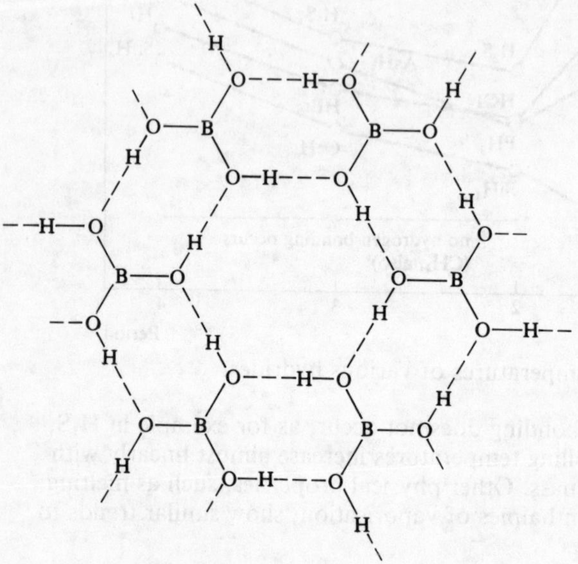

Fig. 4.32 The structure of orthoboric acid.

Three-dimensional structures

The classic example of this structure is ice, which has the form of the diamond lattice (Fig. 4.33).

The anomalous behaviour of water provides further evidence for the existence of hydrogen bonds. At 0°C (273 K), melting occurs with a

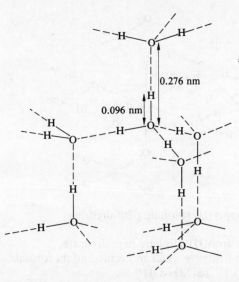

Fig. 4.33 Part of the structure of ice. The oxygen atoms are situated tetrahedrally to one another (cf. diamond). As the dimensions indicate, the hydrogen atoms do not lie midway between the oxygen atoms.

reduction in volume instead of the normal expansion. This is caused by the open structure of ice breaking down by the disruption of hydrogen bonds. The structure partially collapses, leading to a decrease in volume. In the liquid state this is opposed by the normal force of expansion. Both are enhanced by increasing temperature. Up to 4°C (277 K) the former predominates, and this is therefore the position of maximum density or minimum volume.

Hydrogen bonding is common in the structures of both natural and man-made fibres and is the cause of much of the strength of these materials. In cellulose, for example, carbohydrate chains are held together by hydrogen bonding involving O——H bonds, while in wool and nylon the chains are hydrogen bonded through N——H bonds.

Salt hydrates

Many hydrated salts have a hydrogen bonded water molecule acting as a bridge between the cation and the anion. This explains why so many salts form monohydrates. Copper(II) sulphate pentahydrate (Fig. 4.34) is a common example of this phenomenon, where the water molecule hydrogen bonded to the sulphate ion is retained after the four molecules coordinated to the Cu^{2+} ion are driven off on heating. The formula of hydrated copper(II) sulphate could thus be written as

100

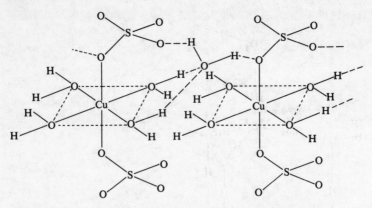

Fig. 4.34 The structure of copper(II) sulphate pentahydrate.

$[Cu(H_2O)_4]^{2+}$ $[SO_4(H_2O)]^{2-}$. Iron(II) sulphate heptahydrate, $FeSO_4 \cdot 7H_2O$, also contains a bridging water molecule and its formula could be written as $[Fe(H_2O)_6]^{2+}$ $[SO_4(H_2O)]^{2-}$.

Chapter 5

Oxidation and reduction

5.1 Electron transfer

Oxidation and reduction are complementary changes which occur whenever an oxidising agent (or 'oxidant') and a reducing agent (or 'reductant') are allowed to react together. The processes are interpreted in terms of the transfer of electrons, e.g.

$$\underset{\text{OXIDANT}}{Fe_2O_3} \quad + \quad \underset{\text{REDUCTANT}}{2Al} \quad = 2Fe + Al_2O_3$$

Reduction

Oxidation

As the iron(III) oxide is reduced to iron, so the aluminium is oxidised to aluminium oxide. Always, in an oxidation−reduction (or 'redox') reaction, the oxidant becomes reduced while the reductant becomes oxidised.

The essential change that aluminium suffers in its oxidation is a loss of electrons:

$$Al = Al^{3+} + 3e^-$$

The electrons are accepted by iron(III) ions in their reduction to iron:

$$Fe^{3+} + 3e^- = Fe$$

'Oxidation' can therefore be defined as electron loss and 'reduction' as electron gain. Oxidation–reduction is essentially a process of *electron transfer* from reducing agent to oxidising agent, and compares with neutralisation which, on the Brønsted–Lowry theory, is a process of *proton transfer* from acid to base.

We can now see why neither oxidation nor reduction can occur in isolation. Electrons originate from one species, which thereby becomes oxidised, and are transferred to another species, which consequently becomes reduced.

Oxidation numbers (oxidation states)

An *oxidation number* can be assigned to an element in any chemical species to indicate the extent to which it is oxidised or reduced. An oxidation number of zero is given to the elements themselves, for they are considered to be in neither an oxidised nor a reduced condition. In compounds, a positive oxidation number indicates that an element is in an oxidised state; the higher the oxidation number, the greater is the extent of oxidation. Conversely, a negative oxidation number shows that an element is in a reduced state. The following paragraphs show how oxidation numbers are computed.

Simple ions

If an element is present in the form of simple ions, its oxidation number is merely the ionic charge. Thus, in iron(II) chloride, Fe^{2+} $(Cl^-)_2$, iron has an oxidation number of $+2$ and chlorine -1.

Molecules

To establish the oxidation number of a particular element in a molecule, we write down the *formal charge* on every atom of that element and then calculate the average. The 'formal charge' is based on the assumption that the shared pair of electrons which constitutes the covalent bond is located at the more electronegative atom (§4.4). For example, in the hydrogen chloride molecule, in which the electron pair is displaced towards the chlorine atom, we assume that the electrons are located *entirely* at the chlorine atom.

$$\overset{\delta^+}{H} \longrightarrow \overset{\delta^-}{Cl} \text{ approximates to } \overset{+}{H} \; \overset{-}{:Cl}$$

In effect, we assume that the molecule approximates to the ionic state represented by $H^+ Cl^-$. Thus, the formal charge on the hydrogen atom is $+1$ and that on the chlorine atom -1. Since, in this particular molecule, there is only one atom of each element, hydrogen has an oxidation number of $+1$ and chlorine -1.

In the same way that the algebraic sum of the ionic charges of an electrovalent compound is zero, so the algebraic sum of the formal charges on the atoms of a covalent compound is also zero.

As another example, consider dinitrogen oxide, N_2O, which may be formulated as N===N----O, where ---- represents a delocalised π bond, or as N≡≡N→O. In computing the oxidation numbers of nitrogen and oxygen in this compound we need to remember that the nitrogen atoms have an identical electronegativity, while the electronegativity of oxygen is greater than that of nitrogen. The N===N and N——O bonds must be considered separately from the delocalised π bond.

N===N and N——O bonds The electrons constituting the N===N bond are formally considered to reside at the midway point between the two atoms, so that the charge on each is zero. However, polarisation of the N——O bond leads to the central nitrogen atom acquiring a charge of $+1$ and the oxygen atom -1:

N===N——O
+1 −1

Delocalised π bond This bond should be treated as a covalent bond involving three atoms. The electron pair is considered to be effectively at the oxygen atom; thus, oxygen gains a charge of -1, and each nitrogen atom $+\frac{1}{2}$:

N------N-----O
$+\frac{1}{2}$ $+\frac{1}{2}$ -1

To summarise, the terminal nitrogen atom has a formal charge of $+\frac{1}{2}$, the central nitrogen atom $+1\frac{1}{2}$, and the oxygen atom -2. The oxidation number of oxygen in this compound is -2, and that of nitrogen the mean of $+\frac{1}{2}$ and $+1\frac{1}{2}$, which is $+1$.

Covalent ions

Covalent ions are treated in essentially the same way as molecules. Consider, for example, the sulphate ion, in which a sulphur atom forms four covalent bonds and two delocalised π bonds with oxygen atoms. Because oxygen is more electronegative than sulphur, the formal charges on the atoms are as follows:

$$
\begin{bmatrix}
O_{-1} \quad\quad _{-1}O \\
_{-\frac{1}{2}}\diagdown {}^{+1+1}\diagup_{-\frac{1}{2}} \\
^{+1}S^{+1} \\
_{-\frac{1}{2}}\diagup {}_{+1+1}\diagdown_{-\frac{1}{2}} \\
O_{-1} \quad\quad _{-1}O
\end{bmatrix}^{2-}
$$

The dinegative charge is equally distributed among the oxygen atoms, so that the oxidation number of oxygen is -2, and that of sulphur $+6$.

A simpler view of the bonding leads to the same conclusion and is therefore justifiable.

$$\begin{bmatrix} O & & O \\ & S & \\ O & & O \end{bmatrix}^{2-} \qquad \text{approximates to} \qquad \begin{matrix} \overset{-2}{O} & & \overset{-2}{O}\ominus \\ & \overset{+6}{S} & \\ \overset{-2}{O} & & \overset{-2}{O}\ominus \end{matrix}$$

As with all covalent ions, the algebraic sum of the formal charges on the atoms is equal to the charge on the ion.

Uses of oxidation numbers

Oxidation numbers are used in chemical nomenclature (Ch. 1). They are also valuable in that if the hydrides, oxides and oxoacids of an element are arranged in order of oxidation number, the chemistry of that element can be seen as part of a logical pattern. Consider the case of nitrogen.

Oxidation number
of nitrogen

		$+5$	N_2O_5	HNO_3	NO_3^-
O	R	$+4$†	N_2O_4, NO_2		
X	E	$+3$	N_2O_3	HNO_2	NO_2^-
I	D	$+2$†	NO		
D	U	$+1$	N_2O		
A	C	0†	N_2		
T	T	-1	NH_2OH		
I	I	-2	N_2H_4		
O	O	-3†	NH_3	NH_4^+	
N	N				

† denotes a relatively stable oxidation state.

The chart helps us to understand why so many substances can appear when nitric acid functions as an oxidising agent. With a feeble reducing agent, such as copper, nitric acid is not extensively reduced and the principal product is nitrogen dioxide, but with a more powerful reductant, e.g. zinc, the nitrogen attains a lower oxidation state and the product may be dinitrogen oxide or even the ammonium ion. Hydrazine, N_2H_4, is a most unlikely product because it is too reactive: reactions tend to stop at relatively stable oxidation states.

The reduction of nitrous acid, in contrast to nitric acid, cannot possibly give nitrogen dioxide because NO_2 is *above* HNO_2 in the chart. Likely products are nitrogen oxide or the ammonium ion, depending on the power of the reducing agent.

The oxidation of ammonia, represented by upward movement on the chart, usually gives nitrogen. If, however, the conditions are severe the ammonia is oxidised further, to nitrogen oxide (§10.5).

The difference between the oxidation numbers of an element in reactant and product is equal to the number of electrons transferred in a redox reaction. Consider, for example, the oxidation of hydroxylamine, NH_2OH, to dinitrogen oxide. The difference in oxidation number, $-1 - (+1) = -2$, represents the number of electrons lost by a molecule of hydroxylamine in its oxidation. The same figure can be derived from the ionic half equation for the oxidation, i.e.

$$NH_2OH = \tfrac{1}{2}N_2O + \tfrac{1}{2}H_2O + 2H^+ + 2e^-$$

Oxidising agents and reducing agents

Oxidising agents

Any chemical species which can gain electrons and become reduced is capable of functioning as an oxidising agent. The more readily electrons are accepted, the more powerful is the oxidising action. Species such as H_2O, HO^- and PO_4^{3-}, in which all the elements are in a relatively stable oxidation state, do not accept electrons readily and are of no practical value as oxidising agents. A measure of the oxidising power of a species in aqueous solution, in the presence of its reduction product, is provided by its standard electrode potential ($E^{\ominus}$) (§5.2). The more positive the $E^{\ominus}$ value, the more powerful is the oxidising action.

Non-metals, such as oxygen and the halogens, serve as oxidising agents because they readily accept electrons:

$$\tfrac{1}{2}O_2 + 2H^+ + 2e^- = H_2O \quad E^{\ominus} = +1.23 \text{ V}$$
$$\tfrac{1}{2}F_2 + e^- = F^- \quad E^{\ominus} = +2.87 \text{ V}$$

Fluorine is the most powerful oxidising agent known. Oxidising power decreases from top to bottom of group 7B, and iodine, although it can be reduced to iodide ions, is not normally regarded as an oxidising agent.

Certain acids and ions which contain an element in a high and relatively unstable oxidation state also function as oxidising agents. Examples are concentrated nitric acid, concentrated sulphuric acid, and cerium(IV), dichromate and permanganate ions. Nitric acid may be reduced to nitrogen dioxide, and sulphuric acid to sulphur dioxide:

$$NO_3^- + 2H^+ + e^- = NO_2 + H_2O \quad\quad E^{\ominus} = +0.81 \text{ V}$$
$$2H_2SO_4 + 2e^- = SO_2 + 2H_2O + SO_4^{2-} \quad E^{\ominus} = +0.17 \text{ V}$$

The cerium(IV) ion is reduced to the more stable cerium(III) ion; and the dichromate ion, which contains chromium(VI), is reduced in acidic solution to the much more stable chromium(III) ion:

$$Ce^{4+} + e^- = Ce^{3+} \quad\quad E^{\ominus} = +1.45 \text{ V}$$
$$\tfrac{1}{2}Cr_2O_7^{2-} + 7H^+ + 3e^- = Cr^{3+} + \tfrac{7}{2}H_2O \quad E^{\ominus} = +1.33 \text{ V}$$

The permanganate ion contains manganese(VII). It is reduced to the manganese(II) ion in strongly acidic solution, to manganese(IV) oxide in weakly acidic or alkaline solution, and to the manganate ion in strongly alkaline solution (§14.7).

Reducing agents

In principle, a reducing agent is a chemical species which is capable of losing electrons, thereby becoming oxidised. Useful reducing agents must have a strong tendency to lose electrons; in water their standard electrode potentials must have negative or low positive values (below approximately $+0.80$ V). The more negative the $E^{\ominus}$ value, the more powerful is the reducing action.

Metals which are near the top of the electrochemical series (§5.2) satisfy this condition, for they are strongly electropositive elements, i.e. they readily form positive ions by the loss of electrons. Sodium, zinc, iron and tin are all well known laboratory reductants.

$$Na^+ + e^- = Na \qquad E^{\ominus} = -2.71 \text{ V}$$
$$Zn^{2+} + 2e^- = Zn \qquad E^{\ominus} = -0.76 \text{ V}$$

Ions and molecules which contain an element in a low and relatively unstable oxidation state may also be used. Of particular importance are sulphur dioxide and the sulphite ion (§11.5), and tin(II) and iron(II) ions:

$$Sn^{4+} + 2e^- = Sn^{2+} \qquad E^{\ominus} = +0.15 \text{ V}$$
$$Fe^{3+} + e^- = Fe^{2+} \qquad E^{\ominus} = +0.77 \text{ V}$$

Substances that act as both oxidants and reductants

If a substance can be both oxidised and reduced, then it will function as either a reducing agent or an oxidising agent, depending upon what reagent is added. When mixed with an oxidant more powerful than itself the substance will become oxidised and thus act as a reductant; conversely, in the presence of a more powerful reductant it will behave as an oxidant. Examples are hydrogen peroxide and sulphur dioxide.

Oxidation number of oxygen		*Oxidation number of sulphur*	
0		$+6$	
-1 $\quad$ H$_2$O$_2$ $\xrightarrow{\text{oxidation}}$ O$_2$		$+4$ $\quad$ SO$_2$ $\xrightarrow{\text{oxidation}}$ H$_2$SO$_4$ or SO$_4^{2-}$	
-2 $\qquad\qquad\xrightarrow{\text{reduction}}$ H$_2$O		0 $\qquad\qquad\xrightarrow{\text{reduction}}$ S	

Most nitrogen containing compounds (see previous chart and §5.3) can act as both oxidising agents and reducing agents. The only exceptions are nitric acid and ammonia and their respective derivatives. Nitric acid is incapable of being oxidised, because it contains nitrogen(V) which is the highest oxidation state of this element, and ammonia cannot be reduced because it contains nitrogen in its lowest possible oxidation state, namely -3.

Disproportionation

In most redox reactions there is electron transfer between two substances, namely a reducing agent and an oxidising agent, but in a few cases there is an electron transfer within a single substance. Some atoms (or molecules or ions) of the substance serve as an electron source and become oxidised, while others accept electrons and are reduced. The phenomenon is known as *disproportionation*.

Because electrons are not transferred elsewhere, the extent to which a substance is oxidised, as shown by the change in oxidation number, is equal to the extent to which it is reduced. Consider, for example, the reaction which occurs when chlorine dissolves in cold, dilute aqueous sodium hydroxide:

$$Cl_2 + 2NaOH = NaCl + NaClO + H_2O$$

Chlorine (oxidation number $= 0$) is partly reduced to the chloride ion (oxidation number $= -1$) and partly oxidised to the hypochlorite ion, in which the oxidation number of chlorine is $+1$. Similar reactions occur when other non-metals dissolve in alkalis.

Most thermal decomposition reactions involve disproportionation. When, for example, ammonium nitrate decomposes on heating, the ammonium ion is oxidised and the nitrate ion is reduced. Four electrons are lost by the former and gained by the latter so that the product, of both processes, is dinitrogen oxide. Similarly, solutions containing ammonium ions and nitrite ions, on heating, give nitrogen by the interionic transfer of three electrons.

5.2 Electrical aspects of oxidation–reduction

Electrode potentials

When a piece of metal is immersed in a solution of its own ions, the atoms on its surface tend to lose electrons and form hydrated cations which pass into the solution, i.e.

$$M(s) = M^{n+}(aq) + ne^-$$

The electrons remain on the metal, which thereby acquires a negative charge relative to the solution. The reverse process also occurs, i.e.

$$M^{n+}(aq) + ne^- = M(s)$$

in which case the metal acquires a positive charge with respect to the solution. After a time a state of dynamic equilibrium is established:

$$M(s) \rightleftharpoons M^{n+}(aq) + ne^-$$

Whether the piece of metal, often called an *electrode* in this context, acquires a positive or a negative charge relative to the solution depends on the position of the equilibrium. If it lies to the right (ionisation more important) the metal is negatively charged, whereas if it lies to the left (deposition more important) the charge is positive. The presence of a charge on the metal means that a potential difference must exist between the electrode and the solution. This is called the *electrode potential* of the metal.

The magnitude of the electrode potential is related to the amount of charge on the metal. This is affected principally by the concentration of ions in solution and the tendency of the metal to form hydrated ions.

Concentration of ions in solution

For a given metal in a solution of its own ions the equilibrium is displaced to the left as the ionic concentration increases. Thus, if the metal carries a negative charge the electrode potential is decreased as some of the negative charge is neutralised by the deposition of ions. The reverse is true if the metal possesses a positive charge.

Tendency to form hydrated ions

For different metals placed in solutions of their ions at the same molar concentration, the position of the equilibrium depends on the tendency of the metal to form hydrated ions. The steps involved in hydrated ion formation are as follows:

$$M(s) = M(g) \qquad \text{atomisation}$$
$$M(g) = M^{n+}(g) + ne^- \qquad \text{ionisation}$$
$$M^{n+}(g) + aq = M^{n+}(aq) \qquad \text{hydration}$$

The overall enthalpy change during the formation of hydrated ions is thus given by

$$\Delta H_{overall} = \Delta H_{atomisation} + \Sigma \Delta H_{ionisation} + \Delta H_{hydration}$$

where $\Sigma \Delta H_{ionisation}$ is the sum of the first n ionisation enthalpies of the metal. For all metals the overall change is endothermic, but the smaller the change the greater is the tendency to form hydrated ions. Thus the alkali metals, which have low ionisation and atomisation enthalpies, are the most ready to form hydrated ions.

For metals which are negatively charged relative to the solution, an increase in the tendency to form hydrated ions leads to greater negative charge and hence to increasingly negative electrode potentials. For positively charged electrodes, as the tendency to form hydrated ions decreases, the positive charge on the metal increases. This leads to high positive electrode potentials.

Measurement of electrode potentials

Because of their dependence on the tendency of metals to form hydrated ions, electrode potentials (together with their signs) provide a quantitative guide to the reactivities of metals in an aqueous environment. Unfortunately, we cannot measure the *absolute* electrode potential of a metal. If we attempt to measure the potential by means of a voltmeter connected between the electrode and the solution, we must of necessity introduce another metal into the solution. This metal will have its own electrode potential which will alter the voltage reading on the voltmeter.

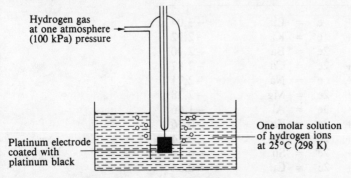

Fig. 5.1 A standard hydrogen electrode.

In practice we choose an arbitrary second electrode against which we can compare all other electrode potentials. The chosen standard is the *standard hydrogen electrode* (SHE) (Fig. 5.1). The electrode reaction occurring in the SHE is:

$$\tfrac{1}{2}H_2(g) \rightleftharpoons H^+(aq) + e^-$$

We arbitrarily assign a potential of 0.00 V to the SHE. This does not mean that the *actual* potential is zero volts. By constructing a voltaic cell (details of which are discussed later) of the SHE and the electrode in its solution, we can obtain the electrode potential of the metal *relative to hydrogen*.

For electrode potentials obtained in this manner to be useful as a guide to the reactivity of metals, they must be measured under the same conditions of concentration and temperature. An electrode potential which relates to a metal immersed in a solution of its own ions of 1 M concentration at a temperature of 25°C (298 K) is known as a *standard electrode potential* $(E^\ominus)$. A definition will be given later.

A list of standard electrode potentials arranged in order of decreasingly negative values is known as the *electrochemical series* (Table 5.1). All the electrode processes shown in Table 5.1 are written, by convention, in the form of reduction from left to right.

When referring to a particular standard electrode potential, we often do so by writing $E^\ominus$ with the subscript 'oxidised form/reduced form', omitting (aq), e.g. $E^\ominus_{Li^+/Li}$. The addendum (aq) has also been omitted in Tables 5.1 and 5.2.

Voltaic cells (galvanic cells)

The standard hydrogen electrode is known as a *half-cell*. A metal immersed in an aqueous solution likewise constitutes a half-cell. Any

Table 5.1 A selection from the electrochemical series, i.e. $E^{\ominus}$ values of important metals, arranged in order of decreasing negative values.

Electrode reaction			$E^{\ominus}$/V
Li^+ +	e^- =	Li	-3.04
K^+ +	e^- =	K	-2.92
Ba^{2+} +	$2e^-$ =	Ba	-2.90
Ca^{2+} +	$2e^-$ =	Ca	-2.87
Na^+ +	e^- =	Na	-2.71
Mg^{2+} +	$2e^-$ =	Mg	-2.38
Al^{3+} +	$3e^-$ =	Al	-1.66
Zn^{2+} +	$2e^-$ =	Zn	-0.76
Fe^{2+} +	$2e^-$ =	Fe	-0.44
Sn^{2+} +	$2e^-$ =	Sn	-0.14
Cu^2 +	$2e^-$ =	Cu	$+0.34$
Ag^+ +	e^- =	Ag	$+0.80$

two half-cells connected together comprise a *voltaic cell* or *galvanic cell*, often called simply a *cell*. Cells are characterised by the following features.

(i) If the two electrodes of the cell are connected by a wire, electrons flow from the negative to the positive electrode.

(ii) Reactions occur at each electrode−solution interface. The combined reactions constitute the *cell reaction*.

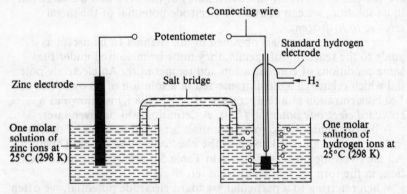

Fig. 5.2 Voltaic cell to measure the $E^{\ominus}$ value of zinc.

Let us consider a cell set up to measure the $E^{\ominus}$ value of zinc (Fig. 5.2). In order to obtain a complete circuit, the two solutions must be in electrical contact with each other. This can be achieved by placing a porous partition between the two solutions, to maintain electrical contact but prevent undue mixing. In accurate work a device called a *salt bridge* (Fig. 5.2) is used. This consists of a U-tube filled with a sol of potassium chloride or potassium nitrate in agar-agar. The device establishes an electrical contact between the solutions, but does not introduce spurious potentials at the points of contact. When the current is flowing the potassium ions in the salt bridge move towards the negatively charged (see below) zinc electrode. The anions (Cl^- or NO_3^-) move in the opposite direction, towards the positively charged (see below) SHE. This results in an excess of potassium ions at one end of the tube and an accumulation of anions at the other. Because the cations and anions travel with the same velocity, the excess of potassium ions at one end is equal to that of anions at the other. Hence a positive charge develops at the zinc electrode end of the tube and a negative charge, equal in magnitude to the positive charge, at the SHE end. The two charges, being equal but of opposite signs, cancel each other out, with the result that they do not affect the potential difference between the zinc electrode and the SHE in the cell.

The zinc electrode of the above cell is negatively charged, and *relative to this electrode* the SHE is positively charged. This is because zinc has a greater tendency than hydrogen to form hydrated ions in solution, i.e. the tendency for $Zn \rightarrow Zn^{2+}(aq) + 2e^-$ is greater than the tendency for $\frac{1}{2}H_2 \rightarrow H^+(aq) + e^-$. Consequently, electrons flow through the external circuit from the point of negative potential (zinc) to that of positive (or lower negative) potential at the SHE.

The potential difference between the electrodes of a cell is known as its *electromotive force* (e.m.f.), represented by E_{cell}, or $E_{cell}^{\ominus}$ if standard conditions apply. For the above cell, $E_{cell}^{\ominus} = 0.76$ V. Since, by convention, $E_{H^+/H_2}^{\ominus} = 0.00$ V, $E_{Zn^{2+}/Zn}^{\ominus} = -0.76$ V. The magnitude of the cell e.m.f. is thus an indication of the greater tendency for zinc to ionise than hydrogen.

If we repeat the experiment with a copper half-cell (i.e. copper immersed in a 1 M solution of $Cu^{2+}(aq)$ ions) instead of zinc, we find that $E_{cell}^{\ominus}$ is 0.34 V and the copper electrode is positive. This arises because hydrogen has a greater tendency to ionise than copper; the value of $E_{cell}^{\ominus}$ again indicates the extent of the tendency.

We are now able to define the 'standard electrode potential' of a half-cell as the cell e.m.f. when a metal immersed in a 1 M solution of its ions at 25°C (298 K) is coupled with a SHE. The sign of $E^{\ominus}$ is the polarity of the electrode in the cell.

In general, the more negative the $E^{\ominus}$ value of a metal, the greater is its tendency to ionise and the higher is its reactivity. The electrochemical series thus gives a quantitative guide to the reactivity of metals when they are immersed in solutions of their own ions. For example, zinc is more reactive than copper because zinc ionises more readily. We could, of course, argue this from ionisation enthalpies, but these are rather abstract in the sense that they apply to isolated metal atoms forming isolated ions. $E^{\ominus}$ values are more practical because they relate to *solid* metal forming hydrated ions in an aqueous environment.

The *Daniell cell* consists of a zinc half-cell and a copper half-cell. Zinc ionises preferentially, and this metal is therefore negative relative to the copper. The conventional representation of such a cell is

$$Zn \mid Zn^{2+}(aq) \parallel Cu^{2+}(aq) \mid Cu$$

A single vertical line represents the interface between substances in different phases. A double line represents the salt bridge connection between the two solutions. Also, by convention, the negative electrode is written on the left-hand side.

If the solutions are both 1 M, the voltage between the zinc and copper electrodes, i.e. the cell e.m.f. ($E_{cell}^{\ominus}$), is the difference between the two $E^{\ominus}$ values. We can demonstrate this on a 'potential diagram'.

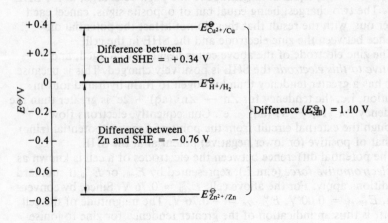

When calculating E_{cell} we again adopt a convention:

$$E_{cell} = E_{right} - E_{left}$$

where E_{right} is the potential of the right-hand electrode (positive) and E_{left} is the potential of the left-hand electrode (negative).

For a Daniell cell consisting of standard electrodes,

$$E_{cell}^{\ominus} = +0.34 - (-0.76) = +1.10 \text{ V}$$

If, in ignorance, we had written the cell the opposite way round, i.e. with the copper electrode on the left, then $E_{cell}^{\ominus} = -1.10$ V. The negative sign immediately indicates the mistake. E_{cell} or $E_{cell}^{\ominus}$ must always be positive.

If the two electrodes are connected by a wire, electrons flow from zinc to copper, i.e. from the point of higher negative potential. The number of electrons on the zinc is thus reduced and the equilibrium

$$Zn \rightleftharpoons Zn^{2+}(aq) + 2e^-$$

is displaced to the right and dissolution of the zinc occurs. At the copper electrode, because there is an increase in the number of electrons, the equilibrium

$$Cu \rightleftharpoons Cu^{2+}(aq) + 2e^-$$

is displaced to the left and copper is deposited. The overall cell reaction is obtained by addition, thus:

at the left-hand electrode $\qquad\qquad\qquad\qquad$ $Zn = Zn^{2+}(aq) + 2e^-$
at the right-hand electrode $\qquad$ $2e^- + Cu^{2+}(aq) = Cu$
∴ cell reaction $\qquad\qquad\qquad\quad$ $Zn + Cu^{2+}(aq) = Zn^{2+}(aq) + Cu$

The net effect is the displacement of copper from solution by zinc.

While the cell is delivering current, zinc is oxidised at the left-hand (negative) electrode and copper(II) ions are reduced at the right-hand (positive) electrode. This important relationship applies to all cells delivering current, i.e.

oxidation occurs at the negative electrode (left),
reduction occurs at the positive electrode (right).

(The two r's, i.e. *r*eduction on the *r*ight, may help in remembering this.)

Cells enable us to predict whether or not reactions occur of their own accord. The displacement of copper by zinc occurs in the Daniell cell; it also occurs if we place pieces of zinc in a solution containing copper(II) ions. As we shall see later, this aspect is useful in predicting the course of redox reactions.

Another example of a cell is

$$Mg \mid Mg^{2+}(aq) \parallel Zn^{2+}(aq) \mid Zn$$

Here we see that *magnesium* is the negative electrode because the $E^{\ominus}$ value of magnesium is more negative than that of zinc. Under standard conditions,

$$E^{\ominus}_{cell} = -0.76 - (-2.37) = +1.61 \text{ V}$$

This can be illustrated by a potential diagram.

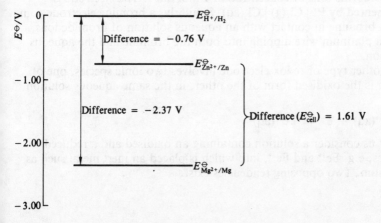

As the cell delivers current, electrons flow from the magnesium to the zinc and the following reactions occur:

$Mg \rightarrow Mg^{2+}(aq) + 2e^-$ and $Zn^{2+}(aq) + 2e^- \rightarrow Zn$
cell reaction $Mg + Zn^{2+}(aq) = Mg^{2+}(aq) + Zn$

Magnesium therefore displaces zinc from solution in the cell. The same reaction also occurs if we place magnesium in a solution of a zinc salt.

The cells used for determining the $E^{\ominus}$ values of zinc and copper can be represented as follows:

$Zn \mid Zn^{2+}(aq)(1 \text{ M}) \mid\mid H^+(aq)(1 \text{ M}) \mid H_2(1 \text{ atm}) \mid Pt$
$Pt \mid H_2(1 \text{ atm}) \mid H^+(aq)(1 \text{ M}) \mid\mid Cu^{2+}(aq)(1 \text{ M}) \mid Cu$

In this instance the concentrations of the various species have been included, but this is not obligatory.

The respective cell reactions are

$$Zn + 2H^+(aq) = Zn^{2+}(aq) + H_2$$
$$\text{and } Cu^{2+}(aq) + H_2 = Cu + 2H^+(aq)$$

Redox electrodes

As we have seen, reversible oxidation−reduction occurs with metal electrodes immersed in solutions of their ions. Reversible oxidation−reduction may also occur with non-metals in contact with their own ions, e.g.

$Cl_2 + 2e^- \rightleftharpoons 2Cl^-$

Such electrodes are often referred to as *redox electrodes*, although they do not differ in principle from the metal electrodes discussed above. Most non-metals are non-conductors of electricity and a piece of platinum is used to make electrical contact, as with hydrogen in the SHE. A chlorine electrode, for example, is similar to a SHE except that hydrogen is replaced by chlorine, and the aqueous solution contains chloride ions of concentration 1 mol dm^{-3}. The electrode is represented by $Pt \mid Cl_2(g) \mid Cl^-(aq)$. Similarly, a bromine electrode comprises bromine in contact with an aqueous solution of bromide ions, with a platinum wire dipping into both the bromine and the aqueous solution.

Another type of redox electrode involves two ionic species, one of which is the oxidised form of the other, in the same aqueous solution, e.g.

$Fe^{3+}(aq) + e^- \rightleftharpoons Fe^{2+}(aq)$

Let us consider a solution containing an oxidised and a reduced species, e.g. Fe^{3+} and Fe^{2+}, into which is placed an inert metal such as platinum. Two opposing tendencies exist.

(i) $Fe^{3+}(aq) + e^- \rightarrow Fe^{2+}(aq)$

The electron is removed from the platinum electrode, which therefore acquires a positive charge.

(ii) $Fe^{2+}(aq) \rightarrow Fe^{3+}(aq) + e^-$

The electron is transferred to the platinum, which therefore acquires a negative charge.

As with a metal electrode immersed in a solution, an equilibrium is rapidly established. If the tendency of the reduced species (e.g. Fe^{2+}) to become oxidised is stronger than that of the oxidised species (e.g. Fe^{3+}) to become reduced, then the platinum carries a negative charge. If the opposite applies the platinum is positively charged. The magnitude of the charge, and hence the potential difference between the platinum and the solution, depends on the oxidising power of one species relative to the reducing power of the other. The more the oxidising power of one species exceeds the reducing power of the other species, the higher is the positive charge on the platinum. Conversely, as the reducing power of the one exceeds the oxidising power of the other so the charge becomes increasingly negative. The sign and magnitude of the charge on the platinum thus serves as a quantitative guide to the net oxidising or reducing power of the two species in solution. However, we cannot measure the potential difference directly. Instead, exactly as for metal electrodes, we use a standard hydrogen electrode and define a *standard electrode potential* ($E^\ominus$), formerly 'standard redox potential'. Thus, the e.m.f. of the cell

$$Pt \mid H_2(1 \text{ atm}) \mid H^+(aq) \parallel Fe^{2+}(aq), Fe^{3+}(aq) \mid Pt$$

together with the sign of the charge on the platinum is called the standard electrode potential of the $Fe^{3+} + e^- \rightleftharpoons Fe^{2+}$ system, when the concentrations of the active species (Fe^{3+} and Fe^{2+}) are each 1 M. We find that $E^\ominus_{cell} = 0.77$ V, and the platinum is positively charged,

$$\therefore E^\ominus_{Fe^{3+}/Fe^{2+}} = +0.77 \text{ V}$$

Similarly, for the $Cr^{3+} + e^- \rightleftharpoons Cr^{2+}$ equilibrium,

$$Pt \mid Cr^{2+}(aq), Cr^{3+}(aq) \parallel H^+(aq) \mid H_2(1 \text{ atm}) \mid Pt \qquad E^\ominus_{cell} = 0.41 \text{ V}$$
$$\therefore E^\ominus_{Cr^{3+}/Cr^{2+}} = -0.41 \text{ V}$$

Standard potentials provide us with a sound basis for comparing the oxidising or reducing powers of different species. For example, the positive sign of the $E^\ominus$ value for the Fe^{3+}/Fe^{2+} electrode shows that hydrogen is a stronger reductant than the $Fe^{2+}(aq)$ ion, while the negative sign of $E^\ominus$ for the Cr^{3+}/Cr^{2+} electrode (Table 5.2) indicates that the $Cr^{2+}(aq)$ ion is a more powerful reductant than hydrogen. The $Cr^{2+}(aq)$ ion must therefore be a stronger reducing agent than the $Fe^{2+}(aq)$ ion. Some standard electrode potentials of various redox elec-

Table 5.2 Standard electrode potentials of some important redox electrodes.

Electrode reaction		$E^{\ominus}/V$
	$Cr^{3+} + e^- = Cr^{2+}$	-0.41
	$Cu^{2+} + e^- = Cu^+$	$+0.15$
	$Sn^{4+} + 2e^- = Sn^{2+}$	$+0.15$
	$\frac{1}{2}I_2 + e^- = I^-$	$+0.54$
	$Fe^{3+} + e^- = Fe^{2+}$	$+0.77$
	$\frac{1}{2}Br_2 + e^- = Br^-$	$+1.07$
	$\frac{1}{2}Cr_2O_7^{2-} + 7H^+ + 3e^- = Cr^{3+} + \frac{7}{2}H_2O$	$+1.33$
	$\frac{1}{2}Cl_2 + e^- = Cl^-$	$+1.36$
	$MnO_4^- + 8H^+ + 5e^- = Mn^{2+} + 4H_2O$	$+1.52$
	$MnO_4^- + 4H^+ + 3e^- = MnO_2 + 2H_2O$	$+1.67$
	$\frac{1}{2}S_2O_8^{2-} + e^- = SO_4^{2-}$	$+2.01$
	$\frac{1}{2}F_2 + e^- = F^-$	$+2.87$

(left margin, vertical: increasing strength as an oxidant ↓; right margin, vertical: decreasing strength as a reductant ↓)

trodes are given in Table 5.2. These should be considered alongside those in Table 5.1.

Standard electrode potentials can be used to predict the direction in which redox reactions occur. Suppose, for example, that we wish to know whether Cr^{2+} will reduce Fe^{3+}, or whether Fe^{2+} will reduce Cr^{3+}. The cell constructed from the two half-cells is

$$Pt \mid Cr^{2+}(aq), Cr^{3+}(aq) \parallel Fe^{2+}(aq), Fe^{3+}(aq) \mid Pt$$

Because $E^{\ominus}_{Cr^{3+}/Cr^{2+}}$ is more negative than $E^{\ominus}_{Fe^{3+}/Fe^{2+}}$, the chromium half-cell forms the negative part of the cell.

$$\therefore E^{\ominus}_{cell} = +0.77 - (-0.41) = 1.18 \text{ V}$$

The half-cell reactions are

$$Cr^{2+}(aq) \rightarrow Cr^{3+}(aq) + e^- \quad \text{and} \quad Fe^{3+}(aq) + e^- \rightarrow Fe^{2+}(aq)$$
$$\therefore \text{cell reaction is } Cr^{2+}(aq) + Fe^{3+}(aq) = Cr^{3+}(aq) + Fe^{2+}(aq)$$

These principles can be applied to all redox reactions.

In Tables 5.1 and 5.2 all species written on the left are potential oxidants, while those on the right are potential reductants. An oxidant (on the left-hand side) will oxidise any species on the right-hand side for which the $E^{\ominus}$ value is less positive. Correspondingly, a reductant will reduce any species on the left-hand side for which the $E^{\ominus}$ value is more positive. Thus, fluorine is the most powerful oxidant that there is, and fluoride ions cannot be oxidised by any other oxidant. Lithium (Table 5.1) is the strongest reductant, and lithium ions cannot be reduced by other reducing agents. Using these principles, we can also see that the permanganate ion, but not the dichromate ion, oxidises the chloride ion to chlorine.

Some species are able to function as oxidants or reductants only in the presence of $H^+(aq)$ or HO^- ions. In these cases the $E^{\ominus}$ values are related to the presence of a 1 M concentration of these ions.

The possibility of disproportionation (§5.1) occurring can be examined by $E^{\ominus}$ values. For example,

$$Cu^{2+}(aq) + e^- = Cu^+(aq) \qquad E^{\ominus} = +0.15 \text{ V}$$
$$Cu^+(aq) + e^- = Cu \qquad E^{\ominus} = +0.52 \text{ V}$$

The cell consisting of these two half-cells is

$$Pt \mid Cu^{2+}(aq), Cu^+(aq) \mid\mid Cu^+(aq) \mid Cu$$
$$\therefore E^{\ominus}_{cell} = +0.52 - (+0.15) = 0.37 \text{ V}$$

The reactions occurring are

$$Cu^+(aq) \rightarrow Cu^{2+}(aq) + e^- \text{ and } Cu^+(aq) + e^- \rightarrow Cu$$
$$\therefore \text{ cell reaction is } Cu^+(aq) + Cu^+(aq) = Cu^{2+}(aq) + Cu$$

i.e. $Cu^+(aq)$ ions disproportionate in solution.

It is also easy to see why some species may function, towards different compounds, as both reducing agents and oxidising agents. Consider hydrogen peroxide in acidic solution, which reduces the permanganate ion but oxidises the iodide ion.

$$MnO_4^- + 8H^+(aq) + 5e^- = Mn^{2+}(aq) + 4H_2O \qquad E^{\ominus} = +1.52 \text{ V}$$
$$O_2 + 2H^+(aq) + 2e^- = H_2O_2 \qquad E^{\ominus} = +0.68 \text{ V}$$

For the cell $Pt \mid O_2 \mid H_2O_2, H^+(aq) \mid\mid MnO_4^-, Mn^{2+}(aq), H^+(aq) \mid Pt$

$$E^{\ominus}_{cell} = +1.52 - (+0.68) = 0.84 \text{ V}$$

The overall reaction which occurs is

$$2MnO_4^- + 6H^+(aq) + 5H_2O_2 = 2Mn^{2+}(aq) + 8H_2O + 5O_2$$

For the reaction with iodide ions,

$$I_2 + 2e^- = 2I^- \qquad E^{\ominus} = +0.54 \text{ V}$$
$$H_2O_2 + 2H^+(aq) + 2e^- = 2H_2O \qquad E^{\ominus} = +1.77 \text{ V}$$

For the cell $Pt \mid I_2 \mid I^- \mid\mid H_2O_2, H^+(aq) \mid Pt, \quad E^{\ominus}_{cell} = 1.23 \text{ V}$

and the reaction occurring is

$$2I^- + 2H^+(aq) + H_2O_2 = I_2 + 2H_2O$$

The redox reactions which occur in voltaic cells also occur if the species concerned are mixed together in a beaker. Standard redox potentials are therefore useful in predicting the possibility of one species oxidising or reducing another. However, as with thermodynamics, we cannot predict rates of reaction; only the possibility of reactions taking place.

118

5.3 Oxidation state diagrams

For any element we can construct an oxidation state diagram, which is a convenient means of presenting and summarising redox data. To obtain such a diagram we need to know the following:

(i) the oxidation state (z) – with the correct sign – of the element in representative ions or molecules, e.g. for chlorine $z = -1$ in Cl^- but $+7$ in ClO_4^-;
(ii) the standard electrode potentials ($E^{\ominus}$) of couples involving the element and these ions or molecules.

A plot of $zE^{\ominus}$ against z gives the *oxidation state diagram*. It is common practice to represent the oxidation state diagrams of several elements on the same graph (Fig. 5.3).

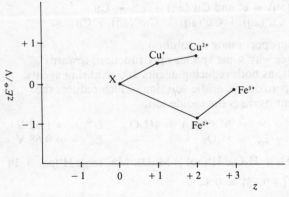

Fig. 5.3 Oxidation state diagrams for copper and iron.

Point X in Fig. 5.3 represents the values of $zE^{\ominus}$ and z for the respective elements in their standard states; at this point z and hence $zE^{\ominus}$ are zero.

The gradient of the line between any two points is $zE^{\ominus}/z$, i.e. the $E^{\ominus}$ value for the couple corresponding to those two points. For example, the gradient of the line between Fe and Fe^{2+} is the standard electrode potential of the couple

$$Fe^{2+} + 2e^- = Fe \qquad E^{\ominus} = -0.44 \text{ V}$$

while that between Fe^{2+} and Fe^{3+} is the standard electrode potential for

$$Fe^{3+} + e^- = Fe^{2+} \qquad E^{\ominus} = +0.77 \text{ V}$$

We are not restricted to a consideration of gradients between adjacent points. For example, the gradient between Fe and Fe^{3+} is the standard electrode potential of the couple

$$Fe^{3+} + 3e^- = Fe \qquad E^{\ominus} = -0.036 \text{ V}$$

In all cases the sign of the gradient is the same as that attached to the $E^{\ominus}$ value.

Standard electrode potentials can be used to predict the possible outcome of a redox reaction. Whenever two couples are mixed together, the one with the more positive $E^{\ominus}$ value will bring about oxidation of the other. Couples with high positive $E^{\ominus}$ values generally behave as oxidising couples, while those with low positive or negative $E^{\ominus}$ values usually act as reducing couples. For example:

(i) $\frac{1}{2}I_2 + e^- = I^-$ $E^{\ominus} = +0.54$ V
(ii) $Fe^{3+} + e^- = Fe^{2+}$ $E^{\ominus} = +0.77$ V
(iii) $Zn^{2+} + 2e^- = Zn$ $E^{\ominus} = -0.76$ V

Couple (ii) will bring about oxidation in both couple (i) and couple (iii); i.e. Fe^{3+} ions will oxidise I^- ions to iodine, and also zinc to Zn^{2+} ions. Couple (iii) will reduce both couple (i) (iodine to I^- ions) and couple (ii) (Fe^{3+} ions to Fe^{2+} ions).

The gradients of oxidation state diagrams, because they are equal to $E^{\ominus}$ values, provide information about the oxidising and reducing powers of couples, as follows:

(i)   the steeper a positive gradient, the more positive is the $E^{\ominus}$ value and the stronger is the oxidising power of the couple;

(ii)   the steeper a negative gradient, the more negative is the $E^{\ominus}$ value and the stronger is the reducing power of the couple.

Since it is the gradients in oxidation state diagrams that are important for comparison purposes, it is convenient to collect all gradients around a single point (Fig. 5.4).

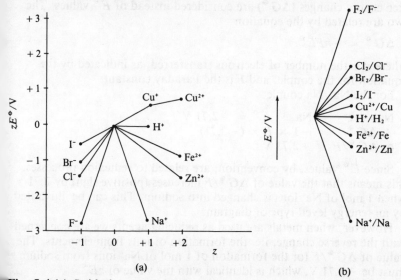

Fig. 5.4 (a) Oxidation state diagrams for several elements, with (b) gradients collected around one point.

It now becomes obvious that the order of oxidising power is

$$F_2 > Cl_2 > Br_2 > I_2 > Cu^{2+} > H^+ > Fe^{2+} > Zn^{2+} > Na^+$$

Conversely, in terms of reducing power, the order is the exact opposite, i.e.

$$Na > Zn > Fe > H_2 > Cu > I^- > Br^- > Cl^- > F^-$$

In general, positive gradients indicate potentially oxidising couples, whereas negative gradients relate to potentially reducing couples. For example, F_2, Cl_2, Br_2, I_2 and Cu^{2+} are all possible oxidants, whereas H_2, Fe, Zn and Na are possible reductants. We must, however, approach this with caution. Whether a particular couple will act as a reductant or as an oxidant depends upon the relative oxidising power of the couple with which it reacts. For example, Fig. 5.4 indicates that bromine is an oxidant, and we find that the bromine couple (i.e. Br_2/Br^-) will bring about oxidation in the I_2/I^- couple:

$$Br_2 + 2I^- = 2Br^- + I_2$$

However, the bromine couple behaves as a *reductant* in its reaction with the Cl_2/Cl^- couple:

$$Cl_2 + 2Br^- = 2Cl^- + Br_2$$

In making specific predictions about oxidation or reduction we must therefore remember that it is the gradient *difference* that is important.

Oxidation state free energy diagrams

These are essentially the same as oxidation state diagrams except that free energy changes ($\Delta G^{\ominus}$) are considered instead of $E^{\ominus}$ values. The two are related by the equation

$$\Delta G^{\ominus} = -nFE^{\ominus}$$

where n is the number of electrons transferred, as indicated by the equation for the couple, and F is the Faraday constant.

For the Na^+/Na couple

$$Na^+ + e^- = Na \quad E^{\ominus} = -2.71 \text{ V}$$
$$\therefore \Delta G^{\ominus} = -1 \times F \times (-2.71)$$
$$\text{or } \Delta G^{\ominus}/F = +2.71 \text{ V}$$

Since $E^{\ominus}$ values, by convention, are related to reduction processes, this means that the value of $\Delta G^{\ominus}/F$ increases (positive sign) by 2.71 V when 1 mol of Na^+ ions is changed into sodium. This can be illustrated by an 'energy level' type of diagram.

However, when metals are used as reducing agents we are concerned with the reverse change, i.e. the formation of ions from elements. The value of $\Delta G^{\ominus}/F$ for the formation of 1 mol of Na^+ ions from sodium must be -2.71 V, which is identical with the value of $zE^{\ominus}$.

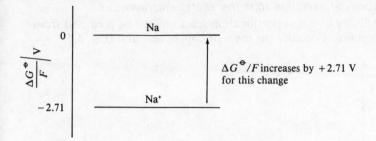

We find that for any couple

$$\Delta G^{\ominus}/F = zE^{\ominus}$$

as the two further examples show.

Copper

$$Cu^{2+} + 2e^{-} = Cu \qquad E^{\ominus} = +0.34 \text{ V}$$
$$\therefore \Delta G^{\ominus}/F = -2(+0.34) = -0.68 \text{ V}$$

i.e. in reducing 1 mol of Cu^{2+} ions to copper the value of $\Delta G^{\ominus}/F$ decreases (negative sign) by 0.68 V. The value of $\Delta G^{\ominus}/F$ for 1 mol of Cu^{2+} ions is thus $+0.68$ V compared with copper, which is again the same as $zE^{\ominus}$.

Chlorine

$$\tfrac{1}{2}Cl_2 + e^{-} = Cl^{-} \qquad E^{\ominus} = +1.36 \text{ V}$$

$\therefore \Delta G^{\ominus}/F$ for 1 mol of Cl^{-} ions relative to chlorine $= -1(+1.36)$ $= -1.36 \text{ V} = zE^{\ominus}$. For non-metals we do not need to reverse the sign of $\Delta G^{\ominus}/F$. Such elements are used as oxidising agents and it is their reduction which concerns us.

For any element we can plot $\Delta G^{\ominus}/F$ (or $\Delta G^{\ominus}$, since F is a constant) against oxidation number (z) to produce an *oxidation state free energy diagram*. A plot of $\Delta G^{\ominus}/F$ against z is identical with one of $zE^{\ominus}$ against z and can be represented by the same diagram (Fig. 5.5).

An oxidation state free energy diagram can be used in exactly the same way as an oxidation state diagram. High points on the diagram represent unstable and potentially oxidising states because the change to lower states is thermodynamically favourable. The height of a point is inversely related to the stability of the ion or molecule which it represents: thus, high points reflect instability and strong oxidising power. Low points indicate the exact opposite, so that the lowest point on the diagram represents the most stable state for that particular element.

122

Applications of oxidation state free energy diagrams

The possibility of disproportionation reactions can be predicted from these diagrams. Consider the cases of copper and iron (Fig. 5.5).

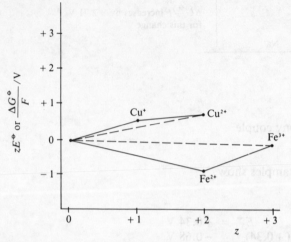

Fig. 5.5 Oxidation state free energy diagrams for copper and iron.

We consider any three states of a given element and draw a line on the diagram between the points for the highest and lowest states, e.g. for copper, Cu and Cu^{2+}. If the point for the intermediate state lies *above* this line then the intermediate state disproportionates into the states above and below it. Thus, for copper, the point for Cu^+ lies above the line drawn between Cu and Cu^{2+}, and disproportionation occurs:

$$2Cu^+ = Cu + Cu^{2+}$$

However, the same is not true for Fe^{2+} because its point falls *below* the line drawn between Fe and Fe^{3+}. In fact the diagram shows that, for iron, +2 is the most stable state because its value of $\Delta G^{\ominus}/F$ is the lowest point on the diagram. (For copper, in contrast, the element itself is more stable than either of its ions).

These diagrams can therefore be used to predict and summarise the solution chemistry of the elements. However, we should always use energy data with caution and remember that thermodynamic (or energetic) feasibility can be affected by kinetic stability. A reaction which may be thermodynamically (or energetically) feasible may not occur in practice. In such cases the rate of the reation is so low (due to kinetic stability) that to all intents and purposes it does not take place. This applies to many disproportionation reactions. We must also remember that, in general, $E^{\ominus}$ and hence $\Delta G^{\ominus}$ values relate to solutions with pH = 0. Changes in pH can affect $E^{\ominus}$ values and so alter the diagrams. The diagrams for some common elements will now be considered.

Nitrogen

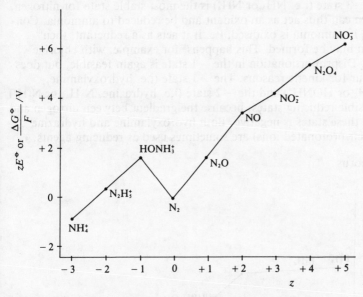

Fig. 5.6 Oxidation state free energy diagram for nitrogen.

Most molecules or ions containing nitrogen in a positive oxidation state are oxidants. The gradients between adjacent points are high and positive, denoting a high oxidising power. If we compare these gradients with those for other couples we can predict the feasibility of redox reactions taking place. For example, by comparison of the following gradients, which can be measured from Figs. 5.4, 5.6 and 5.8, we can say that HNO_3 (i.e. NO_3^- ions in acidic solution) oxidises I^- or Fe^{2+} ions, but not Cl^- ions.

Couple	Gradient/V
NO_3^-/NO	+0.96
I_2/I^-	+0.54
Fe^{3+}/Fe^{2+}	+0.77
Cl_2/Cl^-	+1.36

Oxidising power is at its greatest in the +5 state (i.e. NO_3^- or HNO_3) but falls with oxidation number: the points on the diagram (Fig. 5.6) become lower as oxidation number decreases. The data indicate that disproportionation should occur from the +2 state (i.e. NO) into the

+1 (i.e. N_2O) and +3 (i.e. NO_2^- or HNO_2) states. That it does not generally occur is due to kinetic stability. Nitrogen in the zero state (i.e. N_2) is more stable than any compound containing nitrogen in a positive state.

The −3 state (i.e. NH_3 or NH_4^+) is the most stable state for nitrogen. Nitrogen can thus act as an oxidant and be reduced to ammonia. Conversely, if ammonia is oxidised, i.e. if it acts as a reductant, then nitrogen may be formed. This happens, for example, with chlorine (§10.5). Disproportionation in the −1 state is again feasible, but does not occur for kinetic reasons. The −1 state (i.e. hydroxylamine, NH_2OH, or $HONH_3^+$) and the −2 state (i.e. hydrazine, N_2H_4, or $N_2H_5^+$) are possible reducing states, because the gradient between nitrogen and each of these states is negative. Both hydroxylamine and hydrazine (and their protonated ions) are sometimes used as reducing agents.

Phosphorus

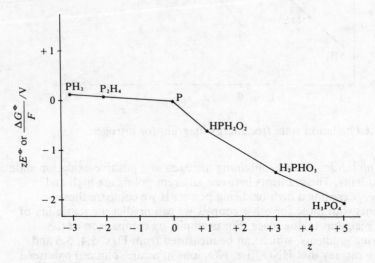

Fig. 5.7 Oxidation state free energy diagram for phosphorus.

The most stable oxidation state for phosphorus is +5, since this appears at the lowest point on the diagram (Fig. 5.7). Molecules or ions containing phosphorus in anything but the +5 state are therefore potential reducing agents, a fact which is also shown by the negative gradients between the couples. Phosphinic acid, HPH_2O_2, is used as a powerful reductant (§10.5).

Chlorine, bromine and iodine

The most stable state for each halogen is −1. Each halogen may thus act as an oxidant, and be reduced to its more stable halide ion. The order of oxidising power is $F_2 > Cl_2 > Br_2 > I_2$, as the gradients

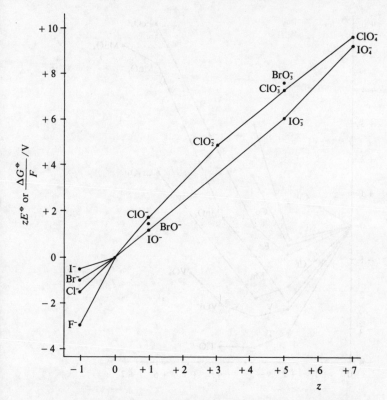

Fig. 5.8 Oxidation state free energy diagrams for the halogens.

between the elemental halogens and the points representing their respective halide ions decrease (Fig. 5.8).

All compounds containing a halogen in a positive oxidation state are oxidants, as indicated by the positive gradients. In general, compounds containing iodine are more stable, and hence weaker oxidants, than those containing chlorine. The situation with bromine is somewhat erratic; e.g. BrO^- is more stable than ClO^-, but the order is reversed with BrO_3^- and ClO_3^-. The +7 state is the least stable and most powerfully oxidising state.

The chlorite ion, ClO_2^-, because it occurs at an apex, is potentially unstable with respect to disproportionation into ClO^- and ClO_3^- ions. In practice it does not decompose in this manner for kinetic reasons.

The first series transition elements

The data in Fig. 5.9 apply to solutions of pH = 0 in the absence of ligands other than water. The solutions thus contain simple hydrated ions, e.g. $[Fe(H_2O)_6]^{2+}$, or oxoanions, e.g. MnO_4^-. Salient points which are evident from the diagram are as follows.

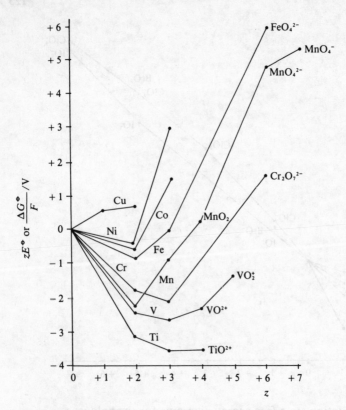

Fig. 5.9 Oxidation state free energy diagrams for the first series transition elements.

(i) The lowest point for each element indicates its most stable state, i.e. +3 for Ti, V and Cr; +2 for Mn, Fe, Co and Ni; 0 for Cu.

(ii) Except for copper the transition elements are all potential reducing agents, as indicated by the negative slopes joining the elements to their lower oxidation states.

(iii) The +3 state becomes decreasingly stable in the order Ti, V, Cr, and the +2 state becomes decreasingly stable from Mn to Cu.

(iv) From Ti to Mn the maximum oxidation state is an oxidising one. The oxidising power in these states is Ti(IV) < V(V) < Cr(VI) < Mn(VII).

(v) The +2 states for Ti, V and Cr are all reducing states, as indicated by the negative gradients between the +2 and +3 states.

(vi) Disproportionation is likely to occur in acidic solution with Mn(III), Mn(VI) and Cu(I). Mn(III) disproportionates into Mn(II) and Mn(IV); Mn(VI) into Mn(IV) and Mn(VII). The case of Cu(I) has already been noted.

(vii) The +3 state for Fe, Co, Ni becomes decreasingly stable and hence increases in oxidising power in that order.

(viii) The +2 state for each element becomes increasingly stable in passing from Ti to Cu. Manganese is anomalous in this respect, for the stability of its +2 state is intermediate between V(II) and Cr(II). The tendency of the metals to form ions, i.e. to act as reducing agents, is in the order: Ti > V > Mn > Cr > Fe > Co > Ni > Cu.

(ix) The +2 state for iron is a reducing one, as shown by the low positive gradient between the +2 and +3 states. Iron(II) compounds are well known reducing agents, being readily oxidised. The same is not generally true, however, for Co and Ni. Although Co(II) and Ni(II) can be oxidised, the $E^{\ominus}$ values for the couples are very high as indicated by the steep gradients between the +2 and +3 states. Very powerful oxidants are therefore required to oxidise Co(II) and Ni(II) compounds under these conditions, and consequently the latter are not usually regarded as reductants.

(x) The above generalisations apply in the absence of ligands other than water. In the presence of other ligands the diagram may change form completely. For example, the $E^{\ominus}$ value for the Co^{3+}/Co^{2+} couple is +1.82 V with water ligands, but +0.10 V with ammonia ligands (§14.1).

(xi) The most stable states of certain transition elements may not be the ones most commonly encountered in their compounds. For example, despite the fact that +3 is the most stable state of both titanium and vanadium, the *most usual state* is +4. The reason is that oxidation from the +3 to the +4 state is easily accomplished, even with quite mild oxidising agents. In view of the fact that we live in an oxidising environment, it is hardly surprising that titanium and vanadium commonly exist in the +4 state.

Consider, also, iron, for which +2 is the most stable state. Because iron(II) is oxidised relatively easily to iron(III) by many oxidants, including the oxygen in our atmosphere, we may be misled into believing that the most stable state is +3.

The above generalisations and diagrams for the transition elements apply only in the absence of oxidants (including atmospheric oxygen) and reductants. In some cases, therefore, conclusions drawn from oxidation state diagrams may be contrary to our common experience. We may predict, for example, that iron(II) is more stable than iron(III), but in the presence of oxidants this may be untrue. Great care is needed in constructing the diagrams to enable sound predictions to be made, particularly in the case of disproportionation reactions.

(xii) A change of pH value can also affect $E^{\ominus}$ values. For example, the diagram for manganese in basic solution (Fig. 5.10) shows that under these conditions Mn(VI) does not disproportionate, because the point for Mn(VI) falls slightly below the straight line drawn between Mn(IV) and Mn(VII).

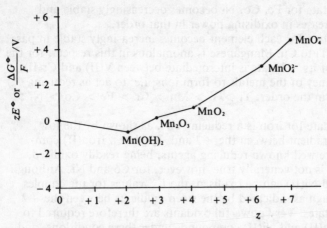

Fig. 5.10 Oxidation state free energy diagram for manganese in basic solution.

5.4 Extraction of metals

Ores

It would be astonishing if metallic sodium occurred naturally. It would be equally surprising if it occurred as sodium azide, NaN_3, despite the fact that nitrogen is a common element, because the compound is unstable. Even if sodium azide had been produced when the earth was formed, it would long ago have decomposed. As is well known, sodium occurs naturally as sodium chloride, sodium carbonate and various sodium aluminosilicates; all are very stable compounds.

Mineral substances are invariably stable. They seldom contain a metal in an unstable valency or oxidation state, and they seldom contain anions other than carbonate, chloride, oxide, phosphate, silicate, sulphate or sulphide. They may well be *reactive* towards certain reagents – Na_2CO_3 and $CaCO_3$ are good examples – but they are *stable*, in the sense that they have relatively large and negative standard free energies of formation. By definition, 'standard free energy of formation' ($\Delta G_f^{\ominus}$) is the change in free energy, under standard conditions, accompanying the formation of 1 mol of a compound from its constituent elements. The more negative the value of $\Delta G_f^{\ominus}$, the more stable is the compound. A study of such values will thus indicate which compounds of an element are most likely to occur as ores. Table 5.3 lists some common compounds of calcium in decreasing order of standard free energy of formation, and it will be seen that only the top four occur naturally.

In general, the standard free energies of formation of carbonates are high, and many metals have an ore of this kind (Table 5.4).

Table 5.3 Standard free energies of formation of various compounds of calcium.

Compound	$\Delta G_f^{\ominus}$/kJ mol^{-1}	Ore
$Ca_3(PO_4)_2$	$-3\,890$	phosphorite
$CaSO_4$	$-1\,320$	anhydrite
CaF_2	$-1\,162$	fluorspar
$CaCO_3$	$-1\,129$	calcite, limestone, etc
$Ca(OH)_2$	-897	none
$Ca(NO_3)_2$	-742	none
$CaCl_2$	-750	none
CaO	-604	none
CaS	-477	none
CaC_2	-67.8	none

Table 5.4 Standard free energies of formation of various compounds.

Element	$\Delta G_f^{\ominus}$/kJ mol^{-1}				Ores
	Carbonate	Chloride	Oxide	Sulphide	
sodium	$-1\,048$	-384	-377 (Na_2O)	—	rock salt, NaCl trona, Na_2CO_3
aluminium	—	-637	$-1\,576$	-492	bauxite, Al_2O_3
zinc	-731	-369	-318	-198	calamine, $ZnCO_3$ zinc blende, ZnS
iron	-674 ($FeCO_3$)	-302 ($FeCl_2$)	-741 (Fe_2O_3)	-167 (FeS_2)	siderite, $FeCO_3$ haematite, Fe_2O_3 pyrites, FeS_2
lead	-626	-314 ($PbCl_2$)	-189 (PbO)	-92.7	cerrusite, $PbCO_3$ galena, PbS
silver	-437	-110	-10.8	-40.2	horn silver, AgCl argentite, Ag_2S metallic silver
gold	—	—	$+163$ (Au_2O_3)	—	metallic gold

Table 5.4 illustrates the principle that $\Delta G_f^{\ominus}$ values depend on the reactivity of the metal. Highly reactive metals, such as sodium and aluminium, release a considerable amount of free energy on forming compounds, whereas other metals release less. Noble metals, notably gold, may *require* free energy for their conversion into compounds: $\Delta G_f^{\ominus}$ for gold(III) oxide has a *positive* value. Certain compounds of gold are thus less stable than the metal itself, which is why gold occurs native, i.e. uncombined.

The compound of a metal for which $\Delta G_f^{\ominus}$ is greatest may not be commercially the most important ore. Since a lot of free energy has been lost in forming the ore, a lot of free energy must be supplied to decompose it; and it may well be advantageous to seek another ore for which the free energy requirement is less. Sodium, for instance, is extracted from sodium chloride ($\Delta G_f^{\ominus} = -384$ kJ mol^{-1}) rather than sodium carbonate ($\Delta G_f^{\ominus} = -1\ 048$ kJ mol^{-1}).

Metals from ores

The conversion of an ore to a metal, known as *smelting*, is a redox reaction in which the ore is reduced. Energy is required, and may be supplied by heating, adding a reducing agent, or applying an electrical potential difference. A combination of heat and a reducing agent is often employed.

Heat alone is insufficient to decompose ores of all but the least reactive metals, for although most compounds (e.g. oxides, sulphides and chlorides) become less stable on heating, the temperatures needed to decompose them are unacceptably high. For example, although silver oxide decomposes at 340 °C (613 K) and mercury(II) oxide at 500 °C (773 K), zinc oxide can be broken down only at about 1 900 °C (2 200 K) and aluminium oxide, calcium oxide and indeed most other metal oxides at over 2 000 °C (2 300 K).

A reducing agent is therefore necessary in most cases, and the one usually chosen on both technical and economic grounds is carbon, in the form of coke. Carbon will reduce many metal oxides to the metal at temperatures below 2 000 °C (2 300 K); it is less effective with sulphides and quite useless with chlorides. Other reducing agents used in special cases include iron (for Sb_2S_3), magnesium or sodium (for $TiCl_4$) and hydrogen (for the oxides of molybdenum and tungsten).

Electrolysis (cathodic reduction) provides the most powerful method of reducing metal compounds to the metal, for virtually any cathode potential can be applied. All the most reactive metals are produced in this way.

Reduction of oxides

Metal oxides are reduced by carbon in accordance with the following general equations:

$$MO + C = M + CO$$
$$2MO + C = 2M + CO_2$$

At room temperature carbon can reduce very few metal oxides, partly because the necessary activation energy is lacking, but principally because the free energy released as carbon changes into carbon monoxide or carbon dioxide is insufficient. However, as the temperature rises, metal oxides become less stable. There is, therefore, for every metal oxide, a certain temperature at which the free energy released in the conversion of carbon to carbon monoxide or carbon dioxide is exactly equal to that required for the reduction of the metal oxide to the metal. At higher temperatures than this, there is a net release of free energy and the reaction is able to occur.

Iron and zinc are the most important metals manufactured by the carbon reduction of oxides. However, in the upper, cooler region of a blast furnace, the principal reductant is carbon monoxide. This is because, at temperatures below 700 °C (973 K), carbon monoxide is a more powerful reducing agent than carbon itself. The gas reduces some iron(III) oxide to spongy iron and the rest to iron(II) oxide which, in the lower, hotter region of the furnace, is reduced to the metal by carbon.

Carbon is unsuitable for the reduction of oxides of calcium and aluminium, partly because temperatures above 2 000 °C (2 300 K) are required, and partly because calcium and aluminium react with carbon to form ionic carbides, CaC_2 and Al_4C_3, which prevent isolation of the metals. Most transition elements form interstitial carbides with carbon. Often, as with iron, a small proportion of the carbide improves the properties of the metal; but if, as with titanium, the carbide spoils the metal then carbon cannot be used in the extraction.

Reduction of sulphides

Sulphides are far more difficult than oxides to reduce with carbon. This is partly because carbon fails to form a lower sulphide, corresponding to CO, and partly because CS_2, unlike CO_2, *requires* free energy for its formation. Hydrogen, too, is an unsatisfactory reducing agent because the standard free energy of formation of hydrogen sulphide is only -33.0 kJ mol^{-1}.

The only metal which is manufactured by the direct reduction of its sulphide is antimony. Usually, as in the case of zinc, a sulphide ore is first converted to the oxide by roasting it in air.

Reduction of chlorides

Chlorides are even more resistant than sulphides to reduction by carbon, because of the difficulty of forming tetrachloromethane at elevated temperatures. One possible reagent for reducing chlorides of the less reactive metals (e.g. tin, lead, silver and copper) is hydrogen, but in practice such metals are best obtained by other routes. The method of chloride reduction is largely confined to the production of titanium by the Kroll process (§14.4).

Electrolytic reduction

The electrolytic production of metals is expensive, but provides the only commercially viable means of obtaining highly reactive elements, notably sodium, magnesium, calcium and aluminium, whose compounds are difficult to reduce by other methods.

Water must be absent, since if it were present hydrogen would be released at the cathode in preference to the metal. Sodium, magnesium and calcium are all made by the electrolysis of their fused chlorides.

Chlorides have the advantage of relatively low melting temperatures. (Oxides, in contrast, have high lattice enthalpies and are almost infusible, while oxosalts tend to decompose to give oxides.) The temperature is kept as low as possible to minimise costs, reduce the reactivity of the chlorine evolved at the anode, and limit the loss of metal through vaporisation.

Aluminium is obtained from its oxide rather than its chloride. (Aluminium chloride is covalent and therefore a non-conductor of electricity.) The difficulty posed by the very high melting temperature of aluminium oxide is overcome by dissolving the compound in molten cryolite (§8.1).

The thermodynamics of metal extraction

Let us first consider the reduction of a metal oxide, MO, by carbon in accordance with the general equation

$$2MO + C = 2M + CO_2$$

The reaction thus involves the transfer of 1 mol of oxygen, O_2, from the metal oxide to the carbon. The standard free energy change ($\Delta G^{\ominus}$) for the reaction can be obtained from the standard free energies of formation of carbon dioxide and the metal oxide:

$$\Delta G^{\ominus} = \Sigma n\Delta G_f^{\ominus}[\text{products}] - \Sigma n\Delta G_f^{\ominus}[\text{reactants}]$$
$$\therefore \Delta G^{\ominus} = \Delta G_f^{\ominus}[\text{CO}_2(g)] - 2\Delta G_f^{\ominus}[\text{MO(s)}]$$

The standard free energy of formation of carbon dioxide is -395 kJ mol^{-1}, and most metal oxides have negative standard free energies of formation, i.e. $\Delta G_f^{\ominus}[\text{MO(s)}]$ is negative. For reduction to occur the standard free energy change ($\Delta G^{\ominus}$) must be negative, which will happen if $2\Delta G_f^{\ominus}[\text{MO(s)}]$ is numerically smaller than $\Delta G_f^{\ominus}[\text{CO}_2(g)] = -395$ kJ mol^{-1}.

At 25 °C (298 K) carbon is unable to reduce most metal oxides because this condition is not fulfilled and $\Delta G^{\ominus}$ is positive. For some metal oxides, e.g. those of mercury and silver, $\Delta G^{\ominus}$ is negative at room temperature, but reduction does not occur because the necessary activation energy is lacking. (This aspect will not be discussed here.) Many metal oxides are reduced by carbon on heating, and to see why this is so we must examine the manner in which standard free energies of formation vary with temperature. The Gibbs free energy equation, $\Delta G^{\ominus} = \Delta H^{\ominus} - T\Delta S^{\ominus}$, may be written as

$$\Delta G^{\ominus} = -\Delta S^{\ominus} \times T + \Delta H^{\ominus}$$

Now since both $\Delta S^{\ominus}$ and $\Delta H^{\ominus}$ are, to a good approximation, independent of temperature, the above equation has the form

$$y = mx + c$$

and a plot of $\Delta G^{\ominus}$ against T will be a straight line of slope $-\Delta S^{\ominus}$. The standard entropy change ($\Delta S^{\ominus}$) for the formation of carbon dioxide is $+3.3$ J K^{-1} mol^{-1}. Therefore $-\Delta S^{\ominus} = -3.3$ J K^{-1} mol^{-1}, and the standard free energy of formation of carbon dioxide ($\Delta G_f^{\ominus}[CO_2(g)]$) becomes more negative with increasing temperature (Fig. 5.11).

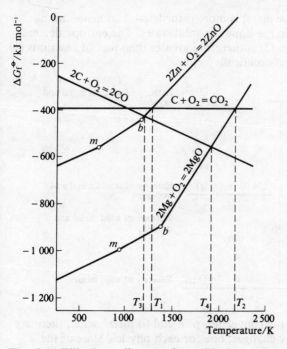

Fig. 5.11 Ellingham diagram for oxide formation. (m = melting temperature and b = boiling temperature of metal.)

For metal oxides, the process is more complex, since the entropy change depends on the physical state of the metal, which alters as the temperature increases. The formation of metal oxides from their elements is always accompanied by a decrease in entropy. For example, in the reaction

$$2M(s) + O_2(g) = 2MO(s) \tag{1}$$

the solid oxide, MO(s), is more ordered than the oxygen gas and the entropy decreases. At temperatures above the melting temperature of the metal, but below that of the oxide, we must consider the reaction

$$2M(l) + O_2(g) = 2MO(s) \tag{2}$$

The liquid metal is more disordered and hence has a higher entropy than the solid metal. There is therefore a greater degree of ordering when the solid metal oxide is formed from the liquid metal than the solid metal. The entropy decrease accompanying reaction (2) is thus greater (i.e. $\Delta S^{\ominus}$ is more negative) than that for reaction (1). Similar considerations apply at temperatures above the boiling temperature of the metal, i.e. for the reaction

$$2M(g) + O_2(g) = 2MO(s) \tag{3}$$

In the gaseous state the metal is more disordered, and hence has a higher entropy, than in the liquid or solid states. The entropy decrease accompanying reaction (3) is therefore greater than that of reactions (1) or (2). This is shown schematically below.

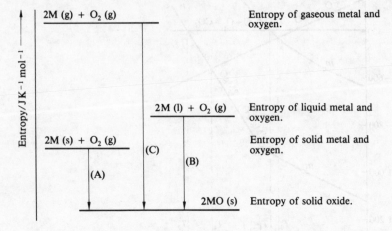

To summarise, for the conversion of metal to metal oxide, there are three constant entropy changes, one for each physical state of the metal. Therefore, if we plot a graph of standard free energy of formation of a metal oxide against temperature, we find that the gradient increases at points corresponding to the melting and boiling temperatures of the metal. This is shown for two metal oxides in Fig. 5.11, which is known as an *Ellingham diagram*. Notice that the graphs have positive slopes because $-\Delta S^{\ominus}$ is positive, and that the gradient increases as the metal melts or boils. Thus, the standard free energies of formation of metal oxides, unlike that of carbon dioxide, become decreasingly negative as the temperature rises.

Let us consider the reduction of zinc oxide, i.e.

$$2ZnO + C = 2Zn + CO_2$$

At temperature T_1 (Fig. 5.11) the graphs relating to standard free energies of formation of 2 mol of zinc oxide and 1 mol of carbon dioxide intersect,

$$\therefore 2\Delta G_f^{\ominus}[ZnO(s)] = \Delta G_f^{\ominus}[CO_2(g)]$$

The standard free energy change for the reaction is then zero. Above this temperature, $2\Delta G_f^{\ominus}[ZnO(s)]$ is numerically smaller than $\Delta G_f^{\ominus}[CO_2(g)]$. Thus, the standard free energy change for the reduction of zinc oxide by carbon is negative and the reaction will proceed of its own accord. That is why, in practice, temperatures in excess of T_1 must be employed. Notice that T_1 is above the boiling temperature of zinc, so that the reaction occurring is

$$2ZnO(s) + C(s) = 2Zn(g) + CO_2(g)$$

Similar considerations apply to the reduction of magnesium oxide:

$$2MgO(s) + C(s) = 2Mg(g) + CO_2(g)$$

Temperatures in excess of T_2 (Fig. 5.11) are required before the standard free energy change becomes negative and the reaction can proceed.

When carbon acts as a reducing agent it may be converted into the monoxide:

$$2MO + 2C = 2M + 2CO$$

Notice that for consistency we are again considering the transfer of one mole of oxygen, O_2, to the carbon from the metal oxide. The standard free energy change for this reaction is given by

$$\Delta G^{\ominus} = 2\Delta G_f^{\ominus}[CO(g)] - 2\Delta G_f^{\ominus}[MO(s)]$$

Since $\Delta G_f^{\ominus}[CO(g)]$ is -137 kJ mol^{-1}, $\Delta G^{\ominus}$ will be negative and the reduction will occur only if $2\Delta G_f^{\ominus}[MO(s)]$ is numerically smaller than $2\Delta G_f^{\ominus}[CO(g)] = -274$ kJ mol^{-1}.

The standard entropy of formation of carbon monoxide ($+89.8$ J K^{-1} mol^{-1}) is greater than that of carbon dioxide ($+3.3$ J K^{-1} mol^{-1}). Therefore the line on the Ellingham diagram (Fig. 5.11) corresponding to the variation of the standard free energy of formation of carbon monoxide has a more pronounced negative slope than that for carbon dioxide. Consider the reduction of zinc oxide. At temperature T_3

$$2\Delta G_f^{\ominus}[ZnO(s)] = 2\Delta G_f^{\ominus}[CO(g)]$$

but above this temperature

$$2\Delta G_f^{\ominus}[ZnO(s)] < 2\Delta G_f^{\ominus}[CO(g)]$$

and the reaction

$$2ZnO(s) + 2C(s) = 2Zn(g) + 2CO(g)$$

will proceed because $\Delta G^{\ominus}$ is negative. Thus at temperatures higher than T_3, but lower than T_1, carbon reduces zinc oxide to form zinc vapour and carbon monoxide. At temperatures in excess of T_1, however, both carbon monoxide and carbon dioxide, in addition to zinc vapour, will be formed.

Ellingham diagrams can also be constructed for the reduction of metal chlorides and metal sulphides.

Chapter 6

Hydrogen

There are three isotopes of hydrogen: protium, ^1_1H, deuterium, ^2_1H or D, and tritium, ^3_1H or T. The ratio of protium to deuterium in nature is approximately 6 000 : 1, and tritium occurs in extremely small quantities. The mixture of isotopes normally encountered is referred to as 'hydrogen' and is given the symbol H. The hydrogen atom has a $1s^1$ configuration.

Under normal conditions hydrogen is a gas, consisting of diatomic molecules, H_2. Because of its low relative molecular mass, $H_2 = 2.016$, hydrogen has very low melting and boiling temperatures. For protium, the melting temperature is $-259\,^\circ C$ (14 K) and the boiling temperature $-252.5\,^\circ C$ (20.7 K).

6.1 Occurrence and isolation of hydrogen

Most of the earth's hydrogen is found in the form of water and organic substances such as oil and coal. Because of its very low mass, elementary hydrogen can escape from the atmosphere and thus occurs in negligible quantities in nature.

Hydrogen is obtained mainly by:

(i)   the reduction of hydrogen compounds, such as water, acids or organic compounds;

(ii) the oxidation of the hydride ion, H⁻.

Reduction methods

Reaction of metals with water or acids

This method involves the reduction of hydrated hydrogen ions, $H^+(aq)$ (§6.3), by the transfer of electrons from metals, i.e.

$$2H^+(aq) + 2e^- = H_2$$

All metals with negative standard electrode potentials can, in principle, reduce hydrogen ions. In practice only the more reactive s-block elements are able to reduce water to hydrogen, but all metals above hydrogen in the electrochemical series reduce non-oxidising acids, e.g. hydrochloric acid or dilute sulphuric acid. In general, the more negative the standard electrode potential of the metal, the more vigorous is the reaction with acids. If an insoluble metal salt is formed, it tends to coat the metal and thus slow down the reaction. Such is the case with, for example, lead. If the acid used is an oxidant, e.g. nitric acid or concentrated sulphuric acid, then hydrogen is not formed (§§10.5 and 11.5).

Reaction of metals with alkalis

Weak metals, i.e. those whose cations can accept HO^- ligands, react with aqueous alkali metal hydroxides to produce hydrogen, e.g.

$$2Al + 2HO^- + 10H_2O = 2[Al(OH)_4(H_2O)_2]^- + 3H_2$$
$$Zn + 2HO^- + 2H_2O = [Zn(OH)_4]^{2-} + H_2$$

These reactions can be regarded as the reduction of water in the presence of hydroxide ions.

Electrolysis

Hydrogen ions are reduced to hydrogen at the cathode during the electrolysis of aqueous solutions of acids, alkalis and many salts.

Oxidation methods

The hydride ion is oxidised to hydrogen at the anode during the electrolysis of the ionic s-block hydrides (§7.5). The reaction of ionic hydrides with water can be regarded as oxidation of the hydride ion and reduction of the hydrogen ion:

$$H^- + H^+(aq) = H_2$$

Industrial methods

Hydrogen is required in vast quantities for the manufacture of such compounds as ammonia and methanol. It is manufactured by a variety of processes.

Electrolysis of sodium chloride solution   Hydrogen is a by-product of the manufacture of sodium hydroxide.

From naphtha Large quantities of hydrogen are now obtained from naphtha by steam reforming. Before the naphtha can be reformed, sulphur compounds must be removed because they deactivate the reforming catalyst. In a typical process naphtha is vaporised, heated to 400 °C (673 K), then mixed with hydrogen and passed over a hydro-desulphurisation catalyst. This converts sulphur compounds to hydrogen sulphide, which is removed by passing the gases over zinc oxide:

$$ZnO + H_2S = ZnS + H_2O$$

The desulphurised naphtha is passed with superheated steam over a nickel reforming catalyst to give a mixture of hydrogen, methane, carbon monoxide and carbon dioxide. After the removal of carbon oxides, hydrogen containing less than 5 per cent of methane is obtained.

From methane In the Texaco process, a mixture of hydrogen and carbon monoxide is produced by treating methane with steam and oxygen at a temperature of 1 100 °C (1 373 K) and a pressure of 30 atm (3 000 kPa).

6.2 The hydrogen economy

There has recently been much speculation concerning the possible use of hydrogen as an energy intermediate. Accessible reserves of oil and natural gas are strictly limited, and early in the next century it is likely that the consumption of these fuels will fall sharply. It is also likely that the use of coal will continue to decline. To compensate for this it is almost certain that there will be a steep increase in the use of electricity, probably from nuclear fission but possibly from new technologies based on solar energy, wave energy or wind energy. However, electricity, regardless of how it is generated, suffers from a lack of flexibility in two important respects.

Generation Power stations, particularly those which use nuclear fuel, do not respond well to fluctuations in demand, e.g. low demand at night, followed by heavy demand in the early morning. They operate best at constant load; but producing unwanted electricity at night is clearly wasteful. Producing nothing at night is equally wasteful as this yields no return on massive capital investment.

Use Electricity is unsuitable for powering cars and lorries. Granted, battery operated vehicles (recharged from the mains at night) are acceptable for town use, but they have a limited range and speed. Granted, too, that developments in battery technology could revolutionise the situation, but all the signs are that the lead–acid battery will remain with us for many years to come.

Both these problems may be solved by the use of an energy-rich chemical intermediate, i.e. a fuel, suitable for use in motor vehicles, which could be manufactured using off-peak electricity. Any intermediate would have to be: (i) simple to manufacture; (ii) simple and safe to use; (iii) economic in both production and use. Various intermediates have been suggested, e.g. methane, methanol and hydrogen, but the one which appears to satisfy these conditions best is hydrogen. It offers a number of outstanding advantages, as follows.

Ease and efficiency of manufacture   Hydrogen is readily available from water. Although electrolysis provides an obvious method, this process is clumsy, capital intensive and inefficient. Thermochemical methods are much more attractive. Numerous routes have been proposed, but the most promising are based on the decomposition of sulphuric acid at temperatures up to 800 °C (1 073 K):

$$2H_2SO_4 = 2H_2O + 2SO_2 + O_2$$

This could be followed by the electrolysis of aqueous sulphur dioxide, which would yield hydrogen and, at the same time, re-form sulphuric acid:

$$SO_2 + 2H_2O \xrightarrow{0.17 \text{ V}} H_2SO_4 + H_2$$

Various other methods of utilising the sulphur dioxide to produce hydrogen have been proposed, and research is continuing.

Flexibility and efficiency in use   Hydrogen, because it is a gas, is more difficult to store and transport than petrol or oil; the use of gas cylinders or vessels for liquid hydrogen poses obvious problems. However, relatively large quantities of hydrogen can be absorbed by certain metals, notably palladium, in forming interstitial hydrides, and this hydrogen can subsequently be released on warming. Vehicles using hydrogen as a fuel, either on its own or mixed with petrol, are remarkably efficient. For example, in town driving, a car powered by hydrogen requires only about half as much energy as one powered by petrol.

Absence of pollution   Because its combustion gives water vapour, hydrogen could not cause atmospheric pollution. There would be no problems associated with unburnt gas, partially burnt gas, or noxious additives.

Safety   Research has shown that in the event of an accident resulting in a hydrogen fire almost all the heat would go upwards. There would be little tendency for it to spread sideways, as happens with petrol; thus there would be less likelihood of serious burns to the occupants of the vehicle.

6.3 The properties of hydrogen

ortho and *para* Hydrogen

The nucleus of a hydrogen (protium) atom possesses spin, just like an electron. Because of this, the hydrogen molecule exists in two forms. In *ortho* hydrogen the two nuclei spin in the same direction, but in the *para* form they possess opposed spins. The two forms exist in equilibrium and have slightly different physical properties but identical chemical properties. At room temperature the ratio of *ortho* to *para* hydrogen is 3 : 1, but close to absolute zero (0 K) the *para* form predominates. The deuterium molecule also exists in *ortho* and *para* forms.

The bonding of hydrogen

At ordinary temperatures hydrogen has a low reactivity. To bring about a reaction with hydrogen, a high temperature, ultraviolet light or the presence of a catalyst is usually required. The cause lies in the strength of the bond in the hydrogen molecule. (The H——H bond dissociation enthalpy is 436 kJ mol^{-1}.) For hydrogen to react this bond must be broken, and the breaking process presents an enthalpy barrier which must be overcome before the reaction can proceed. Heat, ultraviolet light or the presence of a catalyst either ruptures or weakens the H——H bond and therefore speeds up the reactions of hydrogen.

Hydrogen, in its compounds, is always monovalent. It achieves this condition by one of three electronic processes, as follows:

(i)   the loss of its electron to form the hydrogen ion, H^+;
(ii)   the gain of one electron to form the hydride ion, H^-;
(iii) the sharing of its electron with one from another atom to form a single covalent bond.

The hydrogen ion

The isolated hydrogen ion, which is in fact a proton, occurs in the hydrogen discharge tube. In aqueous or other solutions, however, the proton never occurs alone, because it is strongly attracted and bound to polar solvent molecules. For example, in aqueous solution, protons are coordinately bonded to water molecules, i.e.

$$\begin{array}{c} H \\ \diagdown \\ O: \rightarrow H^+ = \\ H \diagup \end{array} \left[\begin{array}{c} H \\ \diagdown \\ O—H \\ H \diagup \end{array} \right]^+$$

The oxonium ion, H_3O^+, which may be described as a monohydrated proton, is formed when *protic acids* are dissolved in water, e.g.

$$HCl + H_2O \rightleftharpoons H_3O^+ + Cl^-$$
$$H_2SO_4 + H_2O \rightleftharpoons H_3O^+ + HSO_4^-$$

There is considerable evidence that the oxonium ion is extensively hydrated in solution, i.e. $H_3O^+(aq)$. This hydrated ion is known as the *hydrogen ion*, and is denoted by either $H^+(aq)$ or H^+. Protons in solution may therefore be represented by H_3O^+, $H^+(aq)$ or H^+, whichever is convenient, but it should be remembered that in these cases H^+ does not represent an isolated proton. The term 'proton' is often used in discussions of acid–base reactions, although it is doubtful whether free protons ever exist in such reactions.

The proton also occurs coordinately bonded to other molecules, e.g. to ammonia as the NH_4^+ ion, to methanol as $CH_3OH_2^+$ and to ethoxyethane (ether) as $(C_2H_5)_2OH^+$.

The hydride ion

Hydrogen has a low electron affinity (-78 kJ mol^{-1}) and is reduced to the hydride ion, H^-, only by the reactive s-block elements (§7.5).

Covalent bonds

With most of the p-block elements hydrogen forms covalently bonded compounds, e.g. NH_3, H_2S and HCl.

Enthalpy changes during the reactions of hydrogen

The enthalpy changes accompanying various reactions of hydrogen are summarised in Table 6.1. The formation of covalent compounds is not shown because the enthalpy changes depend on the other elements involved.

Table 6.1 Enthalpy changes accompanying the reactions of hydrogen.

Overall change	Steps	Enthalpy change of each step/kJ mol^{-1}	Overall enthalpy change/kJ mol^{-1}
(a) $\frac{1}{2}H_2(g) = H(g)$	$\frac{1}{2}H_2(g) = H(g)$	$+218$	$+218$
(b) $\frac{1}{2}H_2(g) = H^+(g) + e^-$	$\frac{1}{2}H_2(g) = H(g)$	$+218$	
	$H(g) = H^+(g) + e^-$	$+1\,310$	$+1\,528$
(c) $\frac{1}{2}H_2(g) = H^+(aq) + e^-$	$\frac{1}{2}H_2(g) = H(g)$	$+218$	
	$H(g) = H^+(g) + e^-$	$+1\,310$	
	$H^+(g) + aq = H^+(aq)$	$-1\,200$	$+328$
(d) $\frac{1}{2}H_2(g) + e^- = H^-(g)$	$\frac{1}{2}H_2(g) = H(g)$	$+218$	
	$H(g) + e^- = H^-(g)$	-70	$+140$

From (b) in Table 6.1 we see that the enthalpy required to form isolated protons, $H^+(g)$, is far in excess of that needed for the other changes. Thus, on enthalpy considerations, the overall changes (a), (c) and (d) are more likely to occur than change (b).

Hydrides

Hydrogen forms binary compounds, known as *hydrides*, with most of the other elements. Notable exceptions are the noble gases. The term 'compound' is perhaps an overstatement when considering the transition elements, but the main group elements do form well defined compounds with hydrogen. The three types of hydride which exist may be designated by means of the periodic table.

s-Block hydrides

Except for beryllium and magnesium, the s-block elements form ionic hydrides containing the hydride ion, H^- (§7.5).

p-Block hydrides

All the elements of groups 4B, 5B, 6B and 7B form covalent mononuclear hydrides, i.e. hydrides which contain one atom of a p-block element (Table 6.2).

Table 6.2 Formulae of the mononuclear hydrides of groups 4B, 5B, 6B and 7B.

Group	4B	5B	6B	7B
formula†	XH_4	XH_3	H_2X	HX
examples	CH_4, SnH_4	NH_3, PH_3	H_2O, H_2S	HF, HI

† X represents one atom of the group element. Notice the conventional manner of writing the formulae.

The X——H bond dissociation enthalpies tend to increase with decreasing radius of atom X. Therefore the stability of the covalent hydrides increases from group 4B to group 7B, and decreases from top to bottom of each group. The hydrides of the metallic elements, e.g. bismuth and lead, are very unstable, while those of the head elements of these groups are comparatively stable.

Some elements form polynuclear hydrides as well as mononuclear hydrides. These contain more than one atom of a p-block element. Carbon is particularly outstanding in this respect, and forms alkanes, alkenes, alkynes and arenes. The remaining p-block elements, notably silicon, germanium, nitrogen, phosphorus, oxygen and sulphur, form a limited number of polynuclear hydrides, e.g. Si_nH_{2n+2}, Ge_nH_{2n+2}, N_2H_4, HN_3, P_2H_4, H_2O_2 and H_2S_n.

Boron forms two series of polynuclear hydrides, with the formulae B_nH_{n+4} and B_nH_{n+6}. All the hydrides of boron, including the simplest, diborane, B_2H_6, are 'electron deficient' (§8.5). Aluminium, beryllium and magnesium form polymeric hydrides, $(AlH_3)_n$, $(BeH_2)_n$ and $(MgH_2)_n$ respectively, which are also electron deficient. No hydride of gallium has yet been identified, although many compounds containing Ga——H bonds are known.

d- and f-Block hydrides

Many d- and f-block elements can absorb hydrogen into the *interstices* (i.e. holes) in their lattices to give products which are often called *interstitial hydrides*. In most cases it appears that free hydrogen atoms are involved, and that there is no direct bonding between the metal and hydrogen. Possibly, therefore, the term 'compound' should not be applied. The metal lattice expands as a result of taking up hydrogen, and so the hydrides have a lower density than the metals from which they are derived.

These hydrides are prepared by heating the metal with hydrogen under pressure, although palladium absorbs hydrogen at room temperature and atmospheric pressure. In view of their nature it is hardly surprising to find that many of these hydrides are non-stoicheiometric, i.e. the ratio of metal to hydrogen is not a sensible whole number. The composition can vary, depending on the conditions of preparation, and reported examples include $TiH_{1.7}$, $PdH_{0.6}$ and $TaH_{0.76}$. Some, however, are stoicheiometric, e.g. UH_3.

Interstitial hydrides are metallic in character because the properties of the host metal are not fundamentally altered by the absorption of hydrogen. When heated, they lose their hydrogen. They are resistant to hydrolysis.

The elements of groups 1B and 2B, also indium and thallium, form hydrides whose nature is far from certain. They are generally described as 'borderline hydrides'. Copper hydride, CuH, the best known hydride in this class, appears to be a definite compound. It is a reducing agent and is stable to water, but reacts with acids to form hydrogen.

Hydride complexes

A hydride complex contains the hydride ion, H^-, coordinated to an atom of another element. The best known examples are the tetrahydroborate(III) ion, $[BH_4]^-$, and the tetrahydridoaluminate(III) ion, $[AlH_4]^-$. Both may be regarded as complexes formed between 'BH_3' or 'AlH_3' and the hydride ion, i.e.

$$BH_3 + H^- = [BH_4]^-$$
$$AlH_3 + H^- = [AlH_4]^-$$

The tetrahydroborate(III) ion is tetrahedral, and the aluminium complex is probably of the same shape.

Sodium tetrahydroborate(III), $Na[BH_4]$, and lithium tetrahydrido-aluminate(III), $Li[AlH_4]$, are important reducing agents. The boron compound is prepared by reacting sodium hydride with trimethyl borate, $(CH_3O)_3B$, at 250 °C (523 K):

$$4NaH + (CH_3O)_3B = Na[BH_4] + 3CH_3ONa$$

The reaction between lithium hydride and anhydrous aluminium chloride in ethoxyethane (ether) can be used to prepare the aluminium compound:

$$4LiH + AlCl_3 = Li[AlH_4] + 3LiCl$$

These compounds function as reductants by acting as sources of the hydride ion. Lithium tetrahydridoaluminate(III) in ethoxyethane solution is an excellent reducing agent, and is widely used in organic chemistry, e.g. for the reduction of carboxylic acids to primary alcohols. In inorganic chemistry it can be used to prepare p-block hydrides from the corresponding halides, e.g.

$$4PCl_3 + 3Li[AlH_4] = 4PH_3 + 3LiCl + 3AlCl_3$$

Lithium tetrahydridoaluminate(III) reacts violently with water:

$$Li[AlH_4] + 4H_2O = LiOH + Al(OH)_3(aq) + 4H_2$$

Sodium tetrahydroborate(III), in contrast, is stable in cold water, but is also an excellent reducing agent.

6.4 The position of hydrogen in the periodic table

On the basis of its electronic configuration and chemical properties, hydrogen could reasonably be placed in group 1A, group 7B or, with imagination, group 4B of the periodic table. Some of the arguments for and against placing hydrogen in these groups are set out in Table 6.3.

Table 6.3 Comparison of hydrogen with the elements of groups 1A, 4B and 7B.

	Properties in which hydrogen displays a resemblance to a periodic group	Properties in which hydrogen displays a difference from a periodic group
group 1A	has an ns^1 configuration forms a monopositive ion	is less reactive than the alkali metals is a non-metal forms diatomic molecules forms covalent bonds forms an anion has a higher electronegativity and a higher ionisation enthalpy than the alkali metals gives an ion, H^+, which does not have an independent existence
group 4B	has a half-full outer shell (cf. C) forms covalent bonds is a non-metal (cf. C and Si)	forms diatomic molecules (contrast C, Si, etc) has an electronegativity which does not fit in with the group trend, i.e. $x_H = 2.1$, $x_C = 2.5$, $x_{Si} = 1.8$, etc
group 7B	is a diatomic non-metal forms covalent bonds has one electron less than the following noble gas in the periodic table forms a mononegative ion	forms cationic species is far less reactive than the halogens has a lower electronegativity than the halogens has a much lower electron affinity than the halogens

As indicated, there are several arguments against putting hydrogen in any of these groups. Many of the alleged similarities, too, are rather artificial because hydrogen does not closely resemble any other element.

It should be regarded as unique and not be placed in any of the periodic groups.

6.5 Deuterium and tritium

Deuterium is sufficiently different from protium to warrant a special mention. The extent to which the isotopes of a given element differ from one another depends on the ratio of their masses. The mass ratio of deuterium to protium is 2 : 1, which is greater than that for any other pair of isotopes, except tritium and protium.

Deuterium is prepared by the electrolysis of deuterium oxide (§11.5). The physical properties of deuterium are significantly different from those of protium (p. 136), e.g. the melting temperature is -254.3 °C (18.9 K), and the boiling temperature is -249.4 °C (23.8 K).

Although the two isotopes are chemically identical, deuterium and its compounds generally react more slowly than their protium counterparts. For example, the reaction between protium and chlorine is three times faster than the corresponding reaction with deuterium.

Tritium is formed continuously in the upper atmosphere by the bombardment of nitrogen with fast neutrons originating from cosmic rays:

$$^{14}_{7}N + ^{1}_{0}n = ^{3}_{1}H + ^{12}_{6}C$$

It can also be obtained by the neutron bombardment of lithium:

$$^{6}_{3}Li + ^{1}_{0}n = ^{3}_{1}H + ^{4}_{2}He$$

Tritium is radioactive and decays into helium-3.

Deuterium and tritium and their compounds can be used to investigate reaction mechanisms. For example, an insight has been gained into the behaviour of ammonia in aqueous solution from the discovery that the ammonia obtained from solution in deuterium oxide has a higher relative molecular mass than ordinary ammonia (NH_3), due to partial conversion into NH_2D. This is attributed to ionisation:

$$NH_3 + D_2O \rightleftharpoons NH_3D^+ + DO^-$$

When the NH_3D^+ ion decomposes in the reverse change the atom of deuterium is not necessarily lost; any of the three atoms of protium could equally well leave instead:

$$NH_3D^+ + DO^- \rightleftharpoons NH_2D + HDO$$

Further reactions with deuterium oxide produce NHD_2 and ND_3.

These observations support the theory that ammonia ionises in water to produce the ammonium ion, in which all four atoms of hydrogen are chemically bonded to the nitrogen atom in an identical manner. Similar results would be obtained by the use of tritium oxide, T_2O. The ammonia obtained in this case would contain NH_2T, NHT_2 and NT_3, and would be radioactive as well as having an increased mass.

Chapter 7

Groups 1A and 2A

The elements of group 1A, often known as the 'alkali metals', are lithium, sodium, potassium, rubidium, caesium and francium. Group 2A comprises beryllium, magnesium, calcium, strontium, barium and radium. Except for beryllium, they are commonly known as the 'alkaline earth metals'. Little is known about francium since it is radioactive and its isotopes have very short half-lives; it is formed from actinium by radioactive decay:

$$^{227}_{89}Ac = {}^{223}_{87}Fr + {}^{4}_{2}He$$

Radium is also radioactive, but its isotopes are more stable than those of francium and its chemistry is well known. Both francium and radium are commonly excluded from general discussions of the s-block elements, but their properties can be deduced from the trends that occur in each group. Some important properties of the s-block elements are given in Tables 7.1 and 7.2.

7.1 Occurrence and isolation of the elements

Group 1A

The chief sources of the alkali metals, of which only sodium and potassium are relatively abundant, are dried-up salt lakes. Lithium occurs principally as a complex aluminosilicate.

The elements are isolated by electrolysis of their fused halides. Aqueous solutions cannot be used because the alkali metals all react

Table 7.1 Some properties of the elements of group 1A.

	Lithium	Sodium	Potassium	Rubidium	Caesium	Francium
character	metal	metal	metal	metal	metal	metal
allotropes	none	none	none	none	none	none
atomic number	3	11	19	37	55	87
relative atomic mass	6.941	22.989 8	39.102	85.467 8	132.906 5	223†
outer electronic configuration	$2s^1$	$3s^1$	$4s^1$	$5s^1$	$6s^1$	$7s^1$
valency	1	1	1	1	1	1
melting temperature/°C	180	97.8	63.7	38.9	28.7	27
boiling temperature/°C	1 330	890	774	688	690	—
enthalpy of atomisation/ kJ mol^{-1}	161.0	109.0	90.0	85.8	78.7	—
$E^{\ominus}$/V	− 3.04	− 2.71	− 2.92	− 2.92	− 2.92	—

† Mass number of the most stable isotope.

Table 7.2 Some properties of the elements of group 2A.

	Beryllium	Magnesium	Calcium	Strontium	Barium	Radium
character	metal	metal	metal	metal	metal	metal
allotropes	none	none	none	none	none	none
atomic number	4	12	20	38	56	88
relative atomic mass	9.012 18	24.305	40.08	87.62	137.34	226†
outer electronic configuration	$2s^2$	$3s^2$	$4s^2$	$5s^2$	$6s^2$	$7s^2$
valency	2	2	2	2	2	2
melting temperature/°C	1 280	650	850	768	714	700
boiling temperature/°C	2 477	1 110	1 487	1 380	1 640	1 140
enthalpy of atomisation/ kJ mol^{-1}	321	150	193	164	176	130
$E^{\ominus}$/V	− 1.85	− 2.38	− 2.87	− 2.89	− 2.90	− 2.92

† Mass number of the most stable isotope.

with water. Sodium, an important metal, is isolated on a large scale by the *Downs process*. The electrolyte is a mixture of sodium chloride and calcium chloride, which melts at approximately 600 °C (873 K). Sodium chloride alone melts at 801 °C (1 074 K); thus by using the mixed electrolyte the cell can be operated at a considerably lower temperature. In this context the calcium chloride is called a 'flux', because it makes the sodium chloride easier to fuse.

The cell contains a graphite anode in the centre, with a cylindrical steel cathode around it. The products of electrolysis, namely chlorine from the anode and a mixture of sodium and calcium at the cathode, are prevented from mixing by a cylindrical steel gauze situated between the two electrodes. The metals produced at the cathode float on the electrolyte and collect under a hood from where they are removed. They can readily be separated from each other because calcium does not dissolve in liquid sodium.

Sodium is used in the manufacture of titanium (§14.4) and tetraethyl-lead. Because of its excellent thermal and electrical conductivities, it is also used as a heat exchange medium in nuclear reactors and in sodium-filled electrical power lines.

Group 2A

Beryllium occurs as a complex aluminosilicate. Important sources of magnesium are carnallite, $MgCl_2 \cdot KCl \cdot 6H_2O$, magnesite, $MgCO_3$, and dolomite, $CaCO_3 \cdot MgCO_3$. Magnesium compounds also occur in sea water. Compounds of calcium account for many minerals, including limestone, $CaCO_3$, anhydrite, $CaSO_4$, and a variety of phosphates, silicates and chlorides. Strontium and barium occur as their sulphates and carbonates. Radium is obtained from uranium minerals, where it is produced by radioactive decay.

Beryllium is isolated by the electrolysis of a fused mixture of beryllium chloride and sodium chloride. Magnesium, the most important element of this group, is extracted by the electrolysis of fused magnesium chloride, produced by heating a mixture of magnesium oxide and coke in a stream of chlorine:

$$MgO + C + Cl_2 = MgCl_2 + CO$$

The magnesium oxide is obtained by heating the carbonate ore or the hydroxide. The latter is precipitated from sea water by the addition of calcium hydroxide:

$$Mg^{2+} + Ca(OH)_2(s) = Mg(OH)_2(s) + Ca^{2+}$$

The remaining elements of group 2A are also prepared by the electrolysis of their fused chlorides.

Beryllium is used for producing wear-resistant alloys. Magnesium is a metal with a low density and is used in the manufacture of light alloys. The remaining metals of this group find little application in industry.

7.2 The structure of the elements

The melting temperatures and enthalpies of atomisation of the group 2A elements are generally higher than those of the group 1A elements. This is a consequence of the greater strength of the metallic bonding in the former. Broadly speaking, the higher the ratio of delocalised bonding electrons to atomic radius, the greater is the strength of the metallic bonding. This ratio is small for group 1A elements, with their relatively large atoms and with only one electron per atom available for metallic bonding. For a given group 2A element the ratio is considerably larger than for the adjacent group 1A element (e.g. Mg and Na) because, for the group 2A element, there are two electrons per atom available for metallic bonding and the atomic radius is smaller.

As the atomic radius increases from top to bottom of the groups, the strength of the metallic bonding decreases. Thus, the melting temperatures and atomisation enthalpies of the group 1A elements, which all crystallise with a body centred cubic lattice, decrease from lithium to caesium. A corresponding decrease is observed in group 2A, but it is more irregular than in group 1A. This is due to another factor which affects metallic bond strength, namely the crystal structure of the metal. Beryllium and magnesium possess a hexagonal close packed structure, and barium crystallises in a body centred cubic lattice. Calcium and strontium change structure when heated from face centred cubic to hexagonal close packed and finally body centred cubic.

7.3 Bonding and valency

The dominant feature of the s-block elements is the formation of ions by the loss of their outer s electrons; group 1A elements form monopositive ions, and group 2A elements dipositive ions.

Ionisation enthalpies

Ionisation enthalpies decrease from top to bottom of each group (Table 7.3). Thus, in group 1A, lithium shows the least tendency to ionise and consequently forms a few covalent compounds (§7.6), but for the remaining elements of the group covalent bond formation is rare. Likewise, in group 2A, beryllium has a rather high ionisation enthalpy and tends to use its $2s^2$ electrons in forming two covalent bonds rather than simple Be^{2+} ions. Indeed, beryllium differs significantly from the other elements of group 2A (§7.6).

The covalent character which is evident in many lithium and magnesium compounds arises from distortion of the anions by the small Li^+ and Mg^{2+} cations (§4.4).

Standard electrode potentials

The ease with which ions are formed under anhydrous conditions is accurately reflected by the ionisation enthalpies of the appropriate elements. However, when ions are formed in aqueous solution they are hydrated. Under such conditions ionisation enthalpies are not always a reliable guide to the overall ease of ion formation, and instead we use standard electrode potentials $(E^{\ominus})$ which, by definition, are a measure of the tendency for the following change to occur:

$$M^{n+}(aq) + ne^- = M(s)$$

The more negative the value of $E^{\ominus}$, the easier is the *reverse* change, i.e. the formation of hydrated ions from the metal.

The $E^{\ominus}$ values in Table 7.1 show that the ease with which the alkali metals form hydrated ions in solution decreases in the order Li > K = Rb = Cs > Na. Thus, lithium shows the strongest tendency to form hydrated ions, even though it has the highest ionisation enthalpy in group 1A.

The anomaly is confirmed by the enthalpy changes for the formation of hydrated ions. Strictly, we should consider $\Delta G^{\ominus}$ values as a guide to the tendency of a reaction to occur, but we can often use $\Delta H^{\ominus}$ values instead when dealing with a series of endothermic changes of the same type and with the same or approximately the same $\Delta S^{\ominus}$ value. (This is because $\Delta G^{\ominus}$ and $\Delta H^{\ominus}$ are related by the Gibbs free energy equation, $\Delta G^{\ominus} = \Delta H^{\ominus} - T\Delta S$.) Thus, for any given series, the likelihood of reaction occurring increases as $\Delta G^{\ominus}$ and hence $\Delta H^{\ominus}$ values become decreasingly positive. If we examine the overall ΔH values for the formation of $M^+(aq)$ ions (Table 7.3), we see that the values are in almost the same order as the $E^{\ominus}$ values. $E^{\ominus}$ values are themselves related to $\Delta G^{\ominus}$ values $(\Delta G^{\ominus} = -nFE^{\ominus})$, and are thus equally reliable.

Table 7.3 Enthalpy changes, in kJ mol^{-1}, for the steps involved in the change $M(s) \rightarrow M^+(aq) + e^-$.

	Lithium	Sodium	Potassium	Rubidium	Caesium
atomisation enthalpy $M(s) \rightarrow M(g)$	+161.0	+109.0	+90.0	+85.8	+78.7
ionisation enthalpy $M(g) \rightarrow M^+(g) + e^-$	+525.0	+500.0	+424.0	+408.0	+382.0
hydration enthalpy $M^+(g) \rightarrow M^+(aq)$	−519.0	−406.0	−322.0	−301.0	−276.0
overall $M(s) \rightarrow M^+(aq) + e^-$	+167.0	+203.0	+192.0	+192.8	+184.7

To resolve the anomaly of lithium we must examine, for all these metals, the enthalpy changes for the various steps leading to the formation of hydrated ions (Table 7.3). We see that the overall change for lithium is the least endothermic because of the high hydration enthalpy of the small lithium ion, which compensates for the high enthalpies of atomisation and ionisation of this element. For sodium it is the unexpectedly high ionisation enthalpy which is principally responsible for the larger amount of energy which is absorbed overall. (By extrapolation from lithium and potassium, the enthalpy of ionisation would be expected to be approximately 476 kJ mol⁻¹.)

In group 2A the order of standard electrode potentials is Ra > Ba > Sr > Ca > Mg > Be (Table 7.2), which is in accordance with the ionisation enthalpies. This is because for these elements the most important factor is the ionisation enthalpy, which decreases from beryllium to radium.

7.4 Reactions of the s-block elements

Most reactions of the s-block elements can be regarded as redox reactions in which the metal, acting as the reductant, becomes oxidised to M^+ ions for group 1A elements or M^{2+} ions for group 2A elements.

Reaction with other elements

The s-block elements, particularly the alkali metals, are extremely reactive and combine with many non-metals. The freshly cut metals have a bright lustre which rapidly disappears as they react with the atmosphere. Most of the s-block elements, except beryllium and magnesium, are therefore stored under liquid paraffin to prevent contact with the air. Beryllium and magnesium tarnish very slowly because a thin protective film of oxide forms on the metal surface (cf. aluminium).

In most cases the reactivity of the s-block elements towards non-metals, such as oxygen or the halogens (§7.5), increases from top to bottom of the groups, as the formation of metal ions becomes easier. In some cases, particularly with nitrogen and carbon, the reverse is true. For example, lithium, alone in group 1A, combines directly with nitrogen to form an ionic nitride:

$$6Li + N_2 = 2Li_3N$$

Only in this case is the lattice enthalpy high enough, because of the small size of the lithium ion, to compensate for the energy absorbed during the formation of ions. Lithium nitride is therefore an exothermic compound ($\Delta H_f^{\ominus}$ [Li_3N] = -198 kJ mol⁻¹) and is stable. Except for beryllium, all the group 2A elements form ionic nitrides, because of the higher lattice enthalpies associated with the dipositive metal ions.

Reaction with water

With the exceptions of beryllium and magnesium, the s-block elements reduce cold water to hydrogen and become oxidised to their hydroxides:

$$2M + 2H_2O = 2M^+(aq) + 2HO^- + H_2 \quad \text{group 1A}$$
$$M + 2H_2O = M^{2+}(aq) + 2HO^- + H_2 \quad \text{group 2A}$$

The group 2A metals are less reactive towards water than the corresponding group 1A elements. Magnesium reacts very slowly with cold

152

water, but more rapidly with boiling water or steam, to form the oxide:

$$Mg + H_2O = MgO + H_2$$

In reactions with water, hydrated metal ions are formed from elements, and we might therefore expect standard electrode potentials to serve as an indication of reactivity. However, this is not the case, because the reactions increase in vigour from top to bottom of each s-block group. The formation of hydrated alkali metal ions from the metals involves two endothermic steps, i.e. atomisation and ionisation, and an exothermic stage, i.e. hydration. Compare, as two extremes, lithium and caesium:

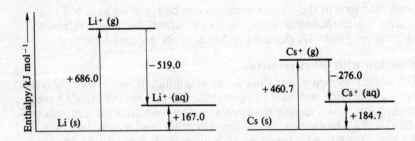

The endothermic steps act as an enthalpy barrier for the reaction. Lithium, with the greater enthalpy barrier, therefore reacts more slowly with water than caesium, which has a lower barrier. For the remaining alkali metals the reactions with water increase in vigour from sodium to rubidium as the enthalpy barrier becomes smaller. Although the enthalpy barrier bears a superficial resemblance to activation energy, it does not represent the latter quantity. When considering the activation energy for these reactions we must include both reactants, i.e. metal and water, and we have neglected the reduction of water in this discussion.

Similar arguments apply to the reactions of the group 2A elements with water, and to the reactions between the s-block elements and alcohols, e.g.

$$2Na + 2ROH = 2RONa + H_2$$

Reaction with ammonia

The alkali metals and calcium, strontium and barium react with liquid ammonia to form hydrogen and metal amides (§10.5). Metal amides are ionic and react readily with water, e.g.

$$NaNH_2 + H_2O = NaOH + NH_3$$

The alkali metals also form amides when heated in ammonia, but the group 2A metals, when similarly treated, produce the nitride or hydride, e.g.

$$3Mg + 2NH_3 = Mg_3N_2 + 3H_2$$
$$3Ca + 2NH_3 = 3CaH_2 + N_2$$

7.5 Compounds of the s-block elements

Hydrides

Except for beryllium, the s-block elements combine directly with hydrogen at temperatures in the range 300–700 °C (573–973 K) to give hydrides. Magnesium hydride, MgH_2, is formed only under high pressures.

$$2M + H_2 = 2MH \qquad \text{group 1A}$$
$$M + H_2 = MH_2 \qquad \text{group 2A}$$

Beryllium hydride, BeH_2, is prepared by reducing beryllium compounds, such as dimethylberyllium, $(CH_3)_2Be$, with lithium tetra-hydridoaluminate(III).

The hydrides of beryllium and magnesium are covalent and polymeric, and are believed to be electron deficient (cf. boranes, §8.5), e.g.

$$\left[\begin{array}{c} H \qquad\qquad H \\ \diagdown \quad / \diagdown \quad / \\ Be \qquad Be \\ / \quad \diagdown \quad / \quad \diagdown \\ H \qquad\qquad H \end{array} \right]_n$$

The remaining hydrides of the s-block elements are ionic and contain the hydride ion, H^-. The alkali metal hydrides possess face centred cubic structures similar to that of sodium chloride, with H^- ions replacing Cl^- ions, but the group 2A metal hydrides have less regular structures.

The presence of the hydride ion in these ionic hydrides can be demonstrated by the electrolysis of the compounds when dissolved in fused alkali metal halides. Hydrogen is evolved at the *anode*, by oxidation of hydride ions, i.e.

$$2H^- = H_2 + 2e^-$$

Lithium hydride is sufficiently stable to be fused without decomposition, but the other ionic hydrides decompose into their respective elements below their melting temperatures.

Ionic hydrides are vigorously hydrolysed by water:

$$H^- + H_2O = H_2 + HO^-$$

Because the hydride ion is readily oxidised to hydrogen, ionic hydrides are powerful reducing agents, e.g.

$$H^- + CO_2 = HCOO^-$$
$$H^- + 2CO = HCOO^- + C$$

Oxides

Beryllium forms one oxide, BeO, which is essentially covalent. The remaining s-block elements form more than one oxide, all of which are ionic (Table 7.4).

Table 7.4 The oxides of the s-block elements.

	Oxides (containing the oxide ion, O^{2-})	Peroxides (containing the peroxide ion, O_2^{2-})	Hyperoxides (containing the hyperoxide ion, O_2^-)
group 1A	M_2O	M_2O_2	MO_2
group 2A	MO	MO_2	none
comments	all the metals	not Be	

Lower oxides

Lithium oxide, Li_2O, and the oxides of group 2A are prepared by heating the elements in oxygen, or by thermal decomposition of their carbonates, nitrates or hydroxides. Sodium oxide, Na_2O, is obtained by heating sodium in a limited supply of oxygen, but the oxides of the heavier alkali metals can be prepared only by indirect methods, such as heating the metal with its nitrate, e.g.

$$10K + 2KNO_3 = 6K_2O + N_2$$

The oxides are strongly basic. Those of group 1A are more basic than those of the corresponding group 2A elements, and basic properties increase with descent of the groups.

The oxides of the s-block elements, with the exception of beryllium, react with water to form the corresponding hydroxides, e.g.

$$Na_2O + H_2O = 2NaOH$$
$$CaO + H_2O = Ca(OH)_2$$

Magnesium oxide reacts very slowly, but the remaining oxides of these two groups are extremely reactive towards water.

Peroxides

The peroxides of the alkali metals are formed by passing oxygen into solutions of the metals in liquid ammonia:

$$2M + O_2 = M_2O_2$$

Sodium peroxide can also be prepared by heating sodium in an excess of oxygen. The hydrated peroxides of magnesium, calcium and strontium are obtained as white precipitates by adding hydrogen peroxide to cold alkaline solutions of their salts, e.g.

$$Ca^{2+} + H_2O_2 + 8H_2O = CaO_2 \cdot 8H_2O(s) + 2H^+(aq)$$

Barium peroxide is prepared by direct combination of the elements at

500 °C (773 K). Higher temperatures should be avoided, because above 800 °C (1 073 K) the peroxide decomposes, i.e.

$$2BaO_2 = 2BaO + O_2$$

The peroxide ion is rather large. Consequently:

(i)   it is easily polarised by cations, especially if their radii are small;
(ii) stable crystal lattices can be formed only with large cations.

Lithium peroxide readily decomposes, because the small lithium ion strongly polarises the peroxide ion and the crystal lattice is unstable. The remaining peroxides become increasingly resistant to heat from top to bottom of the groups, because the polarising power of the cation decreases and more stable lattices are formed.

The peroxides of the alkali metals react readily with acids and with water at 0 °C (273 K) to produce hydrogen peroxide, e.g.

$$Na_2O_2 + 2HCl = 2NaCl + H_2O_2$$
$$Na_2O_2 + 2H_2O = 2NaOH + H_2O_2$$

At higher temperatures oxygen is formed by decomposition of the hydrogen peroxide:

$$2Na_2O_2 + 2H_2O = 4NaOH + O_2$$

Oxygen is also liberated from peroxides by treatment with acidic oxides, e.g.

$$2Na_2O_2 + 2CO_2 = 2Na_2CO_3 + O_2$$

Hyperoxides (formerly 'superoxides')

Hyperoxides are highly coloured compounds, in contrast to the oxides and peroxides which are colourless. The hyperoxides of potassium, rubidium and caesium are produced by burning the elements in air or oxygen, e.g.

$$K + O_2 = KO_2$$

Sodium hyperoxide, NaO_2, is prepared by heating sodium or its peroxide with oxygen at 450 °C (723 K) and a pressure of 300 atm (3×10^4 kPa). The very unstable lithium hyperoxide, LiO_2, is believed to be formed when oxygen is passed into a solution of lithium in liquid ammonia at −78 °C (195 K).

The hyperoxide ion, O_2^-, resembles the peroxide ion in being stable only in combination with large cations. The stability of hyperoxides therefore increases from lithium to caesium.

Hyperoxides react with water and acids at 0 °C (273 K), e.g.

$$2KO_2 + 2H_2O = 2KOH + H_2O_2 + O_2$$
$$2KO_2 + 2HCl = 2KCl + H_2O_2 + O_2$$

As with peroxides, the hydrogen peroxide decomposes at higher temperatures to give oxygen. Oxygen is also formed with acidic oxides, e.g.

$$4KO_2 + 2CO_2 = 2K_2CO_3 + 3O_2$$

Halides

Group 1A halides are ionic, with the general formula MX. Except for lithium halides they possess the expected properties of ionic compounds, e.g. high melting temperature, solubility in water but insolubility in organic solvents.

Lithium halides, because they contain the small Li^+ ion, strongly resemble the corresponding magnesium halides (§7.6) in their physical properties. Thus, lithium fluoride is an ionic solid with a high lattice enthalpy; it has a high melting temperature (867 °C (1 140 K)) and is sparingly soluble in water. The chloride, bromide and iodide have fairly low melting temperatures (e.g. for LiCl 607 °C (880 K)), indicating a substantial degree of covalent character in their bonding. Anion distortion due to the small Li^+ ion (Fajans' rules) is the reason for this.

The chloride, bromide and iodide of lithium, in addition to being very soluble in water, also dissolve in oxygen-containing organic solvents, e.g. ethanol and propanone. No doubt the strong attraction between the small Li^+ ion and the polar organic molecules facilitates this dissolution.

Beryllium halides are all covalent, while those of the remaining group 2A elements are ionic. Magnesium halides strongly resemble the corresponding lithium halides (§7.6). Here the small Mg^{2+} ion is responsible, in the same way as the Li^+ ion in lithium compounds. Because of the small size of the F^- ion, alkaline earth fluorides have high lattice enthalpies and are sparingly soluble in water. The remaining halides, however, all dissolve in water.

Carbides

All the s-block elements form ionic carbides. The commonest are those containing the acetylide ion, written $[C\equiv C]^{2-}$ or C_2^{2-}. All acetylides react with water to form ethyne:

$$C_2^{2-} + 2H_2O = C_2H_2 + 2HO^-$$

The acetylides of the group 1A elements (i.e. M_2C_2), also BeC_2 and MgC_2, are produced when the elements are heated with ethyne. The acetylides of the remaining elements are made by heating their oxides with carbon at very high temperatures (c. 2 000 °C (2 300 K)). Only lithium and sodium in group 1A combine directly with carbon on heating to form acetylides; the remaining alkali metals form interstitial carbides (§9.6).

Other carbides of the group 2A elements are known. They are produced at much higher temperatures than those employed for acetylide formation. For example, at temperatures in excess of 1 000 °C (1 273 K) beryllium reacts with carbon or a hydrocarbon to form beryllium carbide, Be_2C, while magnesium under similar conditions gives Mg_2C_3. Beryllium carbide contains the carbide ion, C^{4-}, and reacts with water to form methane:

$$Be_2C + 4H_2O = CH_4 + 2Be(OH)_2$$
i.e. $$C^{4-} + 4H_2O = CH_4 + 4HO^-$$

Magnesium carbide, Mg_2C_3, forms propyne, $CH_3C{\equiv}CH$, on treatment with water. Because of this it is believed to contain the anion $[C{-}C{\equiv}C]^{4-}$:

$$Mg_2C_3 + 4H_2O = CH_3C{\equiv}CH + 2Mg(OH)_2$$
i.e. $$[C{-}C{\equiv}C]^{4-} + 4H_2O = CH_3C{\equiv}CH + 4HO^-$$

7.6 Anomalous properties of the head elements

Lithium

In many respects lithium strongly resembles magnesium but differs from the other alkali metals (Table 7.5). This is an example of a diagonal relationship (§3.5).

Table 7.5 A comparison of lithium with the other group 1A metals and with magnesium.

Lithium	Sodium, potassium, rubidium and caesium	Magnesium
combines directly with nitrogen to form a nitride, Li_3N	do not combine directly with nitrogen gas	forms a nitride, Mg_3N_2, by direct combination
combines directly with oxygen to form an oxide, Li_2O	form peroxides and hyperoxides	with oxygen forms only an oxide, MgO
carbonate and hydroxide decompose into Li_2O on heating	carbonates and hydroxides are thermally stable	carbonate and hydroxide give MgO on heating
lithium nitrate gives Li_2O + NO_2 + O_2 on heating	nitrates produce stable nitrites (NO_2^-) and O_2 on heating	magnesium nitrate gives MgO + NO_2 + O_2 on heating
lithium hydrogencarbonate exists only in solution	solid hydrogencarbonates exist	magnesium hydrogencarbonate exists only in solution
fluoride, carbonate, phosphate, ethanedioate and hydroxide are sparingly soluble	corresponding salts are more soluble	salts show similar solubilities to those of lithium
chloride, bromide and iodide are soluble in organic solvents	corresponding halides are less soluble in organic solvents	halides show similar solubilities to those of lithium

The cause of these anomalies is the small size of the lithium ion, Li^+, which results in:

(i) high lattice enthalpy of the compounds. This is responsible for their low solubility in water, and also for the formation of a nitride.

(ii) anion distortion. This causes some compounds to have covalent characteristics, e.g. solubility in organic solvents. It is also responsible for the thermal instability of the hydroxide and salts with oxoanions, e.g. the nitrate and carbonate.

Lithium also forms several true covalent compounds, e.g. $Li—CH_3$, which may be compared with the Grignard reagents formed by magnesium.

Beryllium

Beryllium differs from the other elements of group 2A in two major respects. First, it reacts with alkali metal hydroxides to form a complex anion:

$$Be + 2HO^- + 2H_2O = H_2 + [Be(OH)_4]^{2-}$$

tetrahydroxoberyllate(II) ion

Second, many compounds of beryllium are essentially covalent and quite unlike the corresponding compounds of the other elements of the group (Table 7.6). The formation of the Be^{2+} ion requires a large amount of energy ($2\,666$ kJ mol^{-1}), so beryllium tends to use its outer electrons to form covalent bonds. Alternatively, in accordance with

Table 7.6 A comparison of beryllium with the other group 2A metals and with aluminium.

Beryllium	Magnesium, calcium, strontium and barium	Aluminium
forms a complex ion with alkalis	do not form hydro complexes	forms a complex ion with alkalis
oxide and hydroxide are amphoteric	oxides and hydroxides are exclusively basic	oxide and hydroxide are amphoteric
anhydrous halides are covalent and ionise in water	halides are ionic	chloride, bromide and iodide are covalent and ionise in water: AlF_3 is ionic
beryllium chloride is dimeric in the vapour phase, i.e. Be_2Cl_4	chlorides are ionic	aluminium chloride is dimeric in the vapour phase, i.e. Al_2Cl_6
beryllium fluoride forms a complex with fluoride ions, i.e. $[BeF_4]^{2-}$	no fluoro-complexes	aluminium fluoride forms a complex with fluoride ions, i.e. $[AlF_6]^{3-}$

Fajans' rules (§4.4), the small Be^{2+} ion is highly polarising and likely to distort anions to produce bonds with a high degree of covalent character.

The oxide and hydroxide of beryllium are essentially covalent and amphoteric. Beryllium does not form a hydrogencarbonate, and the carbonate, $BeCO_3$, is very unstable and can be prepared only in an atmosphere of carbon dioxide. A basic carbonate is precipitated from a solution of a beryllium salt by adding a soluble carbonate. The halides of beryllium are covalent but ionise in water; cf. aluminium halides (§8.5), e.g.

$$BeF_2 + 4H_2O = [Be(H_2O)_4]^{2+} + 2F^-$$

In the hydrated beryllium ion there are four molecules of water coordinated tetrahedrally around the central ion, i.e.

$$\begin{bmatrix} & H_2O & \\ & | & \\ H_2O \diagdown Be \diagup & OH_2 \\ & | & \\ & H_2O & \end{bmatrix}^{2+}$$

Solutions of the $[Be(H_2O)_4]^{2+}$ ion, like those of the $[Al(H_2O)_6]^{3+}$ ion, are acidic because of hydrolysis:

$$[Be(H_2O)_4]^{2+} + H_2O \rightleftharpoons [Be(OH)(H_2O)_3]^+ + H_3O^+$$

In much of its other chemistry beryllium resembles aluminium rather than the remaining members of group 2A (Table 7.6). This is another example of a diagonal relationship.

7.7 Estimation of the s-block elements

The most versatile and useful techniques for determining the s-block elements are flame photometry and atomic absorption spectroscopy. Gravimetric or, in some cases, volumetric methods may be used if neither of these is available.

Flame photometry

Flame photometry is the most useful method for estimating the important s-block elements. It is based on the emission of radiation by excited atoms in a flame, and is therefore applicable only to elements whose atoms can be sufficiently excited to emit visible radiation in a mains gas/air flame. In other words, it is restricted to those elements which emit visible light in the flame test, namely the elements of group 1A; also calcium, strontium and barium. A solution of the compound is injected into the flame and the intensity of the emitted light, after passing through a filter to remove unwanted radiation, is measured by a detector. The intensity of emitted light is proportional to the number of excited atoms in the flame, which in turn is proportional to the concentration of the solution.

At first a *calibration graph* is plotted of intensity against concentration for standard solutions. The graph is then used to determine the concentrations of unknown solutions from the intensity of the light they emit in the flame.

Atomic absorption spectroscopy (AA spectroscopy)

Atomic absorption spectroscopy is the converse of flame photometry in that it involves the *absorption* of radiation by *unexcited* atoms in a flame. A solution of the sample to be analysed is vaporised and converted into atoms by injection into a flame through which passes a beam of light from a special lamp. The light originates from excited atoms of an element in the lamp. If the lamp and the flame contain the same element, then the light is of exactly the right wavelength to be absorbed by the unexcited atoms in the flame. For example, sodium atoms in the flame will absorb only from a sodium-containing lamp; other elements do not absorb sodium light because the wavelengths of the sodium light do not correspond to their energy level differences.

An atomic absorption spectrophotometer measures the reduction in intensity of the light beam after passing through the flame. The reduction in intensity (i.e. the amount of light absorbed from the incident beam) is proportional to the number of unexcited atoms in the flame, which in turn is proportional to the concentration of the injected solution. A calibration graph can be plotted of reduction in intensity against the concentration of standard solutions, and from this can be obtained the concentrations of unknown solutions.

Despite the fact that a different lamp is required for each element to be determined, atomic absorption spectroscopy is widely used in analytical laboratories. This is because it is reliable, rapid, applicable to many elements, and has a high sensitivity even at extremely low concentrations.

Gravimetric methods

Lithium On adding a solution of sodium aluminate(III) to a solution of Li^+ ions at a pH of 12.5–13.0, a white precipitate is formed of lithium aluminate(III). This is filtered off, heated at 500–550 °C (773–823 K), and weighed as $2Li_2O \cdot 5Al_2O_3$.

Sodium Sodium is precipitated as sodium zinc uranyl ethanoate, $NaZn(UO_2)_3(CH_3COO)_9 \cdot 6H_2O$, by adding a large excess of zinc uranyl ethanoate to a solution of Na^+ ions. Alternatively, magnesium uranyl ethanoate may be used to give a precipitate of sodium magnesium uranyl ethanoate, $NaMg(UO_2)_3(CH_3COO)_9 \cdot 6.5H_2O$. The precipitate, after filtration, is dried at 70 °C (343 K). Care is needed in both these methods since the precipitated sodium salts are moderately soluble in water. Lithium must be absent as it, too, forms insoluble salts under these conditions.

Potassium Several precipitating reagents are available for this element. In general, all other metal ions (except Na^+) and NH_4^+ ions must be absent, otherwise they are precipitated along with the potassium salt. The precipitated potassium salt is filtered off, dried and weighed.

Potassium hexachloroplatinate(IV), $K_2[PtCl_6]$, is precipitated by the addition of hexachloroplatinic(IV) acid, $H_2[PtCl_6]$. As an alternative, the cheaper perchloric acid, $HClO_4$, can be used to precipitate potassium perchlorate, $KClO_4$. Perchloric acid, however, is liable to react explosively with organic materials and should always be used with the utmost care.

Another method involves the use of sodium hexanitrocobaltate(III). A precipitate of the salt $K_2Na[Co(NO_2)_6]$ is formed when a solution of this reagent is added to one of K^+ ions in the presence of dilute nitric acid. Unfortunately, the composition of the precipitate may vary. A better (although more expensive) method employs sodium tetraphenylborate(III) as the precipitating reagent. This salt contains the anion $[B(C_6H_5)_4]^-$ which forms the insoluble salt $K[B(C_6H_5)_4]$ with potassium ions.

Magnesium Magnesium is precipitated as ammonium magnesium phosphate 6-water by adding HPO_4^{2-} ions and aqueous ammonia to a solution containing Mg^{2+} ions. The precipitate should be washed with dilute ammonia, since it is moderately soluble in water. After filtration, the precipitate may be dried in a desiccator and weighed as $MgNH_4PO_4 \cdot 6H_2O$, or heated to 1 000 °C (1 273 K) to convert it to the diphosphate, $Mg_2P_2O_7$. A disadvantage is that magnesium phosphate, $Mg_3(PO_4)_2$, is likely to be coprecipitated with the ammonium magnesium phosphate.

In the absence of other metal ions, except those of the alkali metals, magnesium can be precipitated by the reagent 8-hydroxyquinoline (oxine) as $Mg(C_9H_6O)_2 \cdot 2H_2O$. Care is needed to avoid coprecipitation of the oxine.

Calcium Calcium is usually precipitated as its ethanedioate (oxalate), $CaC_2O_4 \cdot H_2O$, by adding ammonium ethanedioate, followed by aqueous ammonia, to a solution of Ca^{2+} ions. After filtration, the precipitate may be dried at 110 °C (383 K). Calcium ethanedioate is hygroscopic, and weighings must be carried out quickly. Alternatively, the precipitate can be heated at 500 °C (773 K) to produce $CaCO_3$, or at 1 200 °C (1 473 K) to form CaO. The former method is preferable as the oxide absorbs atmospheric carbon dioxide.

Barium Barium is usually estimated as its highly insoluble sulphate, $BaSO_4$, in the absence of calcium, strontium or lead. A digestion period is necessary to increase the particle size, and filtration through a fine pore paper is essential. The filter paper is removed by ignition in a crucible at 900 °C (1 173 K). Care must be exercised because carbon, from the charring of the paper, reduces barium sulphate to the sulphide above 600 °C (873 K).

Strontium In the absence of calcium, barium or lead, strontium may be determined by precipitation as the sulphate, $SrSO_4$. The details are the same as for barium.

Volumetric methods

A solution containing calcium or magnesium ions can be titrated very conveniently against one of ethylenediaminetetraacetic acid (H_4 edta). The operation is generally referred to as a *complexometric titration*, because it involves the formation of a cyclic complex or *chelate* between metal ions and the ethylenediaminetetraacetate anion (edta).

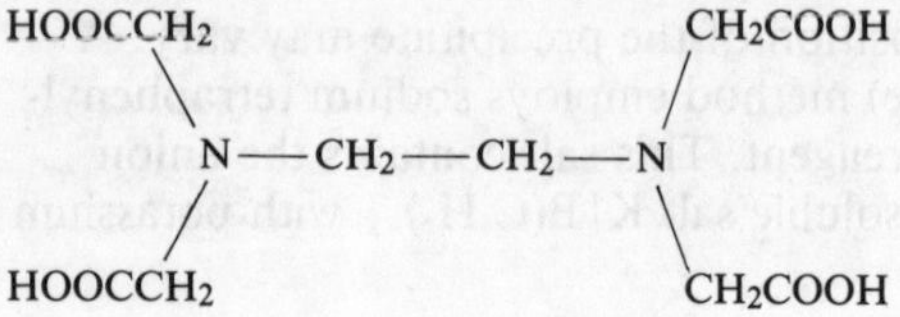

molecule of H_4 edta

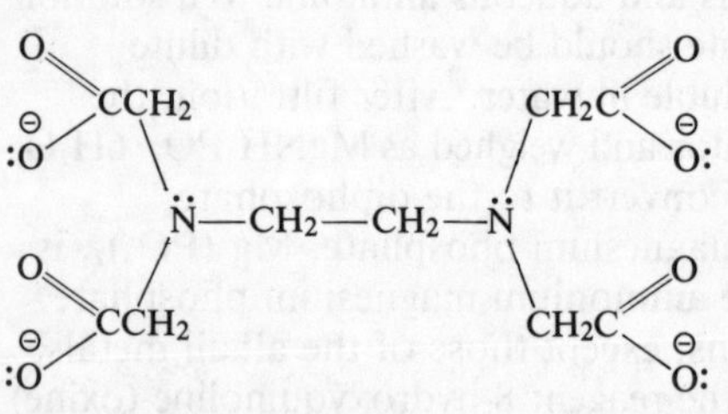

edta anion

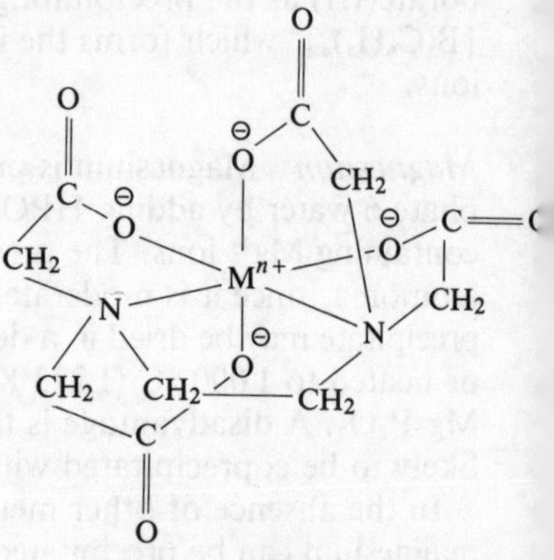

chelate or complex of metal ions, M^{n+}, and the edta anion

Dots denote lone pairs of electrons used in forming chelates

Instead of H_4 edta itself, which is sparingly soluble in water, the disodium salt is generally used. This is available as a dihydrate in a sufficient state of purity to be adopted as a primary standard.

Most metal ions form 1 : 1 complexes with edta,

∴ $1 dm^3$ 1 M edta ≡ 1 mol M^{n+} ions

The complexes form best in alkaline solution, and it is normal practice to buffer the solution at pH 10 with a suitable buffering agent.

Indicators used in edta titrations are coloured substances which are themselves complexing agents. With metal ions, the indicator forms a complex whose colour differs from that of the free indicator. At the equivalence point the indicator is displaced from its complex by edta, and a colour change occurs as the free indicator is re-formed.

At the start: indicator + M^{n+} = M-indicator complex
colour A   colour B

At the equivalence point: M-indicator complex + edta = Medta + indicator
                        colour B   colour A

The indicators may also act as acid−base indicators; hence there is an additional need to buffer the solutions to prevent marked pH changes from occurring during titration.

Both calcium and magnesium can be estimated in solution by titration with edta. Since Mg^{2+} ions complex rather slowly with edta at room temperature, it is advisable, when estimating this metal, to warm the solution to approximately 40 °C (313 K) prior to titrating with edta.

If calcium and magnesium are present in the same solution, e.g. in hard water, they can be estimated together. If required, calcium alone can be determined in the presence of magnesium by using a selective indicator which changes colour when the Ca^{2+} ions are titrated. Alternatively, NaOH or KOH can be added to the solution before titration to precipitate the Mg^{2+} ions as $Mg(OH)_2$.

Chapter 8

Group 3B

Group 3B comprises the elements boron, aluminium, gallium, indium and thallium (Table 8.1).

Table 8.1 Some properties of the elements of group 3B.

	Boron	Aluminium	Gallium	Indium	Thallium
character	non-metal	metal	metal	metal	metal
allotropes	three	none	none	none	none
atomic number	5	13	31	49	81
relative atomic mass	10.81	26.981 5	69.72	114.82	204.37
outer electronic configuration	$2s^2 2p^1$	$3s^2 3p^1$	$4s^2 4p^1$	$5s^2 5p^1$	$6s^2 6p^1$
valencies	3	3	1, 3	1, 3	1, 3
melting temperature/°C	2 300	660	29.8	157	304
boiling temperature/°C	3 930	2 470	2 400	2 000	1 460

8.1 Occurrence and isolation of the elements

Boron

The principal sources of boron are hydrated disodium tetraborate (borax), $Na_2B_4O_7 \cdot 10H_2O$, and boric acid, H_3BO_3. Impure boron is obtained by reducing the oxide, B_2O_3, with magnesium at high temperatures:

$$B_2O_3 + 3Mg = 2B + 3MgO$$

Pure crystalline boron can be prepared by several methods, but always with difficulty, e.g.

(i) the decomposition of boron triiodide, BI_3, at very high temperatures. This is conveniently achieved by electrically heating a metal filament to approximately $2\,000\,°C$ $(2\,273\,K)$ in the vapour of the iodide. The filament is usually made of tantalum or tungsten, both of which have very high melting temperatures.

(ii) the passage of boron tribromide and hydrogen over a heated tantalum filament:

$$2BBr_3 + 3H_2 = 2B + 6HBr$$

In methods (i) and (ii) the boron is deposited on the filament.

(iii) the decomposition of diborane at $700\,°C$ $(973\,K)$:

$$B_2H_6 = 2B + 3H_2$$

Aluminium

Aluminium is the most abundant metallic element, and its compounds are widely distributed in the earth's crust. Examples include clays, mica, feldspars, cryolite, i.e. sodium hexafluoroaluminate(III), $Na_3[AlF_6]$, and the oxide, Al_2O_3. Anhydrous forms of the oxide, namely emery, corundum and ruby, are used as abrasives or gem stones, but the hydrated form, bauxite, $Al_2O_3(aq)$, is the principal ore from which aluminium is obtained.

Impure bauxite is purified by dissolution in aqueous sodium hydroxide. This produces a solution of sodium aluminate and sodium silicate; the latter results from the presence of silica and silicates in the ore.

$$Al_2O_3(aq) + 2HO^- + 7H_2O = 2[Al(OH)_4(H_2O)_2]^-$$

Insoluble impurities, chiefly iron(III) oxide, are removed by filtration. Carbon dioxide is then blown through the filtrate to precipitate pure aluminium hydroxide (§8.5), which is filtered off and heated to yield the pure oxide:

$$2[Al(OH)_4(H_2O)_2]^- + CO_2 + H_2O = 2[Al(OH)_3(H_2O)_3](s) + CO_3^{2-}$$
$$2[Al(OH)_3(H_2O)_3] = Al_2O_3 + 9H_2O$$

The pure oxide is dissolved in molten cryolite at 700–1 000 °C (973–1 273 K) and electrolysed. Aluminium is liberated at the cathode and oxygen at the anode:

$$Al^{3+} + 3e^- = Al$$
$$2O^{2-} = O_2 + 4e^-$$

Low voltages, approximately 6 V, must be employed to avoid decomposition of the cryolite. The cryolite thus acts as a solvent for the oxide. Currents in the region of 30 000 A are required, and a cheap source of electricity, such as hydroelectric power, is necessary for economic viability. The cell is operated on a continuous basis. Periodically, molten aluminium is removed from the floor of the cell, where it collects, and fresh aluminium oxide is added.

Gallium, indium and thallium

Gallium, indium and thallium, unlike aluminium, can be obtained by the electrolysis of aqueous solutions of their salts. This is because the hydrogen overpotentials of these metals are exceptionally high.

8.2 The structure of the elements

Boron is a non-metal and exists in three allotropic forms, each containing different arrangements of covalently bonded B_{12} units. An amorphous form of boron is also known, but is extremely difficult to prepare in a pure state. The remaining elements of this group are metallic and do not exhibit allotropy.

8.3 Bonding and valency

The elements of this group each have three outer electrons (i.e. ns^2 np^1) and exhibit a valency of three (+3 oxidation state). A monovalent state becomes progressively more stable as atomic number increases, and is particularly important for thallium.

Boron

The formation of boron anions, B^{5-}, is energetically unfavourable, and boron is therefore covalently bonded in all its compounds. With metals, it forms a number of binary compounds called *borides*; examples include CaB_6, AlB_2 and Cr_3B_4. In general, borides contain chains, layers, clusters or single atoms of boron, with metal atoms occupying holes in the structure.

Boron also forms compounds with many non-metals, e.g. BF_3 and B_2O_3. In all cases the covalency of boron is three, and is achieved by the promotion of an electron from the 2s orbital into a vacant 2p orbital to produce an atom with three unpaired electrons, i.e.

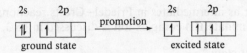

Many compounds of trivalent boron act as Lewis acids by accepting a lone pair of electrons into the remaining vacant p orbital. In this way boron attains its maximum covalency or coordination number of four. The other elements of group 3B can utilise vacant d orbitals in their outermost shells and accept further electron pairs to increase their coordination number to six.

Aluminium, gallium, indium and thallium

These elements are metallic and can lose their outer electrons to form tripositive ions. However, there are very few compounds which contain non-complexed cations. For example, the only simple ionic compounds of aluminium are the anhydrous fluoride, AlF_3, the oxide, Al_2O_3, the perchlorate, $Al(ClO_4)_3$, and the carbide, Al_4C_3.

Many of the compounds of these elements are either covalent or else contain complexed cations.

Covalency

The non-complexed ions have a high surface charge density, which tends to promote anion distortion to give bonds which are best described as polar covalent (§4.4). To support this argument we can consider the energy required to form the trivalent cations from the atoms. The removal of three electrons requires the absorption of a large amount of energy; consequently the atoms tend to use their outer electrons to form covalent bonds. Before this can happen, one of the paired s electrons must be promoted into a vacant p orbital (cf. boron).

Coordination

The high surface charge density of the ions favours complex formation because it increases the attraction of the ions for polar species capable of acting as ligands. Of particular importance is the hexaaqua-aluminium(III) ion, $[Al(H_2O)_6]^{3+}$, which occurs in many hydrated aluminium salts and solutions of aluminium compounds. The ion is stabilised by the high hydration enthalpy of the Al^{3+} ion, which largely offsets the ionisation enthalpy required in its formation, i.e.

$$Al(g) = Al^{3+}(g) + 3e^- \quad \Delta H = +5\,143 \text{ kJ mol}^{-1}$$
$$Al^{3+}(g) + 6H_2O = [Al(H_2O)_6]^{3+} \quad \Delta H = -4\,690 \text{ kJ mol}^{-1}$$

Other important complexes of aluminium include the octahedral hexa-fluoroaluminate(III) ion, $[AlF_6]^{3-}$, and the tetrahedral tetrachloro-aluminate(III) ion, $[AlCl_4]^-$, which are formed by reaction between aluminium halides and the appropriate halide ions in the absence of water. The chloro-complex and the corresponding bromo-complex,

[AlBr$_4$]$^-$, occur as intermediates in Friedel−Crafts reactions. The tetrahydridoaluminate(III) complex ion is discussed in §6.3.

The monovalent state

Bonding in the monovalent state (+ 1 oxidation state) involves the outermost p electron. Monovalent aluminium species exist at high temperatures only, because on cooling disproportionation occurs, e.g.

$$3AlF \rightleftharpoons 2Al + AlF_3$$

A few gallium(I) and indium(I) species have been isolated but on the whole they are not regarded as important compounds of these elements. Thallium(I) compounds, however, are numerous and more stable than thallium(III) compounds. In consequence, thallium(III) compounds, unlike aluminium(III) compounds, act as oxidising agents. The thallium(I) ion, Tl$^+$, has a similar radius to that of the K$^+$, Rb$^+$ and Ag$^+$ ions, and because of this there are many similarities between compounds possessing these ions. For example, the hydroxide and oxide of thallium(I), TlOH and Tl$_2$O respectively, are strong bases which are soluble in water (cf. potassium and rubidium). The sulphide, Tl$_2$S, the chromate, Tl$_2$CrO$_4$, and the halides of thallium(I), except for the fluoride, are insoluble in water (cf. silver).

8.4 Reactions of the group 3B elements

Amorphous boron is a brown powder which is reasonably reactive at high temperatures. The crystalline forms of boron have a black, shiny appearance and are very inert.

Aluminium is a silvery white metal with a low density. It is moderately reactive, but in air a thin, impervious oxide film forms on the surface of the metal, which protects it from prolonged attack. A thicker, more protective film of the oxide can be applied to aluminium by the process of *anodising*, in which the metal is made anodic in an electrolyte of either sulphuric acid (5−80 per cent) or chromic acid (3 per cent). The oxide film so produced is hydrated and may be dyed for decorative purposes.

Pure aluminium is of limited use because of its softness, but its light-weight alloys, especially those with magnesium, are used extensively in aircraft and ship construction, and for window frames and motor car components.

Boron and aluminium are the most important members of group 3B and are usually discussed together (Table 8.2). In general, the reactions of boron are much slower than those of aluminium.

Gallium, indium and thallium are soft, white, reactive metals. Gallium is notable in that it has the longest liquid range of any known substance (Table 8.1).

Gallium and indium dissolve in acids to give solutions containing

Table 8.2 The products of some reactions of boron and aluminium.

Reagent	Boron	Aluminium
oxygen, when heated	B_2O_3	Al_2O_3
nitrogen, when heated	BN	AlN
non-oxidising acids, e.g.		
HCl or dilute H_2SO_4	no reaction	$[Al(H_2O)_6]^{3+} + H_2$
hot concentrated H_2SO_4	H_3BO_3 (slow reaction)	$Al_2(SO_4)_3 + SO_2$
HNO_3	H_3BO_3 (slow reaction)	no reaction; Al is passivated
alkalis	borates (slow reaction)	aluminates $+ H_2$
H_2O at 700 °C (973 K)	B_2O_3	Al_2O_3
sulphur, when heated	B_2S_3	Al_2S_3
halogens	boron halides, BX_3	aluminium halides, AlX_3

hydrated gallium(III) ions and indium(III) ions respectively:

$$2M + 6H^+ = 2M^{3+}(aq) + 3H_2 \qquad (M = Ga \text{ or } In)$$

Thallium, however, dissolves in acids to produce the stable thallium(I) ion. Gallium resembles aluminium by dissolving in aqueous alkalis to form gallate(III) ions, possibly of similar constitution to the aluminate(III) ions.

8.5 Compounds of the group 3B elements

Hydrides of boron and aluminium

A large number of boron hydrides are known. Most of them are extremely reactive and air sensitive, but they can be handled satisfactorily in a vacuum. The expected hydride, borane, BH_3, has not yet been isolated, but it has been detected as a reaction intermediate. Stable complexes of borane, however, are known, e.g. $OC \rightarrow BH_3$, $(CH_3)_3N \rightarrow BH_3$ and $H_3N \rightarrow BH_3$.

The simplest known hydride of boron is diborane, B_2H_6, prepared by reacting sodium tetrahydroborate(III), $Na[BH_4]$, with dilute sulphuric acid, or by reducing boron trichloride with lithium tetrahydridoaluminate(III) in ether solution:

$$2Na[BH_4] + H_2SO_4 = B_2H_6 + 2H_2 + Na_2SO_4$$
$$4BCl_3 + 3Li[AlH_4] = 2B_2H_6 + 3LiCl + 3AlCl_3$$

Geometrically, the diborane molecule resembles that of the aluminium chloride dimer (p. 175), i.e.

The four terminal hydrogen atoms (H_t) form a rectangular plane which contains the two boron atoms. The two bridging hydrogen atoms (H_b) lie one above and one below this plane. There are insufficient electrons to form electron pair bonds between all of the adjacent atoms, and diborane is said to be an *electron deficient compound*. Bonding orbitals embracing three nuclei instead of two are involved, but details are beyond the scope of this book. All the hydrides of boron are similarly electron deficient.

Diborane reacts violently with air or water, but reacts less vigorously with Lewis bases, such as carbon monoxide or trimethylamine, to form complexes of borane (see above). The hydride ion also acts as a donor, to form the tetrahydroborate(III) ion:

$$B_2H_6 + 2H^- = 2[BH_4]^-$$

A white precipitate of polymeric aluminium hydride, $(AlH_3)_n$, is obtained when lithium hydride is added slowly to a solution of aluminium chloride in ethoxyethane (ether). This, the only hydride of aluminium, is believed to be electron deficient. With an excess of lithium hydride, a solution of lithium tetrahydridoaluminate(III) (commonly called lithium aluminium hydride) is obtained:

$$(AlH_3)_n + nLiH = nLi[AlH_4]$$

Sodium tetrahydroborate(III) (commonly called sodium borohydride), $Na[BH_4]$, and lithium tetrahydridoaluminate(III) are powerful reducing agents. They are used, particularly, for the conversion of non-metal chlorides to hydrides and for the reduction of carbonyl compounds in organic chemistry (§6.3).

Oxygen compounds of boron

Oxides

Boron oxide, B_2O_3, is the most important. It is formed by the dehydration of boric acid (also known as orthoboric acid) at 700 °C (973 K):

$$2H_3BO_3 = B_2O_3 + 3H_2O$$

Boron oxide is weakly acidic, and with water slowly re-forms boric acid. Metal borates, many of which have polymeric structures, are formed when boron oxide is fused with metal oxides.

Boron forms another oxide, of formula $(BO)_n$. It is polymeric, and contains B——B bonds and B——O——B bonds.

Oxoacids

If a hot, concentrated solution of disodium tetraborate, $Na_2B_4O_7$, is acidified and cooled, white flaky crystals of boric acid, H_3BO_3, separate out:

$$Na_2B_4O_7 + 2HCl + 5H_2O = 4H_3BO_3 + 2NaCl$$

This is the commonest oxoacid of boron, but two others can be obtained from it by the action of heat; namely metaboric acid, $(HBO_2)_n$, and tetraboric acid, $H_2B_4O_7$:

$$4nH_3BO_3 \xrightarrow[-4nH_2O]{\text{heat}} 4(HBO_2)_n \xrightarrow[-nH_2O]{\text{heat}} nH_2B_4O_7$$

In crystalline boric acid the trigonal planar molecules are hydrogen bonded together (Fig. 4.32). Boric acid is a very weak monoprotic acid, and also behaves as a Lewis acid by accepting an electron pair from a water molecule:

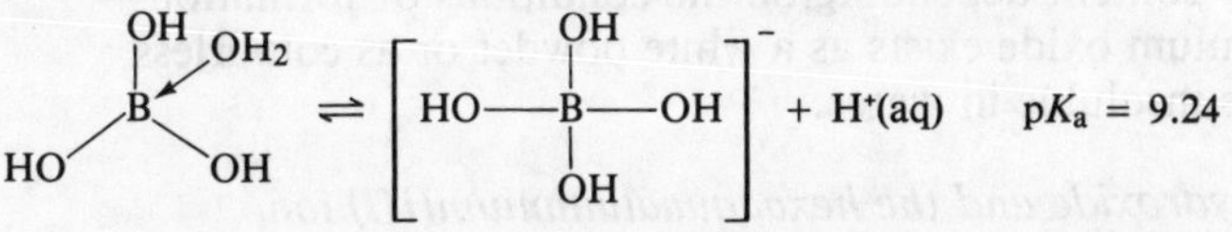

The acid strength is considerably enhanced by the addition of certain polyhydroxy compounds, such as 1,2,3-propanetriol (glycerol). In the presence of these compounds, boric acid behaves as a strong monoprotic acid because of the formation of complexes:

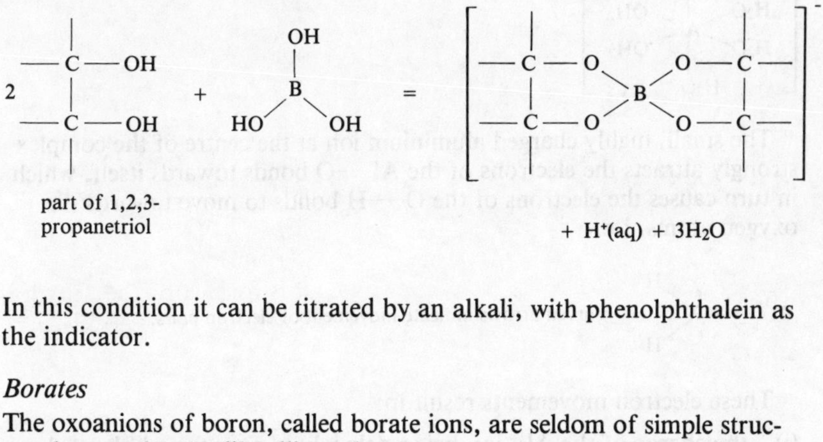

In this condition it can be titrated by an alkali, with phenolphthalein as the indicator.

Borates

The oxoanions of boron, called borate ions, are seldom of simple structure because boron, like silicon, has a strong tendency to form polymeric structures. Both cyclic and linear polymeric anions are known, based on BO_3 and BO_4 units. The commonest borate, hydrated disodium tetraborate (borax), $Na_2B_4O_7 \cdot 10H_2O$, forms alkaline solutions in water because of salt hydrolysis, and can be titrated by hydrochloric acid with methyl red as an indicator:

$$Na_2B_4O_7 + 2HCl + 5H_2O = 2NaCl + 4H_3BO_3$$

i.e.

$$1 \text{ mol } Na_2B_4O_7 \equiv 2 \text{ mol } HCl$$

Oxygen compounds of aluminium

Aluminium oxide (alumina)

Two forms of anhydrous aluminium oxide are known: α-Al_2O_3, which is very hard, resistant to hydration and inert to both acids and alkalis, and γ-Al_2O_3, which readily hydrates and dissolves slowly in acids or alkalis. Corundum is α-Al_2O_3, and emery is a mixture of α-Al_2O_3 and other metallic oxides such as Fe_3O_4. Traces of other metals, which sometimes occur in natural corundum, impart characteristic colours to the crystals. For example, ruby is α-Al_2O_3 containing a small proportion of chromium. The hydrated forms of aluminium oxide have a variable water content depending on the conditions of formation

Pure aluminium oxide exists as a white powder or as colourless crystals and is insoluble in water.

Aluminium hydroxide and the hexaaquaaluminium(III) ion

Solutions of aluminium salts contain the hydrated aluminium(III) ion, $[Al(H_2O)_6]^{3+}$, in which the six water molecules are octahedrally coordinated around the Al^{3+} ion, i.e.

$$\left[\begin{array}{c} H_2O \\ H_2O \diagdown \underset{\displaystyle |}{Al} \diagup OH_2 \\ H_2O \diagup \diagdown OH_2 \\ H_2O \end{array} \right]^{3+}$$

The small, highly charged aluminium ion at the centre of the complex strongly attracts the electrons of the Al—O bonds towards itself, which in turn causes the electrons of the O—H bonds to move towards the oxygen atoms, i.e.

$$Al^{3+}\!-\!\!O\!\!\begin{array}{c} H \\ H \end{array}$$

curved arrows indicate movement of electron pairs.

These electron movements result in:

(i) the charge of the Al^{3+} ion being delocalised over the whole of the complex;

(ii) a greater partial positive charge residing on the hydrogen atom of a coordinated water molecule than on a non-coordinated molecule;

(iii) a weakening of the O—H bond in a coordinated water molecule compared with that in a non-coordinated molecule. Coordinated water molecules therefore attract bases and lose protons more readily than non-coordinated water molecules.

The hexaaquaaluminium(III) ion functions as an acid by donating protons to bases. In aqueous solution, for example, where solvent water functions as a base, oxonium ions are formed and the solution is acidic:

$$[Al(H_2O)_6]^{3+} + H_2O \rightleftharpoons [Al(OH)(H_2O)_5]^{2+} + H_3O^+ \quad pK_1 = 4.9$$
$$[Al(OH)(H_2O)_5]^{2+} + H_2O \rightleftharpoons [Al(OH)_2(H_2O)_4]^+ + H_3O^+$$

Both reactions are regarded as examples of hydrolysis, because water molecules are split up. In the presence of species which are stronger bases than water, e.g. ammonia and the ions CO_3^{2-}, HO^-, S^{2-} and CN^-, a third proton is lost and a neutral, insoluble complex is formed,

$$[Al(OH)_2(H_2O)_4]^+ + HO^- \rightleftharpoons H_2O + [Al(OH)_3(H_2O)_3](s)$$
hydrated aluminium hydroxide

These strong bases act both by removal of oxonium ions, which displaces the previous equilibria to the right, and also by direct proton removal from the cationic complexes. This explains why, when a carbonate is added to an aluminium salt, carbon dioxide is evolved and a white gelatinous precipitate of aluminium hydroxide is formed:

$$2[Al(OH)_2(H_2O)_4]^+ + CO_3^{2-} \rightleftharpoons 2[Al(OH)_3(H_2O)_3](s) + H_2O + CO_2(g)$$

The formula of aluminium hydroxide is often written as $Al(OH)_3(aq)$ for simplicity. The sulphide ion and the cyanide ion also precipitate aluminium hydroxide from solutions of the aluminium(III) ion, and produce hydrogen sulphide and hydrogen cyanide respectively:

$$2[Al(OH)_2(H_2O)_4]^+ + S^{2-} \rightleftharpoons 2[Al(OH)_3(H_2O)_3](s) + H_2S(g)$$
$$[Al(OH)_2(H_2O)_4]^+ + CN^- \rightleftharpoons [Al(OH)_3(H_2O)_3](s) + HCN(g)$$

The hydrated ions of other trivalent metals, e.g. $[Cr(H_2O)_6]^{3+}$ (§14.6) and $[Fe(H_2O)_6]^{3+}$ (§14.8) behave in a similar manner to the hexaaqua-aluminium(III) ion in solution and when treated with carbonate ions.

In the presence of excess hydroxide ions, further protons are removed from aluminium hydroxide to produce soluble aluminate(III) ions:

$$[Al(OH)_3(H_2O)_3] + HO^- \rightleftharpoons [Al(OH)_4(H_2O)_2]^- + H_2O$$
$$[Al(OH)_4(H_2O)_2]^- + HO^- \rightleftharpoons [Al(OH)_5(H_2O)]^{2-} + H_2O$$
$$[Al(OH)_5(H_2O)]^{2-} + HO^- \rightleftharpoons [Al(OH)_6]^{3-} + H_2O$$

The addition of acid displaces the equilibria to the left, by removing hydroxide ions so that aluminium hydroxide is ultimately reprecipitated. This explains the use of carbon dioxide in the preparation of pure aluminium hydroxide for the manufacture of aluminium (§8.1). Aluminium hydroxide in turn is soluble in acids, and if the concentration of acid is high enough the hexaaquaaluminium(III) ion is formed.

The hexaaquaaluminium(III) ion and aluminate(III) ions are also formed when aluminium dissolves in acids and alkalis respectively:

$$2Al + 6H^+(aq) + 12H_2O = 2[Al(H_2O)_6]^{3+} + 3H_2$$
$$2Al + 2HO^- + 10H_2O = 2[Al(OH)_4(H_2O)_2]^- + 3H_2$$

Freshly prepared aluminium hydroxide is readily soluble in both acids and alkalis, but this property is rapidly lost on standing because the hydroxide changes into a hydrated form of aluminium oxide which is less reactive towards these reagents.

Oxygen compounds of gallium, indium and thallium

In keeping with the developing metallic character from gallium to thallium, oxides and hydroxides become increasingly basic. The oxide and hydroxide of gallium, Ga_2O_3 and $Ga(OH)_3$, are amphoteric, while the corresponding compounds of indium are basic. Thallium forms an oxide and a hydroxide in both the monovalent state (i.e. Tl_2O and $TlOH$) and the trivalent state (i.e. Tl_2O_3 and $Tl(OH)_3$). All these compounds are basic.

The hydrated trivalent ions, $[M(H_2O)_6]^{3+}$, where M represents Ga, In or Tl, resemble the corresponding aluminium ion in being acidic in aqueous solution.

Halides of boron

The trihalides BF_3, BCl_3 and BBr_3 are prepared by direct combination of the elements. Boron trifluoride can also be made by heating boron oxide with either hydrofluoric acid or a mixture of an ionic fluoride and concentrated sulphuric acid:

$$B_2O_3 + 6HF = 2BF_3 + 3H_2O$$
$$B_2O_3 + 3CaF_2 + 3H_2SO_4 = 3CaSO_4 + 3H_2O + 2BF_3$$

The iodide, BI_3, is prepared by reacting sodium tetrahydroborate(III) with iodine, or boron trichloride with hydrogen iodide at red heat.

Each of the boron trihalide molecules is trigonal planar in shape (§4.6), and functions as a powerful Lewis acid by accepting a lone pair of electrons into the vacant p orbital in the outermost shell, e.g.

tetrafluoroborate(III) ion

The latter compound is called ammonia—boron trifluoride(1/1), where (1/1) denotes the molar ratio of the constituents.

Boron trifluoride is a most useful and powerful Lewis acid, and is used as a catalyst in organic reactions. It reacts with a large excess of water to produce boric acid and tetrafluoroboric(III) acid:

$$4BF_3 + 3H_2O = 3HBF_4 + H_3BO_3$$

In contrast to boric acid, tetrafluoroboric(III) acid is a strong acid, being completely ionised in aqueous solution. With smaller amounts of water, boron trifluoride forms unstable hydrates, e.g. $BF_3 \cdot H_2O$.

The chloride, bromide and iodide of boron are vigorously hydrolysed by water in a reaction which is believed to involve the coordination of a water molecule, followed by the elimination of a hydrogen halide, e.g.

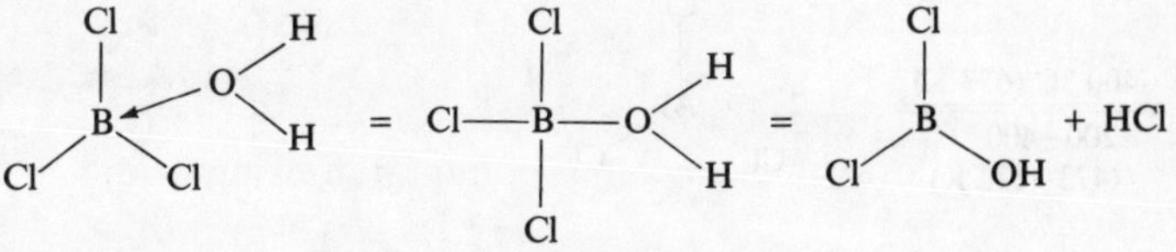

(written as $HBOCl_2$)

This reaction is followed by two other similar steps:

$$HBOCl_2 + H_2O = H_2BO_2Cl + HCl$$
$$H_2BO_2Cl + H_2O = H_3BO_3 + HCl$$

The overall reaction is:

$$BCl_3 + 3H_2O = H_3BO_3 + 3HCl$$

The complex ions $[BCl_4]^-$, $[BBr_4]^-$ and $[BI_4]^-$ are less stable than the tetrafluoroborate(III) ion, and exist only in combination with large cations of low polarising power.

Halides of aluminium

The halides of aluminium are prepared by direct combination of the elements or by heating aluminium in a stream of the hydrogen halide:

$$2Al + 3X_2 = 2AlX_3$$
$$2Al + 6HX = 2AlX_3 + 3H_2$$

X = F, Cl, Br or I

Aluminium fluoride is essentially ionic, i.e. $Al^{3+}(F^-)_3$, and does not react with water or dissolve in organic solvents. In contrast, the chloride, bromide and iodide of aluminium are covalent in the anhydrous state, ionise in water, and dissolve in organic solvents such as benzene.

Anhydrous aluminium chloride possesses a complex polymeric structure in the solid state. At approximately 200 °C (473 K) it sublimes readily to form a vapour which contains dimeric molecules, i.e.

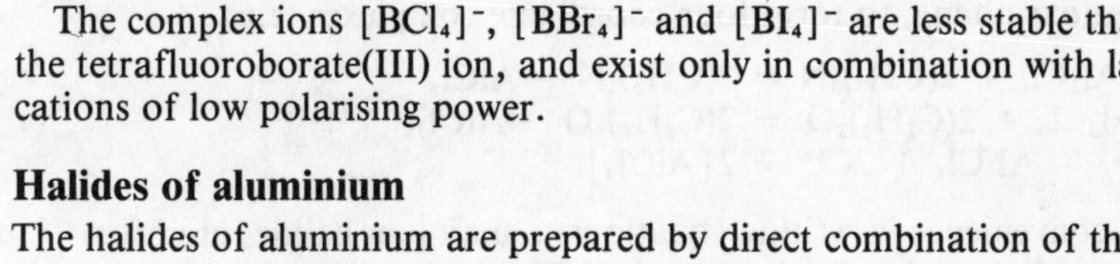

In the dimer each aluminium atom is bonded to four chlorine atoms.

The four terminal chlorine atoms (Cl_t) lie at the corners of a rectangular plane which contains the two aluminium atoms. The two bridging chlorine atoms (Cl_b) are situated one above and one below this plane. Each bridging chlorine atom has a covalency of two, which may be envisaged as comprising a normal covalent bond and a coordinate bond, although in fact we cannot distinguish between them (§4.3). Above 400 °C (673 K), the dimeric Al_2Cl_6 molecules break down reversibly to form molecules of the monomer which are trigonal planar in shape, i.e.

$$Al_2Cl_6 \underset{\substack{200-400\ °C \\ (473-673\ K)}}{\overset{400\ °C\ (673\ K)}{\rightleftharpoons}} 2\quad \begin{array}{c} Cl \\ | \\ Al \\ Cl \quad\quad Cl \end{array}$$

Al_2Cl_6 molecules are also present in solutions of anhydrous aluminium chloride in benzene, as may be shown by measuring the depression of the freezing temperature.

In the solid state the anhydrous bromide and iodide of aluminium contain discrete dimeric molecules, i.e. Al_2Br_6 and Al_2I_6 respectively. They behave in a similar manner to the chloride when heated.

The anhydrous aluminium halides, except for the fluoride, behave as powerful Lewis acids. For example, in benzene solution the aluminium halide dimers are split by electron pair donors, such as trimethylamine or ethoxyethane, to form four-coordinate complexes, e.g.

$$Al_2Cl_6 + 2(CH_3)_3N = 2(CH_3)_3N{-}AlCl_3$$
$$Al_2Cl_6 + 2(C_2H_5)_2O = 2(C_2H_5)_2O{-}AlCl_3$$
$$Al_2Cl_6 + 2Cl^- = 2[AlCl_4]^-$$

For convenience in writing equations, aluminium halides are often represented by the simple formula AlX_3.

The anhydrous chloride, bromide and iodide of aluminium ionise in water, e.g.

$$AlCl_3(s) + 6H_2O = [Al(H_2O)_6]^{3+} + 3Cl^-$$

During this reaction, which is exothermic and irreversible, aluminium–chlorine covalent bonds are broken. The necessary energy is provided by the hydration enthalpy of the small aluminium(III) ion. The hydrated aluminium ions undergo hydrolysis in solution (p. 173), but since all the water molecules coordinated to the Al^{3+} ion are not affected we often refer to the reaction as 'partial hydrolysis'. In contrast, the halides of boron are said to be 'completely hydrolysed', because every water molecule that is involved in the reaction is cleaved.

The white hydrated halides of aluminium can be obtained by adding water to the anhydrous compounds, or by dissolving aluminium or aluminium hydroxide in the appropriate hydrohalic acid. The crystals so obtained, e.g. $AlCl_3 \cdot 6H_2O$, contain hexaaquaaluminium(III) ions:

$$2Al + 6HCl + 12H_2O = 2[Al(H_2O)_6]^{3+} + 6Cl^- + 3H_2$$

Anhydrous aluminium halides cannot be prepared by heating the hydrated salts because hydrolysis occurs to give aluminium hydroxide, e.g.

$$[Al(H_2O)_6]^{3+} + 3Cl^- = [Al(OH)_3(H_2O)_3] + 3HCl(g)$$

Unlike the anhydrous compounds, hydrated aluminium halides do not function as Lewis acids.

Halides of gallium, indium and thallium

The trihalides of gallium, GaX_3, and indium, InX_3, closely resemble those of aluminium, both structurally and chemically. The trihalides of thallium, however, are unstable and decompose into the monohalides when heated, e.g.

$$TlCl_3 = TlCl + Cl_2$$

Gallium forms so-called 'dihalides' of stoicheiometric formula GaX_2. However, these compounds do not contain divalent gallium, but are salts of the type $Ga^+[GaX_4]^-$. A number of similar indium and thallium compounds are also known.

Other important compounds of aluminium

Aluminium sulphate and alums

White crystals of aluminium sulphate, $Al_2(SO_4)_3 \cdot 18H_2O$, are prepared by dissolving aluminium, its oxide or its hydroxide in moderately concentrated sulphuric acid.

The *alums* have the general formula $M_2^ISO_4 \cdot M_2^{III}(SO_4)_3 \cdot 24H_2O$, where:

M^I represents a monopositive ion, i.e. Na^+, K^+, Rb^+ or NH_4^+ (not Li^+);
M^{III} represents a tripositive ion, i.e. Al^{3+}, Cr^{3+}, Mn^{3+} or Fe^{3+}.

Alums form octahedrally shaped crystals and are isomorphous with one another, i.e. the arrangement of the constituent ions, $[M^I(H_2O)_6]^+$, $[M^{III}(H_2O)_6]^{3+}$ and SO_4^{2-} within the crystal is the same irrespective of their identity. Alums are therefore known as *double salts*, because they consist essentially of two salts within one crystal. In solution they behave as simple mixtures of the constituent salts.

Alums are prepared by evaporation of a solution containing equimolar amounts of the two sulphates, $M_2^ISO_4$ and $M_2^{III}(SO_4)_3$. Because they are isomorphous, it is possible to form an *overgrowth* of one alum on another, i.e. to grow crystals of one alum around those of another. Many of the common alums still retain their trivial names, e.g.

$(NH_4)_2SO_4 \cdot Fe_2(SO_4)_3 \cdot 24H_2O$	iron alum
$K_2SO_4 \cdot Cr_2(SO_4)_3 \cdot 24H_2O$	chrome alum
$K_2SO_4 \cdot Al_2(SO_4)_3 \cdot 24H_2O$	alum

Aluminium sulphide

When heated, aluminium combines exothermically with sulphur to form aluminium sulphide, Al_2S_3, a covalent compound which is rapidly hydrolysed by water:

$$Al_2S_3 + 12H_2O = 2[Al(H_2O)_6]^{3+} + 3S^{2-} \quad \text{(cf. } AlCl_3\text{)}$$
$$2[Al(H_2O)_6]^{3+} + 3S^{2-} = 2[Al(OH)_3(H_2O)_3] + 3H_2S \quad \text{(p. 173)}$$

8.6 Diagonal relationship between boron and silicon

Table 8.3 A comparison of boron with the other elements of group 3B and with silicon.

Boron	Aluminium, gallium, indium and thallium	Silicon
non-metal with high melting temperature; non-conductor of electricity	metals with typical metallic properties; melting temperatures are rather low compared with those of most other metals	non-metal with high melting temperature; non-conductor of electricity
oxide, B_2O_3, is covalent, polymeric, glassy and acidic	oxides are ionic and amphoteric or basic	oxide, SiO_2, is covalent, polymeric, glassy and acidic
halides are covalent and completely hydrolysed by water	some halides are ionic; hydrolysis, if it occurs, is partial	halides are all covalent and completely hydrolysed by water
forms a series of hydrides	do not form series of hydrides	forms a series of hydrides
forms binary compounds with metals, e.g. CaB_6	form alloys with metals	forms binary compounds with metals, e.g. Mg_2Si

We have seen (§3.5) that the head element of a particular group of the periodic table may resemble the second element of the next group to it. Boron in many respects resembles silicon rather than the other elements of group 3B (Table 8.3).

Chapter 9

Group 4B

The elements of group 4B are carbon, silicon, germanium, tin and lead. The increase in metallic character from top to bottom of the group, which results from the decreasing ionisation enthalpies of the elements, is very pronounced. Carbon and silicon are distinctly non-metallic, tin and lead are typical metals, while germanium possesses the properties of both metals and non-metals. Some important properties of the elements are given in Table 9.1.

9.1 Occurrence and isolation of the elements

Carbon

There are two allotropes of carbon, namely graphite and diamond. Graphite, although occurring naturally in Sri Lanka, Germany and the USA, is largely manufactured by the *Acheson process*, in which coke and a small amount of silica are heated in an electric furnace for several hours in the absence of air.

Natural diamonds are sparsely distributed about the world, South Africa being the main source. Diamonds for industrial purposes are also obtained synthetically.

Amorphous carbon (§9.2) is produced by heating organic materials, e.g. coal, oil or sugar, in the absence of air.

Silicon

Pure silicon is produced either by reducing the tetrachloride with

Table 9.1 Some properties of the elements of group 4B.

	Carbon	Silicon	Germanium	Tin	Lead
character	non-metal	non-metal	semi-metal	metal	metal
allotropes	diamond, graphite	none	none	α-tin, β-tin, γ-tin	none
atomic number	6	14	32	50	82
relative atomic mass	12.011	28.086	72.59	118.69	207.2
outer electronic configuration	$2s^22p^2$	$3s^23p^2$	$4s^24p^2$	$5s^25p^2$	$6s^26p^2$
valencies	4	4	2†, 4	2†, 4	2, 4†
melting temperature/°C	3 730‡ (sublimes)	1 410	937	232§	327
boiling temperature/°C	4 830‡	2 360	2 830	2 270§	1 744

† Denotes a relatively unstable state.
‡ Data for graphite.
§ Data for β-tin.

hydrogen, or by the thermal decomposition of silane, SiH_4:

$$SiCl_4 + 2H_2 = Si + 4HCl$$
$$SiH_4 = Si + 2H_2$$

Impure silicon is obtained by heating silica with carbon:

$$SiO_2 + 2C = Si + 2CO$$

Super-pure silicon, which is used in microchips, is made from the pure element by zone refining.

Germanium

The ash from certain coals contains up to 1 per cent of germanium. The element is obtained by reduction of germanium(IV) oxide with hydrogen at red heat:

$$GeO_2 + 2H_2 = Ge + 2H_2O$$

Super-pure germanium for use in transistors is made by zone refining.

Tin

Impure tin(IV) oxide, known as cassiterite or tinstone, occurs in Malaya,

Germany, Nigeria and Cornwall. Reduction of the heated ore with coke produces crude tin, which is refined by heating it in a furnace with a sloping hearth until the tin melts and flows away from less fusible impurities, such as iron.

$$SnO_2 + 2C = Sn + 2CO$$

The molten tin is further purified by stirring it in air, when the remaining metallic impurities are converted to an oxide scum which is skimmed off. Very pure tin is obtained by electrolytic refining.

Lead

Galena, PbS, the most abundant lead ore, is found in the Americas, Germany and Australia. The ore, mixed with quartz, is roasted in air to oxidise the sulphide to the oxide. Any lead(II) sulphate formed at this stage is converted to the silicate by reaction with silica:

$$2PbS + 3O_2 = 2PbO + 2SO_2$$
$$PbSO_4 + SiO_2 = PbSiO_3 + SO_3$$

The mixture of oxide and silicate is then mixed with coke and lime-stone and heated in a small blast furnace when the following reactions occur:

$$PbO + C = Pb + CO \quad \text{in the hotter, lower regions}$$
$$PbO + CO = Pb + CO_2 \quad \text{in the cooler, upper regions}$$
$$PbSiO_3 + CaO + CO = Pb + CaSiO_3 + CO_2$$

Crude lead is purified by heating it in a furnace, where the impurities form a scum which floats on the molten metal. Alternatively, the crude lead is made the anode in a cell containing an electrolyte of lead(II) hexafluorosilicate(IV). On electrolysis, pure lead is deposited on the cathode. Some valuable by-products, notably silver and bismuth, are obtained from the sludge which collects beneath the anode.

9.2 The structure of the elements

Carbon

Carbon can form a two-dimensional and a three-dimensional atomic crystal (Fig. 9.1).

In diamond the carbon atoms are tetrahedrally surrounded by and covalently bonded to one another in a three-dimensional framework. This gives a crystal of great strength and hardness, which is a non-conductor of electricity.

Graphite possesses a *layer lattice*. Within each layer, or two-dimensional framework, the carbon atoms are covalently bonded together to form a hexagonal pattern. Each carbon atom uses three of its four outer electrons to form localised covalent bonds to its nearest

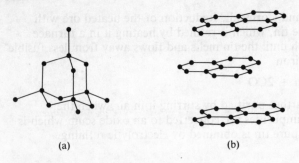

| (a) | (b) |

Fig. 9.1 The arrangement of carbon atoms in (a) diamond, (b) graphite.

neighbours. The remaining electrons, one from each carbon atom, combine to form a delocalised orbital extending over the whole of the layer. These delocalised electrons are free to move anywhere within a given layer, but cannot move from one to another. They will migrate under an applied electrical potential, thus making a graphite crystal an electrical conductor in the plane of the layers, but not in a direction perpendicular to them.

In a crystal of graphite the layers are stacked together like a pack of cards, with only weak van der Waals' forces holding them together. The distance between adjacent layers is much greater than that between neighbouring atoms within a layer, and it is impossible for the carbon atoms of one layer to form covalent bonds with those of another.

Graphite has a relatively low density (2.25 g cm^{-3}, compared with 3.51 g cm^{-3} for diamond), owing to its open structure. The ease with which this structure can be distorted accounts for the softness of graphite and its use as a lubricant. van der Waals' forces are readily overcome, allowing the layers to slide freely over one another.

The type of allotropy exhibited by carbon is known as *monotropy*, and is characterised by the following points.

(i) There is no definite temperature at which one allotrope changes into another.

(ii) One allotrope is more stable than the others. The unstable forms are said to be *metastable*.

(iii) The change from a metastable form to the stable allotrope is generally very slow.

At ordinary temperatures diamond is the metastable form of carbon because it possesses a higher free energy than graphite:

$$C(diamond) = C(graphite) \quad \Delta G^{\ominus} = -2.9 \text{ kJ mol}^{-1}$$

Nevertheless, diamond does not change into graphite at room temperature and pressure because of the very high activation energy associated with the moving of atoms within a solid structure.

The change from graphite to diamond is endothermic and accompanied by a decrease in volume. It is therefore favoured by high temperatures and high pressures. Industrial diamonds are manufactured by heating graphite to approximately 2 000 °C (2 273 K) at a pressure in the region of 10^5 atm (10^7 kPa) in the presence of a nickel catalyst. A recent report states that fairly large diamonds can be grown by heating small diamonds in a stream of methane at 1 000 °C (1 273 K).

Charcoals, soot and lampblack, known collectively as *amorphous carbon*, are microcrystalline forms of graphite. Because of its finely divided state, amorphous carbon has an enormous surface area and readily absorbs solutes from solutions, or large volumes of gases and liquids. For maximum effectiveness, amorphous carbon needs to be activated by heating it in steam at 1 000 °C (1 273 K).

Silicon and germanium

These two elements exist in only one structural form, which is similar to diamond. There are no structures comparable with that of graphite.

Tin

Tin displays a type of allotropy known as *enantiotropy*, which is characterised by the following points.

(i)   The change from one allotrope to another occurs at a definite temperature, known as the *transition temperature*.
(ii) At the transition temperature between two allotropes, both forms have equal stability.
(iii) Below the transition temperature one allotrope is stable, while above this temperature the other is stable.
(iv) The allotropes are easily interconverted.

The three allotropes of tin and the transition temperatures are as follows:

$$\alpha\text{-tin} \underset{}{\overset{13.2\,°C\,(286.4\,K)}{\rightleftharpoons}} \beta\text{-tin} \underset{}{\overset{161\,°C\,(434\,K)}{\rightleftharpoons}} \gamma\text{-tin}$$
(grey tin)   (white tin)   (rhombic tin)

The change from β-tin to α-tin is slow above temperatures of $-50\,°C$ (223 K) unless some α-tin is already present. The α-form has the diamond type of structure, but the β- and γ-allotropes have metallic structures. In adopting both metallic and non-metallic structures tin is an unusual element.

Lead

Lead does not exhibit allotropy and exists in a metallic form only.

9.3 Bonding and valency

The elements of group 4B each possess four outer electrons in an $ns^2\,np^2$ configuration, and may bond ionically or covalently.

Ionic bonding

Carbon can gain four electrons per atom to form the carbide ion, C^{4-} (§7.5). The metallic elements of the group, tin and lead, may form M^{4+} ions by the loss of all four outer electrons or M^{2+} ions by the loss of the two p electrons.

Covalent bonding

The formation of four covalent bonds is the dominant feature of the chemistry of carbon and silicon, and is common to the other elements of the group. The oxidation state may vary from -4 to $+4$ for carbon, although the remaining elements nearly always have positive oxidation numbers of 2 or 4. In addition, germanium, tin and lead commonly exhibit a covalency of two by using their unpaired p electrons.

The stability of the tetravalent and divalent states for germanium, tin and lead is shown below.

	Ge	Sn	Pb

increasing stability of divalent state $\longrightarrow$

$\longleftarrow$ increasing stability of tetravalent state

more stable state	4	4	2

Thus germanium and tin in the divalent state ($+2$ oxidation state) act as reducing agents, because they tend to lose electrons and switch to the more stable tetravalent state ($+4$ oxidation state). For ionic tin(II) compounds,

$$Sn^{2+} \rightarrow Sn^{4+} + 2e^-$$

For lead the opposite is true, and lead(IV) compounds act as oxidising agents:

$$Pb^{4+} + 2e^- \rightarrow Pb^{2+}$$

Maximum covalency

With the exception of carbon, the elements of group 4B have vacant d orbitals in their outermost shells which can be used to form coordinate bonds with donors. In such cases the elements achieve their maximum covalency of six, e.g.

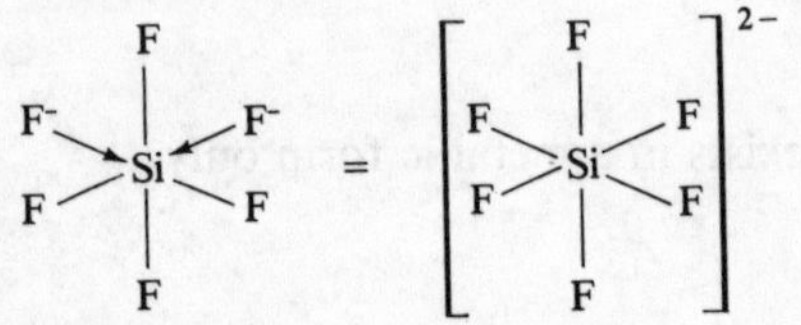

hexafluorosilicate(IV) ion
(octahedral)

Examples of other six-coordinate complexes include: $[GeCl_6]^{2-}$, $[SnBr_6]^{2-}$, $[PbCl_6]^{2-}$ and $[Sn(OH)_6]^{2-}$. The last may be compared with the aluminate(III) ion, $[Al(OH)_6]^{3-}$. Complexes of the type $[SiX_6]^{2-}$, where X represents Cl, Br or I, do not exist because of the difficulty of accommodating six of these large halogen atoms around a silicon atom.

9.4 The unique properties of carbon

Carbon differs in many respects from the other members of the group.

Maximum covalency

The maximum covalency of carbon is four, due to the absence of d orbitals in the outermost shell. This accounts for many of the differences which occur between carbon compounds and the corresponding compounds of the other group 4B elements. For example, the tetrahalides of carbon do not react with water, in contrast to silicon tetrachloride (§9.6).

Bond strength

The C—C bond is considerably stronger than the Si—Si, Ge—Ge, Sn—Sn and Pb—Pb bonds. This accounts for the strong tendency of carbon to form molecules containing chains of carbon atoms covalently bonded together, a property referred to as *catenation*. Carbon also forms exceptionally strong bonds with other elements, such as hydrogen, oxygen, sulphur, nitrogen and the halogens. These two factors account for the immense number of compounds which are studied under the heading of 'organic chemistry'. In contrast, the weaker Si—Si and Si—H bonds result in the silanes being relatively few in number and far more reactive than the alkanes. The Si—O bond is stronger than the Si—Si bond, and the chemistry of silicon is characterised by chains and rings of alternating silicon and oxygen atoms, in the same way that organic chemistry features chain and ring structures held together by strong bonds between carbon atoms.

Multiple bonding

Carbon is the only element of group 4B which is able to form stable multiple bonds with itself or other elements, e.g. C=C, C≡C, C≡N, C=O and C=S. Consequently there are no compounds of silicon and the heavier elements which correspond to the alkenes, alkynes, aldehydes, ketones or nitriles. Even compounds with similar stoicheiometric formulae, e.g. CO_2 and SiO_2, are totally different from one another.

9.5 Reactions of the group 4B elements

Table 9.2 The products of some reactions of carbon and silicon.

Reagent	Carbon	Silicon
oxygen at 700 °C (973 K)	CO_2 or CO	SiO_2
fluorine	CF_4	SiF_4
chlorine	no reaction	$SiCl_4$
sulphur at 900 °C (1 173 K)	CS_2	SiS_2
heated metals	metal carbides	metal silicides
oxidising acids, e.g. HNO_3	CO_2	partly oxidised to SiO_2
hydrofluoric acid	no reaction	H_2SiF_6
alkalis	no reaction	silicates and hydrogen

Although many differences exist between carbon and silicon, it is instructive to compare their chemistry. Some important reactions of these elements are given in Table 9.2. Amorphous carbon is more reactive than graphite because its broken crystal structure allows easy access of reagents. Diamond is less reactive than graphite.

Germanium, tin and lead form a family and are conveniently discussed together. Some of their important reactions are presented in Table 9.3.

Table 9.3 The products of some reactions of germanium, tin and lead.

Reagent	Germanium	Tin	Lead
air or oxygen on heating	GeO_2	SnO_2	PbO or Pb_3O_4
chlorine	$GeCl_4$	$SnCl_4$	$PbCl_2$
heated sulphur	GeS_2	SnS_2	PbS
concentrated HNO_3	GeO_2	SnO_2	$Pb(NO_3)_2$
concentrated HCl	no reaction	$SnCl_2$	$PbCl_2$
concentrated H_2SO_4	GeO_2	$Sn(SO_4)_2$	$PbSO_4$
alkalis	$[Ge(OH)_6]^{2-}$	$[Sn(OH)_6]^{2-}$	$[Pb(OH)_6]^{4-}$
heated metals	alloy formation	alloy formation	alloy formation

We can see from their reactions that germanium and tin, in contrast to lead, have a distinct preference for the tetravalent state. The reaction of lead with dilute hydrochloric acid or cold concentrated sulphuric acid is slow, because the insoluble lead salts which are formed tend to coat the metal surface. Attack by hot concentrated sulphuric acid is more rapid because lead sulphate is soluble under these conditions. Warm concentrated hydrochloric acid is effective because it dissolves lead(II) chloride to form the tetrachloroplumbate(II) ion, $[PbCl_4]^{2-}$ (§9.7).

9.6 Compounds of carbon and silicon

Most compounds of carbon are classically considered under the heading of 'organic chemistry', leaving a relatively small number of compounds, principally oxides, tetrahalides, cyanides and carbonates, together with the properties of the element itself, to be studied in 'inorganic chemistry'.

Oxides of carbon

Carbon dioxide

Carbon dioxide is formed whenever carbon or its compounds are burned in an excess of oxygen or air. It is more conveniently produced by:

(i)   the thermal decomposition of carbonates or hydrogencarbonates;
(ii) the action of a dilute acid on a carbonate or a hydrogencarbonate:

$$CO_3^{2-} + 2H^+(aq) = CO_2 + H_2O$$
$$HCO_3^- + H^+(aq) = CO_2 + H_2O$$

(iii) the fermentation of sugars in the presence of zymase, an enzyme contained in yeast cells, e.g.

$$C_6H_{12}O_6 = 2C_2H_5OH + 2CO_2$$
glucose

(iv) the steam reforming of hydrocarbons (§6.1).

The carbon dioxide molecule is linear and can be represented as:

$$O{=}C{=}O \qquad \text{bond length} = 0.116 \text{ nm}$$

The bonding is more complex than this, however, owing to extensive delocalisation of π electrons which produces bonds that are intermediate in character between $C{=}O$ (bond length, 0.122 nm) and $C{\equiv}O$ (bond length, 0.110 nm).

At temperatures in excess of 1 700 °C (1 973 K) carbon dioxide decomposes into carbon monoxide and oxygen:

$$2CO_2 = 2CO + O_2$$

When heated with reactive metals, such as sodium or magnesium, reduction occurs:

$$2Na + 2CO_2 = Na_2CO_3 + CO$$
$$2Mg + CO_2 = 2MgO + C$$

Carbon dioxide is weakly acidic and reacts with strongly basic oxides or hydroxides to form carbonates:

$$Na_2O + CO_2 = Na_2CO_3$$
$$Ca(OH)_2 + CO_2 = CaCO_3 + H_2O$$

The formation of insoluble calcium carbonate from a saturated solution of calcium hydroxide ('lime water') is used as a test for carbon dioxide.

The calcium carbonate dissolves if an excess of carbon dioxide is used, owing to the formation of the hydrogencarbonate:

$$CaCO_3 + H_2O + CO_2 = Ca(HCO_3)_2$$

Carbon monoxide

Carbon monoxide, a colourless, odourless, toxic gas, is produced whenever carbon or its compounds are burned in a deficiency of oxygen. In the laboratory it may be prepared by:

(i)   passing carbon dioxide over carbon at 700 °C (973 K);
(ii) dehydrating methanoic acid or ethanedioic acid with either concentrated sulphuric acid or phosphorus(V) oxide:

$$HCOOH = CO + H_2O$$
$$(COOH)_2 = CO + CO_2 + H_2O$$

The carbon dioxide can be removed by passing the gases through aqueous sodium hydroxide.

Industrially, carbon monoxide is produced in the steam reforming of hydrocarbons (§6.1).

Carbon monoxide can act as a ligand (§5.3), by donating the lone pair of electrons on the carbon atom. The oxygen atom does not donate in this case, possibly due to its higher electronegativity. Two examples of complexes of carbon monoxide are tetracarbonylnickel(0) and penta-carbonyliron(0), in each of which the oxidation state of the metal is zero.

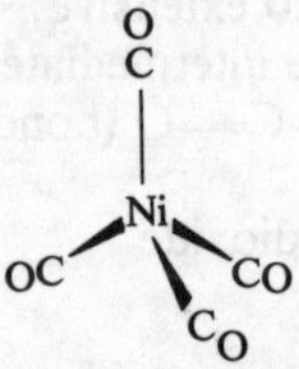

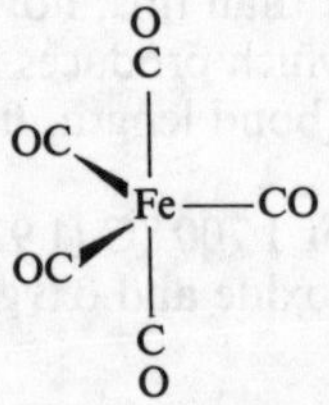

The bonding in metal carbonyls involves the donation of electrons from carbon to the metal, and a back donation of electrons from the metal d orbitals into vacant antibonding orbitals (§4.1) on the carbon monoxide molecule.

Carbon monoxide is weakly acidic, and reacts with sodium hydroxide at 200 °C (473 K) and 10 atm (1 000 kPa) to produce sodium methanoate:

$$NaOH + CO = HCOONa$$

Despite being the anhydride of methanoic acid, it does not form this acid with water. At room temperature a neutral solution is formed, and at elevated temperatures an oxidation–reduction reaction occurs to give carbon dioxide and hydrogen:

$$CO + H_2O = CO_2 + H_2$$

Carbon monoxide is readily oxidised, and burns in air with a characteristic blue flame:

$$2CO + O_2 = 2CO_2$$

It reduces many heated metallic oxides to metals (§5.4).

The reaction with diiodine pentaoxide, I_2O_5, occurs quantitatively at 90 °C (363 K) and may be used to analyse gas mixtures containing carbon monoxide. The liberated iodine is titrated with sodium thiosulphate:

$$I_2O_5 + 5CO = I_2 + 5CO_2$$
$$I_2 + 2Na_2S_2O_3 = 2NaI + Na_2S_4O_6$$
$$\therefore \text{ 5 mol } CO \equiv \text{ 1 mol } I_2 \equiv \text{ 2 mol } Na_2S_2O_3$$

Carbon monoxide is also oxidised by chlorine (in the presence of light and a charcoal catalyst) and by heated sulphur:

$$CO + Cl_2 = O{=}C\diagup^{Cl}_{\diagdown Cl} \qquad \text{carbonyl chloride (phosgene)}$$

$$CO + S = O{=}C{=}S \qquad \text{carbonyl sulphide}$$

Solutions of copper(I) chloride in ammonia or hydrochloric acid readily absorb carbon monoxide.

Carbonic acid and its salts

Carbon dioxide is fairly soluble in water, 1 volume of CO_2 dissolving in 1.71 volumes of water at 0 °C (273 K) and a pressure of 1 atm (100 kPa). Most of the dissolved gas is present as a weakly bound hydrate, $CO_2(aq)$, but approximately 1 per cent reacts with water to produce a weak diprotic acid, H_2CO_3, called carbonic acid:

$$CO_2(g) + aq \rightleftharpoons CO_2(aq) \rightleftharpoons H_2CO_3$$
$$H_2CO_3 \rightleftharpoons H^+(aq) + HCO_3^- \qquad pK_1 = 3.7$$
$$HCO_3^- \rightleftharpoons H^+(aq) + CO_3^{2-} \qquad pK_2 = 10.32$$

Carbonic acid is very unstable and has not been isolated in the pure state.

Two series of salts derived from carbonic acid are known, namely the carbonates and the hydrogencarbonates, and of particular importance are those of the s-block elements. The carbonate ion, which is present in these compounds, is planar, and because of delocalised π bonding the carbon−oxygen bonds are equivalent (Fig. 9.2(a)). Crystalline hydrogencarbonates of the alkali metals are of interest as they contain very long chains of HCO_3^- ions linked together by hydrogen bonds (Fig. 9.2(b)).

Carbonates are insoluble in water, with the exception of the ammonium salt and those of the alkali metals. The hydrogencarbonates of

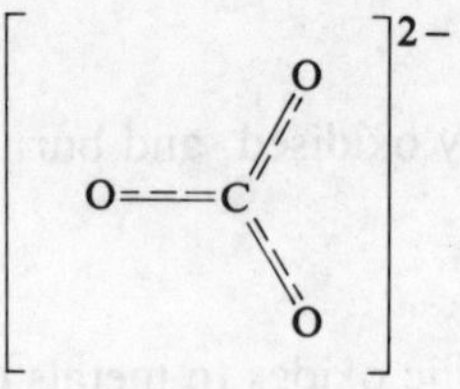

(a)

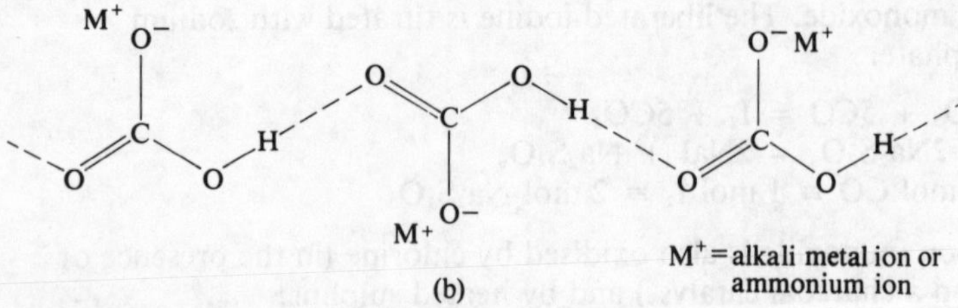

M^+ = alkali metal ion or ammonium ion

(b)

Fig. 9.2 (a) The structure of the carbonate ion. Typical C—O distance = 0.129 nm. (b) Part of the chain structure in crystalline hydrogen-carbonates.

the alkali metals, except for lithium, are the only ones which can be obtained in the crystalline state. All other hydrogencarbonates decompose on evaporation of the solution, e.g.

$$Ca(HCO_3)_2 = CaCO_3 + CO_2 + H_2O$$

Because of salt hydrolysis, both carbonates and hydrogencarbonates form alkaline solutions, i.e.

$$CO_3^{2-} + H_2O \rightleftharpoons HCO_3^- + HO^-$$
$$HCO_3^- + H_2O \rightleftharpoons H_2CO_3 + HO^-$$

This occurs to a greater extent with the CO_3^{2-} ion than the HCO_3^- ion. Thus, 0.1 M solutions of sodium carbonate and sodium hydrogen-carbonate have pH values of 11.5 and 8.5 respectively.

All metal carbonates are thermally unstable and decompose into the metal oxide and carbon dioxide on heating. Normally, decomposition occurs below the melting temperature of the carbonate, but alkali metal carbonates, except lithium carbonate, can be fused without appreciable decomposition. Hydrogencarbonates are less stable than the corresponding carbonates and decompose below 100 °C (373 K), e.g.

$$CaCO_3 = CaO + CO_2$$
$$2NaHCO_3 = Na_2CO_3 + CO_2 + H_2O$$

The carbonate and hydrogencarbonate ions are readily distorted by the electrical field associated with cations. The greater the distortion the lower is the thermal stability (§7.6). Thus, the group 2A carbonates become increasingly stable from magnesium to barium as the surface charge density of the cation decreases. Group 2A hydrogencarbonates, and lithium hydrogencarbonate, are stable only in solution because the close approach of a cation, as a prerequisite to forming a crystalline salt, is sufficient to decompose the hydrogencarbonate ion.

Precipitation reactions of carbonates and hydrogencarbonates

Soluble carbonates react with solutions of metal salts to form various products.

Precipitation of a hydroxide or oxide

The hydrated trivalent ions Al^{3+}, Fe^{3+} and Cr^{3+} are acidic in solution and act as acids towards the carbonate ion, e.g.

$$2[Al(OH)_2(H_2O)_4]^+ + CO_3^{2-} = 2[Al(OH)_3(H_2O)_3] + CO_2 + H_2O$$
(§8.5)

In many cases the precipitated hydroxide changes rapidly into a hydrated oxide.

Precipitation of a normal carbonate

The divalent ions Ca^{2+}, Sr^{2+} and Ba^{2+} do not greatly polarise neighbouring water molecules and are neutral or weakly acidic in solution. In these cases the normal carbonate is precipitated by adding a soluble carbonate:

$$M^{2+} + CO_3^{2-} = MCO_3(s) \qquad (M = Ca, Sr \text{ or } Ba)$$

Precipitation of a basic carbonate

In between these two extremes are other hydrated divalent metal ions, notably Cu^{2+}, Mg^{2+}, Fe^{2+} and Pb^{2+}. When a soluble carbonate is added to solutions of these ions a precipitate of a basic carbonate is formed which contains the metal ions, hydroxide ions and carbonate ions. For example, malachite, $CuCO_3 \cdot Cu(OH)_2$ or $Cu_2CO_3(OH)_2$, a naturally occurring basic copper carbonate, possesses a structure with an extended arrangement of Cu^{2+}, CO_3^{2-} and HO^- ions, and white lead, $2PbCO_3 \cdot Pb(OH)_2$ or $Pb_3CO_3(OH)_2$, consists of an array of Pb^{2+} and CO_3^{2-} ions interleaved with layers of $Pb(OH)_2$.

The term 'basic' indicates that the compound is intermediate between the normal salt and the base, i.e. the hydroxide. Basic salts other than carbonates are known, and many of these contain regular arrays of metal ions, hydroxide ions and the relevant anions, e.g. hydroxyapatite, $3Ca_3(PO_4)_2 \cdot Ca(OH)_2$ or $Ca_5(PO_4)_3(OH)$, and basic lead(II) chloride, $PbCl_2 \cdot Pb(OH)_2$ or $PbCl(OH)$.

The hydrogencarbonate ion is a weaker base than the carbonate ion and is less efficient at ionising coordinated water molecules in hydrated cations. Therefore, some metal ions, which form basic carbonates when treated with the carbonate ion, do not form basic salts with the

192

hydrogencarbonate ion. The precipitate obtained is usually a carbonate because most hydrogencarbonates are unstable, particularly if heated, e.g.

$$Mg^{2+} + 2HCO_3^- \xrightarrow{50\,°C\,(323\,K)} MgCO_3(s) + H_2O + CO_2$$

Oxides of silicon

Silicon forms a very unstable monoxide, SiO, and a very stable dioxide, SiO_2, which is a colourless glassy solid with a high melting temperature. Silicon dioxide is *trimorphic*, i.e. it exists in three forms. In order of decreasing stability at room temperature they are quartz, cristobalite and tridymite. Structurally, each form consists of an infinite three-dimensional array in which each silicon atom is surrounded tetrahedrally by four oxygen atoms (Fig. 9.3). The formula SiO_2 does not, therefore, represent a molecule, and for this reason the name 'silica' is often preferred to silicon dioxide (cf. carbon dioxide). Silica adopts this structure because, unlike carbon, silicon cannot form multiple bonds.

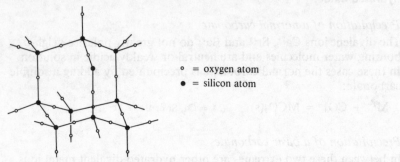

○ = oxygen atom
● = silicon atom

Fig. 9.3 The structure of silica.

The high stability of silica is shown by its high enthalpy of formation. $\Delta H_f^{\ominus}$ [SiO_2(quartz)] = $-859\,kJ\,mol^{-1}$. The high value is due to:

(i) the relatively low atomisation enthalpy of silicon, which is a consequence of the weakness of the Si—Si bond;
(ii) the high bond dissociation enthalpy of the Si—O bond.

Silica is insoluble in water and chemically rather inert. It does, however, function as a weakly acidic oxide and reacts, for example, with fused alkali metal hydroxides or carbonates to produce silicates, e.g.

$2NaOH + SiO_2 = Na_2SiO_3 + H_2O$
$Na_2CO_3 + SiO_2 = Na_2SiO_3 + CO_2$

The only other common reagent to attack silica is hydrofluoric acid, with which it forms silicon tetrafluoride and hexafluorosilicic(IV) acid:

$SiO_2 + 4HF = SiF_4 + 2H_2O$
$SiF_4 + 2HF = H_2SiF_6$

Silicates, glass and silica gel

Silicates bear no resemblance to carbonates (cf. SiO_2 and CO_2), a fact which is due to the inability of silicon to form multiple bonds. A large number of silicate ions are known, most of which are polymeric in nature. Silicates are often represented by their stoicheiometric formulae, but this does not imply the existence of simple anions. For example, the anion in sodium silicate, Na_2SiO_3, is polymeric and not SiO_3^{2-} as the formula suggests.

Silicates are insoluble in water, except for those of the alkali metals. Solutions of these silicates are alkaline because of salt hydrolysis. Sodium silicate, known as 'water glass', is used in preserving and cleansing solutions.

Glass, a supercooled liquid, is essentially a mixture of the silicates of sodium and calcium, or potassium and calcium. Various modified glasses are made by incorporating other elements into the basic glass formulation. This is done by adding the oxides or carbonates of the elements concerned to molten glass. Some common elements which are used to impart special properties are as follows: aluminium and boron (heat resistance, as in Pyrex), lithium (added strength), lead (high refractive index for cut glass or flint glass) and phosphorus (crown glass). Coloured glass is produced by adding various metal oxides to molten glass, e.g. cobalt oxide gives a blue glass.

If a solution of a silicate is acidified, a gel (i.e. jelly) of hydrated silica is formed:

$$SiO_3^{2-} + 2H^+(aq) = SiO_2(aq) + H_2O$$

Similar gels are also obtained by hydrolysing silicon halides. If the gel is heated it loses most of its water to give a brittle solid, known as *silica gel*, which readily absorbs moisture and is used as a desiccant. When saturated with water, silica gel can be dried at 110 °C (383 K) any number of times and re-used without loss of drying efficiency. Silica gel is also used as a catalyst, a catalyst support, and a chromatographic support.

The tetrahalomethanes

Tetrafluoromethane and tetrachloromethane are stable compounds, in contrast to the bromo- and iodo-compounds which are unstable because of the difficulty of accommodating four large halogen atoms around a small carbon atom.

Tetrachloromethane is prepared by reacting chlorine with either methane or carbon disulphide:

$$CH_4 \xrightarrow{Cl_2} CH_3Cl \xrightarrow{Cl_2} CH_2Cl_2 \xrightarrow{Cl_2} CHCl_3 \xrightarrow{Cl_2} CCl_4$$
$$CS_2 + 3Cl_2 = CCl_4 + S_2Cl_2$$
$$2S_2Cl_2 + CS_2 = CCl_4 + 6S$$

Tetrachloromethane is used as a solvent, although it must be handled with care because it is extremely toxic. Chemically, it is rather inert, e.g. it is resistant to hydrolysis, even though the reaction is thermodynamically favourable:

$$CCl_4(l) + 2H_2O(l) = CO_2(g) + 4HCl(g) \quad \Delta G^{\ominus} = -233.6 \text{ kJ mol}^{-1}$$

This is an example of kinetic stability.

Silicon tetrahalides

All four tetrahalides of silicon exist, i.e. SiX_4, where X represents F, Cl, Br or I. In addition, several catenated halides containing Si—Si bonds are known, e.g. Si_6Cl_{14}, Si_2F_6 and Si_2I_6, but these are less important than the tetrahalides. Silicon tetrafluoride is conveniently prepared by the action of hydrofluoric acid on silica, while the other halides are formed by direct combination of the heated elements.

Silicon tetrahalides have a tetrahedral structure. In contrast to the corresponding halides of carbon they are rapidly attacked by water, which indicates that a favourable pathway exists for the hydrolysis. The reaction is stepwise. Each stage involves the formation of a coordinate bond between a water molecule and the silicon atom, followed by the elimination of a molecule of hydrogen halide, e.g.

The final product to be expected from the hydrolysis is $Si(OH)_4$, but this has not been isolated since it undergoes condensation polymerisation to form hydrated silica, $SiO_2(aq)$.

In forming a coordinate bond with a water molecule, the silicon atom uses one of its vacant 3d orbitals. Carbon has no d orbitals in its outermost shell and cannot coordinate water molecules in this manner, which accounts for the kinetic stability of its halides.

The hydrolysis of silicon tetrafluoride differs from that of the other halides because hydrofluoric acid attacks any unhydrolysed fluoride to produce hexafluorosilicic(IV) acid, which is a strong acid containing the hexafluorosilicate(IV) ion:

$$SiF_4 + 2H_2O = SiO_2(aq) + 4HF$$
$$SiF_4 + 2HF = 2H^+(aq) + [SiF_6]^{2-}$$

Silanes (silicon hydrides)

The silanes have the general formula Si_nH_{2n+2}, where n ranges from 1 to 6, and are named according to the number of silicon atoms they contain. For example, SiH_4 is called silane, Si_2H_6 is disilane, and Si_3H_8

is trisilane. A mixture of silanes is obtained by treating magnesium silicide with a dilute acid in the absence of air. The mixture may be separated by fractional distillation or gas chromatography. Individual silanes can be prepared by the reduction of silicon halides with lithium tetrahydridoaluminate(III), e.g.

$$SiCl_4 + Li[AlH_4] = SiH_4 + LiCl + AlCl_3$$
$$2Si_2Cl_6 + 3Li[AlH_4] = 2Si_2H_6 + 3LiCl + 3AlCl_3$$

Structurally, the silanes resemble the alkanes, but chemically they are far more reactive. This is due to the weakness of the Si—H and Si—Si bonds and the existence of vacant 3d orbitals on the silicon atom.

The silanes are spontaneously flammable in air, e.g.

$$SiH_4 + 2O_2 = SiO_2 + 2H_2O$$

In the absence of air, many of them decompose slowly into silicon and hydrogen at room temperature. They are rapidly hydrolysed by water in the presence of traces of alkali, e.g.

$$Si_2H_6 + 4H_2O = 2SiO_2(aq) + 7H_2$$

There are no unsaturated silicon hydrides corresponding to alkenes, alkynes or benzene.

Carbides and silicides

Carbides

Binary compounds between carbon and elements of lower electronegativity are termed *carbides*, although hydrocarbons are usually excluded from this category. There are three structural types, namely ionic, covalent and interstitial.

Aluminium carbide, Al_4C_3, and beryllium carbide, Be_2C, contain the carbide ion, C^{4-}. They are generally prepared by direct combination of the elements at high temperatures, and they yield methane on hydrolysis with water, e.g.

$$Al_4C_3 + 12H_2O = 3CH_4 + 4Al(OH)_3$$

Most carbides of the s-block elements contain the acetylide ion, $[C{\equiv}C]^{2-}$, and are hydrolysed to give ethyne (§7.5). Because of this they are named as 'acetylides' rather than 'carbides'; e.g. CaC_2, calcium acetylide. One of the carbides of magnesium, Mg_2C_3, probably contains the $[C{-}C{\equiv}C]^{4-}$ ion (§7.5).

The best known covalent carbide, silicon carbide or 'carborundum', is prepared by heating silica with carbon at 1 800 °C (2 073 K):

$$SiO_2 + 3C = SiC + 2CO$$

It forms an atomic crystal similar to that of diamond, with alternate silicon and carbon atoms throughout the lattice. Because of its structure, silicon carbide is very hard and is an important abrasive.

A covalent carbide, B_4C, is also formed by boron.

Interstitial carbides can arise because carbon atoms, being small, are able to enter the *interstices* (i.e. spaces) between the atoms of certain crystalline metals. Such compounds are often non-stoicheiometric, because there is no bonding between the metal and carbon atoms, and they possess properties which are essentially those of the host metal. They are resistant to hydrolysis and are generally very hard. Some, e.g. tungsten carbide, are used for the tips of cutting tools.

Silicides

Binary compounds between metals and silicon are called *silicides*. They are prepared at high temperatures by direct combination of the elements, or by reduction of silica with an excess of a reactive metal, e.g.

$$4Mg + SiO_2 = Mg_2Si + 2MgO$$

Silicides range from essentially ionic compounds, e.g. Ca_2Si, to those with alloy-type structures, e.g. Cr_3Si.

9.7 Compounds of germanium, tin and lead

Oxides

The oxides of these elements are:

GeO	SnO	PbO	(divalent or $+2$ oxidation state)
GeO$_2$	SnO$_2$	PbO$_2$	(tetravalent or $+4$ oxidation state)
		Pb$_3$O$_4$	(mixed oxide)

All the oxides are amphoteric, but basic character increases from germanium to lead, and is more pronounced in the divalent state than in the tetravalent state. Lead, alone in this group, forms a mixed oxide.

Germanium(II) oxide

A yellow precipitate of hydrated germanium(II) oxide, GeO(aq), is obtained by the addition of alkali to a solution of a germanium(IV) compound that has been reduced with phosphinic acid, HPH_2O_2. The black anhydrous oxide is obtained by dehydration of the hydrated oxide at 650 °C (923 K).

Germanium(II) oxide is readily oxidised to germanium(IV) oxide, GeO_2, by oxygen. It dissolves in alkalis to produce the germanate(II) ion, GeO_2^{2-} or possibly $[Ge(OH)_4(aq)]^{2-}$, and forms germanium(II) salts with acids.

Germanium(IV) oxide

Anhydrous germanium(IV) oxide is obtained as a white powder by heating germanium in oxygen. A hydrated form can be prepared by dissolving germanium in concentrated nitric acid, or by hydrolysing germanium(IV) chloride with an excess of water:

$$Ge + O_2 = GeO_2$$
$$Ge + 4HNO_3 = GeO_2(aq) + 4NO_2 + 2H_2O$$
$$GeCl_4 + 2H_2O \rightleftharpoons GeO_2(aq) + 4HCl$$

At room temperature germanium(IV) oxide is ionic, i.e. $Ge^{4+}(O^{2-})_2$, with a similar structure to that of rutile (Fig. 14.10), but above 1 033 °C (1 306 K) it has a silica type of structure. In forming an oxide which has both ionic and covalent structures, germanium exhibits both metallic and non-metallic character.

Germanium(IV) oxide dissolves in an excess of concentrated hydrochloric acid to form germanium(IV) chloride. With alkalis germanate(IV) species are produced, which are oxoanions containing germanium, e.g. $[GeO(OH)_3]^-$ or $[Ge(OH)_6]^{2-}$. Like all germanium(IV) compounds, the oxide does not possess any oxidising or reducing properties.

Tin(II) oxide

Anhydrous tin(II) oxide is prepared by heating tin(II) ethanedioate:

$$(COO)_2Sn = SnO + CO + CO_2$$

The hydrated oxide, SnO(aq), which is produced as a white precipitate by adding a limited quantity of alkali to a tin(II) salt, can be dehydrated at 120 °C (393 K) to give the blue-black anhydrous compound.

Tin(II) oxide dissolves readily in acids to form tin(II) salts, and in alkalis to form stannate(II) ions, possibly $[Sn(OH)_6]^{4-}$, e.g.

$$SnO + 2HCl = SnCl_2 + H_2O$$
$$SnO + 4HO^- + H_2O = [Sn(OH)_6]^{4-}$$

A solution of the stannate(II) ion is a powerful reducing agent.

Tin(IV) oxide

Tin(IV) oxide can be prepared by methods similar to those used for germanium(IV) oxide. Hydrated forms of the oxide, which vary widely in their water content, readily become anhydrous on heating. Tin(IV) oxide is ionic, i.e. $Sn^{4+}(O^{2-})_2$, with the rutile type of structure (Fig. 14.10).

Tin(IV) oxide dissolves in acids or alkalis, particularly fused alkalis, e.g.

$$SnO_2 + 2H_2SO_4 = Sn(SO_4)_2 + 2H_2O$$
$$SnO_2 + 2HO^- + 2H_2O = [Sn(OH)_6]^{2-}$$

The octahedral hexahydroxostannate(IV) ion, $[Sn(OH)_6]^{2-}$, comprises six hydroxide ions coordinated to a tin(IV) ion, and may be compared with the hexahydroxoaluminate(III) ion, $[Al(OH)_6]^{3-}$. Like all tin(IV) compounds, the oxide does not function either as an oxidant or as a reductant.

The reaction of tin with concentrated nitric acid possibly involves the formation of hydrated tin(IV) ions, which undergo extensive hydrolysis because of the high surface charge density of the tin(IV) ion (cf. Al^{3+}):

$$(x-4)H_2O + Sn + 4NO_3^- + 8H^+(aq) = [Sn(H_2O)_x]^{4+} + 4NO_2$$
$$[Sn(H_2O)_x]^{4+} + H_2O \rightleftharpoons [Sn(OH)(H_2O)_{x-1}]^{3+} + H_3O^+$$
$$[Sn(OH)(H_2O)_{x-1}]^{3+} + H_2O \rightleftharpoons [Sn(OH)_2(H_2O)_{x-2}]^{2+} + H_3O^+$$

The loss of two more hydrogen ions would produce hydrated tin(IV) hydroxide, i.e. $[Sn(OH)_4(H_2O)_{x-4}]$. However, there is no evidence for the existence of this species, presumably because it rapidly changes into the hydrated oxide:

$$[Sn(OH)_4(H_2O)_{x-4}] \rightleftharpoons SnO_2(aq) + (x-2)H_2O$$

With an excess of alkali, further ionisation would produce anionic species, e.g. $[Sn(OH)_6]^{2-}$.

Lead(II) oxide

This compound exists in two different structural forms, litharge (red) and massicot (yellow). The stable form at room temperature is litharge, but the change from massicot to litharge is very slow under these conditions. Lead(II) oxide can be prepared by the thermal decomposition of lead(IV) oxide or certain other lead(II) compounds, e.g. the carbonate, hydroxide or nitrate. At temperatures below 550 °C (823 K) litharge is formed, but above 650 °C (923 K) the product is massicot.

Lead(II) oxide is the most basic group 4B oxide and dissolves in acids to produce lead(II) salts, although the reaction may be slow if the resulting salt is insoluble and forms a coating on the surface of the oxide particles. Lead(II) oxide also dissolves slowly in solutions of alkalis to give anionic plumbate(II) species, possibly $[Pb(OH)_6]^{4-}$; cf. tin(II) oxide.

The only hydroxide apparently formed by the elements of this group, lead(II) hydroxide, $Pb(OH)_2$, is produced as a white precipitate by adding limited alkali to a solution of a lead(II) salt:

$$Pb^{2+}(aq) + 2HO^- = Pb(OH)_2$$

Like the oxide, lead(II) hydroxide is amphoteric and possesses no oxidising or reducing properties.

Lead(IV) oxide

A brown precipitate of lead(IV) oxide, PbO_2, is formed by:

(i) oxidising the lead(II) ion with the hypochlorite ion in alkaline solution:

$$Pb^{2+} + 2HO^- + ClO^- = PbO_2 + H_2O + Cl^-$$

(ii) treating trilead tetraoxide with dilute nitric acid:

$$Pb_3O_4 + 4HNO_3 = 2Pb(NO_3)_2 + PbO_2 + 2H_2O$$

(iii) the electrolytic oxidation of a lead(II) salt:

$$Pb^{2+} + 2HO^- = PbO_2 + 2H^+(aq) + 2e^-$$ (at the anode)

Lead(IV) oxide is similar in structure to rutile (Fig. 14.10). Above 300 °C (573 K) it decomposes into lead(II) oxide and oxygen:

$$2PbO_2 = 2PbO + O_2$$

Lead(IV) oxide is a very powerful oxidising agent. For example, it oxidises both sulphur dioxide and warm concentrated hydrochloric acid:

$$PbO_2 + SO_2 = PbSO_4$$
$$PbO_2 + 4HCl = PbCl_2 + Cl_2 + 2H_2O$$

At 0 °C (273 K) lead(IV) oxide dissolves in concentrated hydrochloric acid to produce the unstable lead(IV) chloride, $PbCl_4$, and with fused alkalis forms the hexahydroxoplumbate(IV) ion, $[Pb(OH)_6]^{2-}$ (cf. SnO_2).

Trilead tetraoxide (dilead(II) lead(IV) oxide)
This orange-red compound is formed by heating lead(II) oxide in air at 300–570 °C (573–843 K). Above 570 °C (843 K) the reverse reaction occurs:

$$6PbO + O_2 \underset{\text{above 570 °C}}{\overset{300-570\,°C}{\rightleftharpoons}} 2Pb_3O_4$$

It is a mixed oxide which, as its name suggests, behaves chemically (but not physically) as a 2 : 1 mixture of lead(II) oxide and lead(IV) oxide. For example, with nitric acid the 'lead(II) part' dissolves, leaving a residue of lead(IV) oxide:

$$Pb_3O_4 + 4HNO_3 = PbO_2 + 2Pb(NO_3)_2 + 2H_2O$$
('$PbO_2 \cdot 2PbO$')

Warm concentrated hydrochloric acid is oxidised to chlorine by the 'lead(IV) part':

$$Pb_3O_4 + 8HCl = 3PbCl_2 + Cl_2 + 4H_2O$$
('$PbO_2 \cdot 2PbO$')

Structurally, the oxide contains a regular array of Pb^{2+}, Pb^{4+} and O^{2-} ions in the ratio 2 : 1 : 4.

Trilead tetraoxide under the commercial name of 'red lead' is used for making anti-rust paints.

Halides
The following discussion is centred chiefly on the chlorides of germanium, tin and lead because they are the most important halides of these elements.

Germanium(II) chloride
This compound is obtained by passing germanium(IV) chloride vapour over heated germanium:

$$Ge + GeCl_4 = 2GeCl_2$$

It forms chloro-complexes, e.g. $[GeCl_3]^-$, with ionic chlorides, and is hydrolysed by water to hydrated germanium(II) oxide. Like all germanium(II) compounds, the chloride is a powerful reducing agent.

Germanium(IV) chloride

Germanium(IV) chloride, a colourless liquid, is prepared by passing chlorine over heated germanium or a mixture of germanium(IV) oxide and carbon:

$$Ge + 2Cl_2 = GeCl_4$$
$$GeO_2 + C + 2Cl_2 = GeCl_4 + CO_2$$

Germanium(IV) chloride is reversibly hydrolysed by water to a white precipitate of hydrated germanium(IV) oxide, and forms the hexachloro-germanate(IV) ion, $[GeCl_6]^{2-}$, with ionic chlorides.

Germanium also forms a fluoro-complex, $[GeF_6]^{2-}$, but not the corresponding bromo- and iodo-complexes, presumably because it is not possible to accommodate these large halogen atoms around a germanium atom.

Tin(II) chloride

The hydrate, $SnCl_2 \cdot 2H_2O$, is prepared by dissolving tin in hydrochloric acid, followed by evaporation of the solution:

$$Sn + 2HCl = SnCl_2(aq) + H_2$$

The anhydrous compound is obtained by passing hydrogen chloride over heated tin. It cannot be prepared by heating the hydrate because hydrolysis occurs and a basic tin(II) chloride is formed:

$$SnCl_2 \cdot 2H_2O = SnCl(OH) + HCl + H_2O$$
$$\text{tin(II) chloride hydroxide}$$

Tin(II) chloride is molecular (bond angle 95°) with a lone pair of electrons on the tin atom. Aqueous solutions of tin(II) chloride appear milky due to the formation, by hydrolysis, of insoluble basic chlorides, e.g.

$$SnCl_2 + H_2O \rightleftharpoons SnCl(OH) + HCl$$

The addition of hydrochloric acid clears the solution by displacing the equilibrium to the left, and also by forming trichlorostannate(II) and tetrachlorostannate(II) ions:

$$SnCl_2 + 2Cl^- \rightleftharpoons [SnCl_3]^- + Cl^- \rightleftharpoons [SnCl_4]^{2-}$$

There is no evidence for the existence of simple hydrated tin(II) ions in solution because of the strong tendency for hydrolysis to occur and produce complex ions containing tin(II).

Tin(II) chloride reduces many substances, e.g. mercury(II) and iron(III) compounds:

$$2HgCl_2 + SnCl_2 = SnCl_4 + Hg_2Cl_2$$
$$Hg_2Cl_2 + SnCl_2 = SnCl_4 + 2Hg$$
$$2Fe^{3+} + 2Cl^- + SnCl_2 = SnCl_4 + 2Fe^{2+}$$

Tin(II) chloride also reduces nitrobenzene to phenylamine (aniline).

Tin(IV) halides

Tin(IV) halides are prepared by methods similar to those used for germanium(IV) chloride. Tin(IV) fluoride appears to be ionic, but the other tin(IV) halides are covalent, with tetrahedral molecules.

In many respects tin(IV) chloride resembles germanium(IV) chloride. It is a colourless liquid which is reversibly hydrolysed by water to give hydrated tin(IV) oxide:

$$SnCl_4 + 2H_2O \rightleftharpoons SnO_2(aq) + 4HCl$$

The white fumes emitted from tin(IV) chloride in moist air are a mixture of hydrogen chloride and a 'smoke' of hydrated tin(IV) oxide produced in this hydrolysis reaction. The reaction with water is thought to involve an ionic stage (cf. aluminium), because the addition of small amounts of water to tin(IV) chloride results in the formation of an ionic compound of formula $SnCl_4 \cdot 5H_2O$. Undoubtedly this compound contains hydrated tin(IV) ions, although their exact nature is not known. Hydrated ions of the type $[Sn(H_2O)_x]^{4+}$ are also formed in solution by the reaction:

$$SnCl_4 + xH_2O = [Sn(H_2O)_x]^{4+} + 4Cl^-$$

but these undergo extensive hydrolysis to produce hydrated tin(IV) oxide. The ease of hydrolysis of tin(IV) halides decreases from the fluoride to the iodide.

The addition of hydrochloric acid to tin(IV) chloride gives the octahedral hexachlorostannate(IV) ion:

$$SnCl_4 + 2Cl^- = [SnCl_6]^{2-}$$

The ammonium salt, $(NH_4)_2[SnCl_6]$, is used as a mordant in dyeing. The other tin(IV) halides form similar halo-complexes, i.e. $[SnF_6]^{2-}$, $[SnBr_6]^{2-}$ and $[SnI_6]^{2-}$, when treated with the appropriate hydrohalic acid.

The tin(IV) halides do not possess oxidising or reducing properties.

Lead(II) halides

The lead(II) halides are sparingly soluble in cold water and are prepared by precipitation reactions,

$$Pb^{2+}(aq) + 2X^-(aq) = PbX_2(s) \qquad (X = F, Cl, Br or I)$$

They are colourless compounds, with the exception of lead(II) iodide, which is yellow. Lead(II) halides are appreciably soluble in hot water and in concentrated solutions of the hydrohalic acids. For example, lead(II) chloride dissolves in hydrochloric acid to form the tetrachloro-plumbate(II) complex:

$$PbCl_2 + 2Cl^- \rightleftharpoons [PbCl_4]^{2-}$$

Lead(II) halides are ionic, but their structures become increasingly covalent from the fluoride to the iodide (§12.6). They do not function as oxidants or reductants.

Lead(IV) halides

Bromine and iodine are unable to oxidise lead(II) to lead(IV). Therefore the only lead(IV) halides to exist are the essentially ionic fluoride and the covalent chloride. Lead(IV) chloride is prepared by passing chlorine through a solution of lead(II) chloride in concentrated hydrochloric acid at 0 °C (273 K). Oxidation to lead(IV) chloride occurs and the hexachloroplumbate(IV) ion is formed:

$$PbCl_2 + Cl_2 = PbCl_4$$
$$PbCl_4 + 2Cl^- = [PbCl_6]^{2-}$$

The addition of ammonium chloride precipitates the ammonium salt of this ion, $(NH_4)_2[PbCl_6]$, which can be filtered off and treated with concentrated sulphuric acid to liberate lead(IV) chloride as a yellow oil:

$$(NH_4)_2[PbCl_6] + H_2SO_4 = PbCl_4 + 2HCl + (NH_4)_2SO_4$$

Lead(IV) chloride is reversibly hydrolysed by water (cf. $SnCl_4$), and decomposes into lead(II) chloride and chlorine on warming.

Sulphides

White germanium(IV) sulphide, GeS_2, and yellow tin(IV) sulphide, SnS_2, are prepared by heating the respective elements with an excess of sulphur. In addition, tin(IV) sulphide is precipitated from solutions containing tin(IV) species by means of hydrogen sulphide.

Black germanium(II) sulphide, GeS, is formed by heating germanium(IV) sulphide with germanium. Tin(II) sulphide, SnS, which is brown, and lead(II) sulphide, PbS, which is black and the only sulphide of lead, are precipitated from solutions of tin(II) or lead(II) compounds respectively by hydrogen sulphide.

Hydrides

Germanium forms a series of hydrides, known as 'germanes', with the general formula Ge_nH_{2n+2}. Germanes containing up to nine germanium atoms are known. They are surprisingly stable to hydrolysis, even with 30 per cent alkali, but react rapidly with oxygen, e.g.

$$GeH_4 + 2O_2 = GeO_2 + 2H_2O$$

The only hydride of tin is stannane, SnH_4, which is prepared by reducing tin(IV) chloride with lithium tetrahydridoaluminate(III):

$$SnCl_4 + Li[AlH_4] = SnH_4 + LiCl + AlCl_3$$

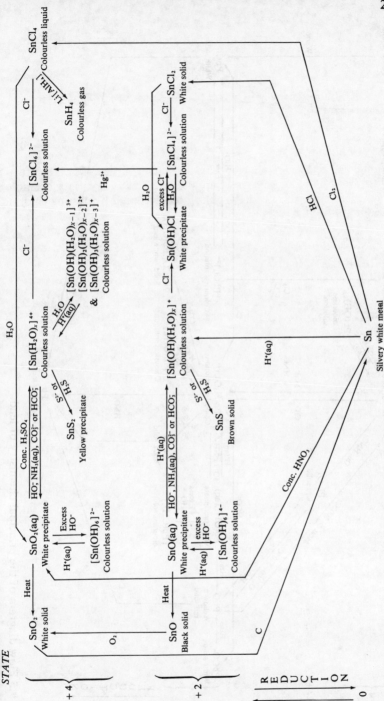

Fig. 9.4 Flow diagram of the principal chemistry of tin.

203

204

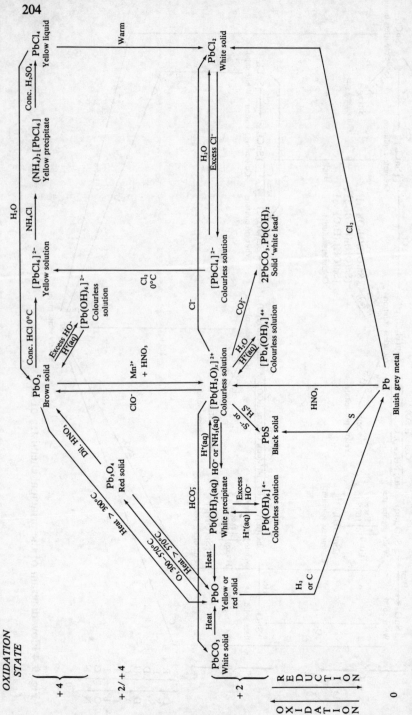

Fig. 9.5 Flow diagram of the principal chemistry of lead.

It is thermally unstable but resistant to hydrolysis.

The very unstable plumbane, PbH_4, is formed in small quantities when a magnesium−lead alloy is dissolved in an acid.

Other common compounds of lead

The only common water-soluble lead(II) salts are the nitrate, $Pb(NO_3)_2$, and the ethanoate, $(CH_3COO)_2Pb \cdot 3H_2O$. In solution, the hydrated lead(II) ion undergoes hydrolysis to give polymeric cations such as $[Pb_4(OH)_4]^{4+}$. Covalent lead(IV) ethanoate, $(CH_3COO)_4Pb$, is used in organic chemistry to oxidise 1,2-diols to aldehydes or ketones.

Tetraethyllead, $(C_2H_5)_4Pb$, which is used in huge quantities as an antiknock agent in petrol, is manufactured by reacting a sodium−lead alloy with chloroethane at 87−100 °C (360−373 K):

$$4NaPb + 4C_2H_5Cl = (C_2H_5)_4Pb + 3Pb + 4NaCl$$

Summary The principal compounds of tin and lead and their inter-relationships are shown in Fig. 9.4 and Fig. 9.5.

Chapter 10

Group 5B

This group comprises the elements nitrogen, phosphorus, arsenic, antimony and bismuth. There are many fundamental differences between nitrogen and the other members of the group, mostly arising from the inability of nitrogen to utilise d orbitals in bonding. Some important properties of the elements are shown in Table 10.1.

10.1 Occurrence and isolation of the elements

Nitrogen

Industrially, nitrogen is obtained by the fractional distillation of liquefied air. In the laboratory, pure nitrogen is prepared by *carefully* heating a solution containing ammonium and nitrite ions:

$$NH_4^+ + NO_2^- = N_2 + 2H_2O$$

Phosphorus

Phosphorus is extracted from various phosphate-containing minerals, the most important of which are apatite, $3Ca_3(PO_4)_2 \cdot CaF_2$, and hydroxyapatite, $3Ca_3(PO_4)_2 \cdot Ca(OH)_2$. When heated to 1 500 °C (1 773 K) with silica and coke in an electric furnace, the following reactions occur:

$$2Ca_3(PO_4)_2 + 6SiO_2 = 6CaSiO_3 + P_4O_{10}$$
$$P_4O_{10} + 10C = 10CO + P_4$$

Table 10.1 Some properties of the elements of group 5B.

	Nitrogen	Phosphorus	Arsenic	Antimony	Bismuth
character	non-metal	non-metal	semi-metal	semi-metal	metal
allotropes	—	white, red, black	non-metallic and metallic	non-metallic and metallic	—
atomic number	7	15	33	51	83
relative atomic mass	14.006 7	30.973 8	74.921 6	121.75	208.980 6
outer electronic configuration	$2s^2 2p^3$	$3s^2 3p^3$	$4s^2 4p^3$	$5s^2 5p^3$	$6s^2 6p^3$
valencies	3	3, 5	3, 5	3, 5	3, 5†
melting temperature/°C	−210	44.2 (white) 590 (red)	—	630	271
boiling temperature/°C	−196	280 (white)	613‡ (sublimes)	1 380	1 560

† Denotes a relatively unstable state.
‡ Data for non-metallic form.

White phosphorus (§10.2) is obtained by condensing the vapours that distil from the furnace.

Arsenic, antimony and bismuth

These elements are obtained by reduction of their oxides with hydrogen or carbon, e.g.

$$Bi_2O_3 + 3H_2 = 2Bi + 3H_2O$$

10.2 The structure of the elements

Nitrogen

At room temperature nitrogen is an unreactive colourless gas consisting of diatomic molecules, N≡N (§4.2). Its low reactivity is due partly to the lack of polarity in the N_2 molecule, and partly to the high bond dissociation enthalpy of the N≡N bond:

$$N_2(g) = 2N(g) \qquad \Delta H^\ominus = +944 \text{ kJ mol}^{-1}$$

It is therefore difficult for charged species to attack the molecule, and difficult to break the N≡N bond. Other molecules containing triple bonds, e.g. alkynes and carbon monoxide, are far more reactive than nitrogen because their bonds are polar and weaker than the N≡N bond.

Phosphorus

Unlike nitrogen, phosphorus is unable to form multiple bonds between its atoms; cf. silicon and carbon. Hence phosphorus cannot form P_2 molecules analogous to N_2. Like carbon, phosphorus exhibits monotropy. The allotropes are usually named according to their colour; namely white phosphorus (sometimes 'yellow phosphorus'), red phosphorus, and black phosphorus. The two principal allotropes are the white and red forms (Table 10.2).

Table 10.2 Some properties of white and red phosphorus.

	White	Red
appearance and colour	yellowy white waxy solid	red-violet powder
density/g cm^{-3}	1.82	2.34
melting temperature	44.2 °C (317.4 K)	590 °C (863 K) (under pressure)
solubility in CS$_2$	soluble	insoluble
ignition temperature in air	~ 35 °C (308 K)	~ 260 °C (533 K)
electrical conductivity	none	none

White phosphorus (P(white))

This is the least stable and by far the most reactive allotrope. It is usually stored under water to protect it from atmospheric oxidation. Because of a complex oxidation process, it emits a faint green light (*phosphorescence*) in air at room temperature.

White phosphorus consists of P_4 molecules in which each phosphorus atom uses its 3p orbitals to form three single bonds (Fig. 10.1(a)). On this basis a bond angle of 90° would be expected, but the

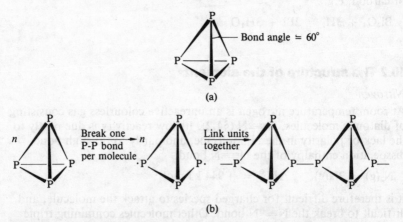

Fig. 10.1 (a) The P_4 molecule of white phosphorus. The phosphorus atoms lie at the corners of a tetrahedron. (b) The suggested structure of red phosphorus and its formation from white phosphorus. Cross-linking also occurs between the chains.

value of 60° in the molecule means that considerable strain is present in the P—P bonds. For this reason the P—P bonds are easily broken, a fact which explains the high reactivity of white phosphorus. The low melting temperature of white phosphorus and its solubility in carbon disulphide are accounted for by the relatively weak van der Waals' forces which exist between the P_4 molecules.

Molecules of P_4 are also present in the liquid and vapour phases of phosphorus.

Red phosphorus (P(red))

Red phosphorus is more stable and far less reactive than the metastable white allotrope. Nevertheless, at room temperature, the change from white to red phosphorus is very slow, taking several years to reach completion. The interconversion of the two forms is detailed below.

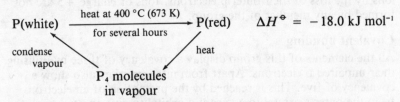

Red phosphorus is polymeric (Fig. 10.1(b)), which accounts for its insolubility, low volatility and in part for its low reactivity. The relief of strain as a P—P bond in a P_4 molecule is broken to form a polymer chain unit also contributes to the low reactivity of red phosphorus.

Black phosphorus

This is the most stable and least reactive allotrope of phosphorus. It is prepared by heating white phosphorus at 350 °C (623 K) for eight days in the presence of a copper or mercury catalyst.

Black phosphorus closely resembles graphite. It forms black flaky crystals with a layer structure, and it conducts electricity.

Arsenic, antimony and bismuth

Bismuth exists in a metallic form only, but both arsenic and antimony exhibit allotropy and exist in stable metallic and unstable non-metallic forms. The latter consist of tetrahedral As_4 and Sb_4 molecules respectively; cf. P_4.

10.3 Bonding and valency

Each element of this group has five outer electrons (i.e. $ns^2\ np^3$) and can enter into ionic or covalent bonding. Electrovalency involves either the loss or gain of three electrons per atom, but various covalencies are possible.

Ionic bonding

Nitrogen forms the nitride ion, N^{3-}, e.g.

$$6Li + N_2 = 2(Li^+)_3 N^{3-}$$

The nitride ion is an exceedingly strong base and is rapidly hydrolysed by water:

$$N^{3-} + 3H_2O = NH_3 + 3HO^-$$

The other elements of the group form anions with increasing difficulty as the non-metallic character decreases. For example, Ca_3P_2 and Mg_3P_2 contain the phosphide ion, P^{3-}, and the arsenide ion, As^{3-}, is believed to exist in Mg_3As_2, but antimony and bismuth do not form the simple anions Sb^{3-} and Bi^{3-}.

Antimony and bismuth are sufficiently metallic to form tripositive ions by the loss of their outer p electrons. Ions of charge $+5$ are not formed by any member of the group.

Covalent bonding

All the elements of this group display a covalency of three by utilising their unpaired p electrons. Apart from nitrogen, they also show a covalency of five. This is reached by the promotion of an electron from the outer s orbital to a vacant d orbital to give an atom with five unpaired electrons with which to form five covalent bonds, i.e.

$$ns^2\ np^3 \xrightarrow{\text{energy}} ns^1\ np^3\ nd^1$$

Because nitrogen has no 2d orbitals it cannot exhibit a covalency of five.

All possible oxidation states from -3 (e.g. NH_3, Li_3N, Ca_3P_2) to $+5$ (e.g. HNO_3, H_3PO_4) are known for nitrogen and phosphorus, but it must be stressed that an oxidation state of $+5$ for nitrogen does not imply that it has a covalency of five. In their compounds, the other elements of the group exist in $+3$ and $+5$ oxidation states only.

Nitrogen and, to a limited extent, phosphorus and arsenic reach a covalency or coordination number of four by donation of the outer lone pair of s electrons. In this way are formed the ammonium ion, NH_4^+, and the phosphonium ion, PH_4^+ (§10.5).

Except for nitrogen, which has no available d orbitals, the elements of the group can accept an electron pair from a donor and thus achieve a covalency or coordination number of six, e.g.

hexafluorophosphate(V) ion

Other examples include $[AsF_6]^-$, $[SbCl_6]^-$ and $[Sb(OH)_6]^-$.

10.4 Reactions of the group 5B elements

The principal reactions of nitrogen and phosphorus, the most important members of this group, are summarised in Table 10.3.

Table 10.3 The products of some reactions of nitrogen and phosphorus.

Reagent	Nitrogen	White phosphorus	Red phosphorus
hydrogen	NH_3	no reaction	no reaction
oxygen	a small amount of NO is formed reversibly at 3 000 °C (3 273 K)	ignites at approximately 35 °C (308 K) to form P_4O_6 and P_4O_{10}	ignites at approximately 260 °C (533 K) to form P_4O_6 and P_4O_{10}
halogens	no reaction	PX_3 and PX_5	PX_3 and PX_5 (reactions are less vigorous than with P (white))
sulphur	no reaction	complex mixture of sulphides	complex mixture of sulphides
heated metals	ionic nitrides or interstitial nitrides	phosphides	phosphides
alkalis, e.g. NaOH, KOH	no reaction	$PH_3 + PH_2O_2^-$	no reaction
oxidising acids, e.g. HNO_3	no reaction	H_3PO_4	H_3PO_4

Some reactions of arsenic, antimony and bismuth are presented in Table 10.4.

Table 10.4 The products of some reactions of arsenic, antimony and bismuth.

Reagent	Arsenic	Antimony	Bismuth
concentrated H_2SO_4	$As_4O_6(aq)$	$Sb_2(SO_4)_3$	$Bi_2(SO_4)_3$
dilute HNO_3	$As_4O_6(aq)$	Sb_4O_6	$Bi(NO_3)_3$
concentrated HNO_3	H_3AsO_4	Sb_2O_5	$Bi(NO_3)_3$
alkalis	AsO_3^{3-}	SbO_3^{3-}	no reaction
oxygen when heated	As_4O_6	Sb_4O_6	Bi_2O_3

10.5 Compounds of nitrogen and phosphorus

Hydrogen compounds of nitrogen

Ammonia

Preparation of ammonia

Ammonia is manufactured in the *Haber process* by the direct combination of nitrogen and hydrogen:

$$\tfrac{1}{2}N_2(g) + \tfrac{3}{2}H_2(g) \rightleftharpoons NH_3(g) \qquad \Delta H^{\ominus} = -46.2 \text{ kJ mol}^{-1}$$

The formation of ammonia is favoured by high pressures and low temperatures. However, at low temperatures equilibrium is established very slowly, even in the presence of a catalyst, and elevated temperatures are necessary to secure a reasonable rate of reaction. Typical pressures for the synthesis of ammonia are 100–1 000 atm (10^4–10^5 kPa), with a temperature of approximately 550 °C (823 K) and a catalyst of finely divided iron containing, as a promoter, a small amount of aluminium oxide. (A 'promoter' increases the efficiency of a catalyst, but is not itself a catalyst.)

In the laboratory, ammonia is usually prepared by heating an ammonium salt with an alkali:

$$NH_4^+ + HO^- = NH_3 + H_2O$$

Water is removed by passing the ammonia over calcium oxide. Other drying agents, e.g. concentrated sulphuric acid or calcium chloride, cannot be used because they react with ammonia.

Ammonia can also be obtained by the hydrolysis of ionic nitrides, e.g. Mg_3N_2 or Li_3N.

Properties of ammonia

Ammonia is a colourless gas with a characteristic odour. Because of hydrogen bonding its boiling temperature, -33.4 °C (239.8 K), is higher than expected (§4.9). The molecule is pyramidal (§4.6). On the nitrogen atom there is a lone pair of electrons which can be donated to other species. For this reason ammonia is a Lewis base, a property which dominates its chemistry.

Aqueous solutions of ammonia

Ammonia is extremely soluble in water, e.g. 1 volume of water dissolves approximately 1 300 volumes of ammonia at 0 °C (273 K) and a pressure of 1 atm (100 kPa). A saturated solution, which contains about 35 per cent of ammonia, is often referred to as '880 ammonia' because it has a density of 0.880 g cm^{-3}. The high solubility results from the ability of ammonia to hydrogen bond with water, i.e.

$$NH_3(g) + H_2O(l) \rightleftharpoons$$

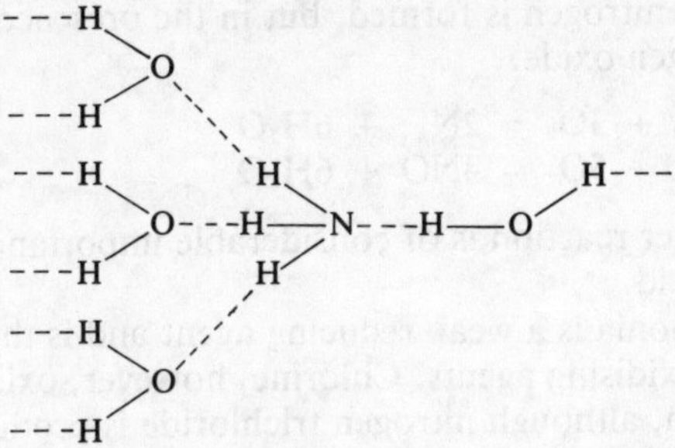

Most of the ammonia is present in solution in this hydrated form, i.e. $NH_3(aq)$, and two unstable hydrates, $NH_3 \cdot H_2O$ and $2NH_3 \cdot H_2O$, can be isolated by crystallising concentrated solutions at a low temperature. However, a small proportion of the dissolved ammonia ionises:

$$NH_3(aq) + H_2O \rightleftharpoons NH_4^+(aq) + HO^-(aq) \qquad pK_b = 4.75$$

A 1 M solution of ammonia is only 0.004 2 M in NH_4^+ and HO^- ions. In view of the very limited extent of this ionisation it is best to refer to solutions of ammonia as *aqueous ammonia* or *ammonia solution* rather than 'ammonium hydroxide'. Because of the relatively low concentration of hydroxide ions, aqueous ammonia is regarded, on the Arrhenius theory, as a weak base.

Basic properties of ammonia

The ammonia molecule has a high affinity for protons and is thus regarded, on the Brønsted−Lowry theory, as a strong base. The ammonium ion, NH_4^+, is formed whenever ammonia reacts with aqueous solutions of acids or with covalent compounds containing acidic hydrogen atoms, e.g. hydrogen chloride:

$$NH_3(g) + H^+(aq) = NH_4^+(aq)$$
$$NH_3(g) + HCl(g) = NH_4^+ Cl^-(s)$$

The basic character of ammonia towards water is fairly limited because water is a weak acid.

The addition of aqueous ammonia to a solution of a metal salt generally produces a precipitate of the metal hydroxide, but this does not always happen for the following reasons:

(i)   the hydroxide may be reasonably soluble;
(ii) the hydroxide ion concentration may not be high enough to exceed the solubility product of the metal hydroxide;
(iii) with excess ammonia the metal ion may form a soluble ammine complex, since ammonia is a Lewis base.

Oxidation of ammonia

At high temperatures ammonia reacts with oxygen. In the absence of a catalyst nitrogen is formed, but in the presence of platinum the product is nitrogen oxide.

$$4NH_3 + 3O_2 = 2N_2 + 6H_2O$$
$$4NH_3 + 5O_2 = 4NO + 6H_2O$$

The latter reaction is of considerable importance in the manufacture of nitric acid.

Ammonia is a weak reducing agent and is therefore stable towards many oxidising agents. Chlorine, however, oxidises ammonia to nitrogen, although nitrogen trichloride is produced if an excess of chlorine is used.

$$2NH_3 + 3Cl_2 = N_2 + 6HCl$$
$$2NH_3 + 6Cl_2 = 2NCl_3 + 6HCl$$

Similarly, the hypochlorite ion oxidises ammonia to nitrogen:

$$2NH_3 + 3ClO^- = N_2 + 3Cl^- + 3H_2O$$

Ammonia also reduces some heated metal oxides to the metal, e.g.

$$2NH_3 + 3CuO = 3Cu + N_2 + 3H_2O$$

Liquid ammonia

Liquid ammonia, which is prepared by compressing the gas, closely resembles water in being an excellent ionising solvent and in undergoing self-ionisation:

$$2NH_3 \rightleftharpoons NH_4^+ + NH_2^- \qquad pK \approx 30 \text{ at } -50 \,°C \,(223 \text{ K})$$
$$2H_2O \rightleftharpoons H_3O^+ + HO^- \qquad pK = 15.74 \text{ at } 25 \,°C \,(298 \text{ K})$$

A system of acids and bases exists in liquid ammonia analogous to that in water. For example, in liquid ammonia acids furnish the ammonium ion, NH_4^+ (cf. H_3O^+), and bases the amide ion, NH_2^- (cf. HO^-). Thus, a neutralisation reaction occurs between ammonium chloride (an acid) and sodium amide (a base):

$$NH_4^+ Cl^- + Na^+ NH_2^- = Na^+ Cl^- + 2NH_3$$

i.e.

$$NH_4^+ + NH_2^- = 2NH_3$$

cf.

$$H_3O^+ + HO^- = 2H_2O$$

Liquid ammonia dissolves the alkali metals and, to a lesser extent, calcium, strontium and barium to produce deep blue solutions which are excellent reducing agents. Evaporation of the ammonia from freshly prepared solutions results in the recovery of the alkali metal or, for the group 2A metals, metal ammines such as $Ca(NH_3)_6$. On standing, the blue solutions slowly become colourless as metal amides are formed, e.g.

$$2Na + 2NH_3 = 2NaNH_2 + H_2$$
$$Ca + 2NH_3 = Ca(NH_2)_2 + H_2$$

Transition metal ions, e.g. Fe^{3+} or Cu^{2+}, catalyse the formation of amides. Metal amides contain the strongly basic amide ion, which readily removes a proton from a water molecule:

$$NH_2^- + H_2O = NH_3 + HO^-$$

The deep blue solutions are excellent electrical conductors and reducing agents, for they contain *solvated electrons*, i.e. free electrons associated with molecules of solvent, e.g.

$$Na = Na^+ + e^-$$
$$e^- + nNH_3 \text{ (l)} = e^-(NH_3)_n$$

Ammonium salts

Ammonia combines with protic acids to form ionic ammonium salts which contain the tetrahedral ammonium ion, NH_4^+. In structure and solubility ammonium salts closely resemble the corresponding compounds of potassium and rubidium. This is due to similarities in ionic radii: NH_4^+ 0.143 nm, K^+ 0.133 nm and Rb^+ 0.148 nm. Like the salts of potassium and rubidium, ammonium salts are generally soluble in water but form anhydrous crystals.

All ammonium salts are thermally unstable. The decomposition products depend on the nature of the anion in the salt.

(i) With anions derived from non-oxidising acids, ammonia and the acid or its decomposition products are obtained, e.g.

$$NH_4Cl \rightleftharpoons NH_3 + HCl$$
$$(NH_4)_2CO_3 \rightleftharpoons 2NH_3 + H_2O + CO_2$$

(ii) Anions derived from oxidising acids oxidise the ammonium ion to nitrogen or one of its oxides, e.g.

$$NH_4NO_2 = N_2 + 2H_2O$$
$$NH_4NO_3 = N_2O + 2H_2O$$
$$(NH_4)_2Cr_2O_7 = N_2 + Cr_2O_3 + 4H_2O$$

The decomposition of ammonium nitrate and ammonium nitrite may occur explosively and should be undertaken with great care.

When ammonium salts are treated with alkalis ammonia is liberated:

$$NH_4^+ + HO^- = NH_3 + H_2O$$

Ammonium salts can be analysed by boiling with alkali and dissolving the expelled ammonia in a known excess of a standard solution of an acid. The amount of acid which is not neutralised is then determined by titration with a standard solution of an alkali.

$$1 \text{ mol } H^+(aq) \equiv 1 \text{ mol } NH_3 \equiv 17 \text{ g } NH_3$$

Hydrazine and hydroxylamine

Hydrazine, NH_2NH_2 or N_2H_4, and hydroxylamine, NH_2OH, are derived from ammonia by the replacement of a hydrogen atom by an NH_2 group or an HO group respectively. They are bases, and therefore form salts with acids. Hydrazine possesses a lone pair of electrons on each nitrogen atom and forms salts containing the hydrazinium(1 +) ion, $N_2H_5^+$, and the hydrazinium(2 +) ion, $N_2H_6^{2+}$. Hydroxylamine forms the hydroxylammonium ion, written as $HONH_3^+$. Both hydrazine and hydroxylamine ionise in water to form weakly alkaline solutions:

$$N_2H_4 + H_2O \rightleftharpoons N_2H_5^+ + HO^- \qquad pK_b = 6.07$$
$$NH_2OH + H_2O \rightleftharpoons HONH_3^+ + HO^- \qquad pK_b = 8.18$$

(cf. $pK_b = 4.75$ for ammonia)

Hydroxylamine is amphoteric, and gives the hydroxylamide ion, $NHOH^-$, on treatment with alkali, e.g.

$$NH_2OH + Na^+ HO^- = Na^+ NHOH^- + H_2O$$

Hydrazine and hydroxylamine can function as oxidants or reductants. For example, they are reduced to the ammonium ion by titanium(III) ions or zinc in acidic solution, and are oxidised to nitrogen by means of bromine or chlorine:

$$N_2H_5^+ + 3H^+(aq) + Zn = 2NH_4^+ + Zn^{2+}$$
$$HONH_3^+ + 2H^+(aq) + Zn = NH_4^+ + Zn^{2+} + H_2O$$
$$N_2H_4 + 2Br_2 = N_2 + 4Br^- + 4H^+(aq)$$
$$2NH_2OH + Br_2 = N_2 + 2Br^- + 2H^+(aq) + 2H_2O$$

Hydrazine and hydroxylamine both undergo addition–elimination reactions with carbonyl compounds, principally aldehydes and ketones.

Hydrogen azide

Hydrogen azide, HN_3, is a weak acid which forms salts containing the azide ion, N_3^-. Both the molecule and the ion possess a linear chain of nitrogen atoms. The azides of heavy metals, e.g. PbN_3, decompose explosively when subjected to mechanical shock and are used in the manufacture of detonators.

Phosphine

Phosphorus forms two hydrides, namely phosphine, PH_3, and diphosphane, P_2H_4. Only the former is considered here.

Phosphine is prepared by warming white phosphorus with a concentrated solution of an alkali metal hydroxide:

$$P_4 + 3HO^- + 3H_2O = PH_3 + 3PH_2O_2^-$$

phosphinate ion

The reaction is an example of disproportionation (§5.1). Pure phosphine is stable in air at room temperature, but when prepared by this method it immediately ignites due to the presence of spontaneously flammable impurities, notably diphosphane and phosphorus vapour. The impurities can be condensed by passing the impure phosphine gas through a freezing mixture. Phosphine is also formed by the hydrolysis of ionic phosphides, or by reducing phosphorus trichloride with an ethereal solution of lithium tetrahydridoaluminate(III):

$$Ca_3P_2 + 6H_2O = 2PH_3 + 3Ca(OH)_2$$
$$4PCl_3 + 3Li[AlH_4] = 4PH_3 + 3LiCl + 3AlCl_3$$

The phosphine molecule is pyramidal, with a bond angle of 93°. Hydrogen bonding does not occur with phosphine (§4.9), and as a result its boiling temperature, -87.4 °C (185.8 K), and solubility in water are much lower than those of ammonia. Solutions of phosphine are unstable and slowly decompose into phosphorus and hydrogen.

Phosphine is a much weaker base than ammonia, because phosphorus and hydrogen have the same electronegativity (Pauling value = 2.1). Consequently, there is no accumulation of negative charge on the phosphorus atom, and the tetrahedral phosphonium ion, PH_4^+, is far less stable than the ammonium ion. This is shown by the fact that phosphonium iodide, one of the most stable phosphonium salts, dissociates above 60 °C (333 K):

$$PH_4I \rightleftharpoons PH_3 + HI$$

Water is a stronger base than phosphine and therefore readily decomposes the phosphonium ion:

$$PH_4^+ + H_2O = PH_3 + H_3O^+$$

Phosphine forms unstable complexes with a number of transition metal ions. The bonding in these complexes involves donation of electrons from the phosphorus atom to the metal ion, and back donation from the metal ion to vacant 3d orbitals on the phosphorus atom. Alkyl and aryl substituted phosphines, e.g. $(CH_3)_3P$ and $(C_6H_5)_3P$, form more stable complexes than phosphine itself.

Phosphine is a stronger reducing agent than ammonia because the P—H bond is readily oxidised to P—OH. For example, phosphine ignites readily in air at 150 °C (423 K):

$$PH_3 + 2O_2 = H_3PO_4$$

Liquid phosphine displays none of the properties of liquid ammonia.

Halides of nitrogen

The trihalides of nitrogen are prepared by oxidising ammonia with an excess of the appropriate halogen:

$$NH_3 + 3X_2 = NX_3 + 3HX \qquad (X = F, Cl, Br \text{ or } I)$$

Nitrogen trifluoride is a stable gas at room temperature and does not react with water or alkalis. The trichloride is an unstable, highly reactive yellow liquid, which is rapidly hydrolysed by water to ammonia and hypochlorous acid:

$$NCl_3 + 3H_2O = NH_3 + 3HClO$$

The reaction is stepwise and involves the formation of a coordinate N—H bond in which the nitrogen atom is the donor:

This is followed by:

$$NHCl_2 + H_2O = NH_2Cl + HClO$$
$$\text{and } NH_2Cl + H_2O = NH_3 + HClO$$

This hydrolysis contrasts with that of most other non-metal halides (e.g. BCl_3, §8.5) where the central atom, unlike nitrogen, acts as an electron *acceptor* towards a water molecule.

Nitrogen tribromide and nitrogen triiodide are known only as addition compounds with ammonia, i.e. $NBr_3 \cdot 6NH_3$ and $NI_3 \cdot xNH_3$. They are coloured solids, purple and black respectively, which are readily hydrolysed by water.

Nitrogen forms another fluoride, dinitrogen difluoride, N_2F_2, which exhibits geometrical isomerism:

represents a lone pair of electrons

cis isomer   *trans* isomer

Halides of phosphorus

Halides of phosphorus are known in both the trivalent and pentavalent states.

Phosphorus trihalides (phosphorus(III) halides)

Phosphorus trihalides are obtained when the halogens are allowed to react with an excess of phosphorus in the absence of oxygen and water. For example, when a slow stream of chlorine is passed over white phosphorus, the chlorine burns in the phosphorus vapour and phosphorus trichloride distils over. The tribromide and triiodide are prepared by slowly adding bromine or iodine to red phosphorus.

Phosphorus trihalides have a pyramidal structure (§4.6) and, with the exception of the fluoride, are vigorously hydrolysed to phosphonic acid by cold water, e.g.

$$PCl_3 + 3H_2O = H_2PHO_3 + 3HCl$$

The reaction is believed to involve the coordination of a water molecule, using a vacant 3d orbital on the phosphorus atom, followed by the elimination of hydrogen chloride; cf. the hydrolysis of BCl_3 (§8.5) and $SiCl_4$ (§9.6).

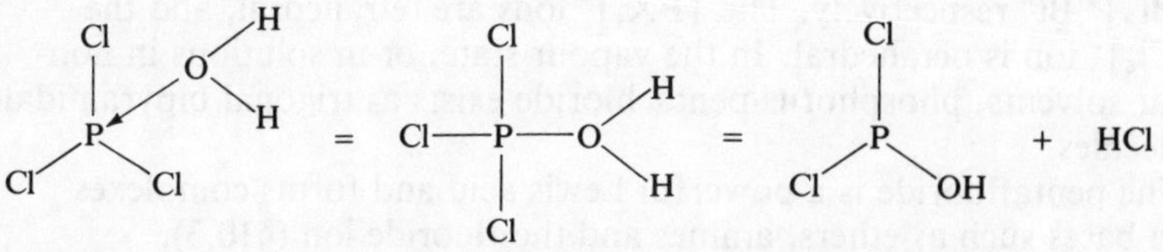

(written as HPOCl₂)

This reaction is followed by two further steps to give H_3PO_3, i.e. $P(OH)_3$, which immediately rearranges into phosphonic acid, H_2PHO_3:

$$HPOCl_2 + H_2O = H_2PO_2Cl + HCl$$
$$H_2PO_2Cl + H_2O = H_2PHO_3 + HCl$$

Similar reactions occur with other molecules which contain hydroxyl groups, e.g. alcohols and carboxylic acids.

Phosphorus trichloride is readily oxidised by oxygen or chlorine:

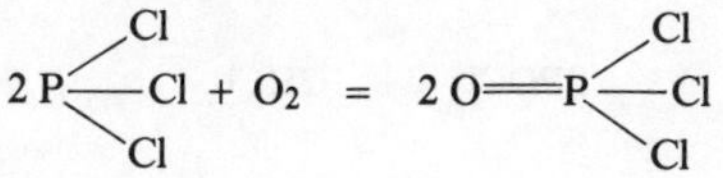

phosphoryl chloride

$$PCl_3 + Cl_2 \rightleftharpoons PCl_5$$

Phosphorus trifluoride forms complexes with transition metals, e.g. $[Ni(PF_3)_4]$. The bonding between the metal atom and the phosphorus atom is similar to that in complexes of phosphine (see above) and carbon monoxide (§9.6).

Phosphorus pentahalides (phosphorus(V) halides)

Phosphorus pentaiodide, PI_5, is unknown. This is probably because of the difficulty of accommodating five large iodine atoms around the smaller phosphorus atom. The chloride is prepared by reacting phosphorus trichloride with an excess of chlorine:

$$PCl_3(g) + Cl_2(g) \rightleftharpoons PCl_5(g) \qquad \Delta H^{\ominus} = -93 \text{ kJ mol}^{-1}$$

The reaction is reversible, and the formation of the pentachloride is favoured by an excess of chlorine and a low temperature. Similar principles apply to the formation of the pentabromide, but, because of the difficulty of handling fluorine, the fluoride is prepared by the reaction between phosphorus pentachloride and calcium fluoride at $300-400 \,^{\circ}\text{C}$ (573-673 K):

$$2PCl_5 + 5CaF_2 = 2PF_5 + 5CaCl_2$$

At room temperature phosphorus pentafluoride is a gas which consists of trigonal bipyramidal molecules (§4.6), while the chloride and bromide are colourless ionic solids of constitution $[PCl_4]^+ [PCl_6]^-$ and $[PBr_4]^+ Br^-$ respectively. The $[PX_4]^+$ ions are tetrahedral, and the $[PCl_6]^-$ ion is octahedral. In the vapour state, or in solutions in nonpolar solvents, phosphorus pentachloride exists as trigonal bipyramidal molecules.

The pentafluoride is a powerful Lewis acid and forms complexes with bases such as ethers, amines and the fluoride ion (§10.3). Phosphorus pentachloride and pentabromide dissociate on heating to form the corresponding trihalide and halogen, but phosphorus pentafluoride is thermally stable.

Phosphorus pentachloride reacts with water, producing first phosphoryl chloride and then orthophosphoric acid:

$$PCl_5 + H_2O = POCl_3 + 2HCl$$
$$POCl_3 + 3H_2O = H_3PO_4 + 3HCl$$

Phosphorus pentachloride is useful for replacing the hydroxyl groups of molecules by chlorine atoms, e.g.

sulphuric acid   sulphuryl chloride

Oxides of nitrogen

Oxides of nitrogen are known in all oxidation states from $+1$ to $+5$ (Table 10.5). They become increasingly acidic as the oxidation number of the nitrogen atom increases. Thus, N_2O and NO are very weakly acidic, but N_2O_5 is strongly acidic. They are all endothermic compounds, due principally to the high bond dissociation enthalpy of the nitrogen molecule.

Dinitrogen oxide

Dinitrogen oxide, a colourless gas, is made by heating ammonium nitrate, but care must be taken as the reaction may be explosive:

Table 10.5 The oxides of nitrogen.

Oxidation number of nitrogen	Formula	Name	$\Delta H_f^{\ominus}$/kJ mol^{-1}
+1	N_2O	dinitrogen oxide	+81.6
+2	NO	nitrogen oxide	+90.4
+3	N_2O_3	dinitrogen trioxide	+92.9
+4	NO_2	nitrogen dioxide	+33.9
+4	N_2O_4	dinitrogen tetraoxide	+9.7
+5	N_2O_5	dinitrogen pentaoxide	+15†

† Data for formation of the gaseous compound.

$$NH_4NO_3 = N_2O + 2H_2O$$

An alternative and safer preparation involves the reaction between hydroxylamine and nitrite ions in acidic solution:

$$NH_2OH + H^+(aq) + NO_2^- = N_2O + 2H_2O$$

Dinitrogen oxide is collected over warm water since it is appreciably soluble in the cold.

The molecule is linear, and involves delocalised π bonding, i.e.

$$N\!\!=\!\!=\!\!=\!\!N\!\!-\!\!-\!\!-\!\!O$$

Dinitrogen oxide is unreactive to most reagents at room temperature. On heating, however, it decomposes into its elements:

$$2N_2O = 2N_2 + O_2$$

Hot substances may cause this decomposition and burn in the oxygen so produced. For example, a glowing splint (hot carbon) re-lights in dinitrogen oxide, just as it does in oxygen, and heated phosphorus burns easily in the gas.

$$C + 2N_2O = CO_2 + 2N_2$$
$$P_4 + 10N_2O = P_4O_{10} + 10N_2$$

Dinitrogen oxide can be distinguished from oxygen by the facts that no reaction occurs with nitrogen oxide, and that an equal volume of nitrogen is produced on passing the gas over heated copper:

$$Cu + N_2O = CuO + N_2$$

Nitrogen oxide

Impure nitrogen oxide gas is formed by reacting copper with concentrated nitric acid which has been diluted with an equal volume of water:

$$3Cu + 8HNO_3 = 3Cu(NO_3)_2 + 2NO + 4H_2O$$

The pure gas is prepared by the reduction in acidic solution of either nitrate ions by iron(II) ions, or nitrite ions by iodide ions:

$$3Fe^{2+} + NO_3^- + 4H^+(aq) = 3Fe^{3+} + NO + 2H_2O$$
$$2I^- + 2NO_2^- + 4H^+(aq) = I_2 + 2NO + 2H_2O$$

Commercially, nitrogen oxide is an intermediate in the production of nitric acid by the oxidation of ammonia.

The nitrogen oxide molecule is often described as 'odd' because it possesses an odd number of electrons. One electron is therefore un-paired and the compound is paramagnetic (§14.1). Like the nitrogen molecule, which has 14 electrons and a triple bond between its atoms, the nitrogen oxide molecule has 15 electrons and, in essence, a triple bond between the nitrogen and oxygen atoms. The extra or odd elec-tron occupies a high energy antibonding orbital and is easily removed to yield the nitrosyl cation, NO^+, which is diamagnetic and isoelec-tronic with the nitrogen molecule. Salts containing the nitrosyl cation are known; e.g. nitrosyl tetrafluoroborate(III), $NOBF_4$, and nitrosyl perchlorate, $NOClO_4$. At low temperatures nitrogen oxide dimerises to the diamagnetic $(NO)_2$.

Nitrogen oxide acts as a ligand by donating the lone pair of electrons on the nitrogen atom, and forms complexes such as the $[Fe(NO)(H_2O)_5]^{2+}$ ion (produced in the brown ring test) and the so-called 'nitroprusside' ion, $[Fe(CN)_5(NO)]^{2-}$.

Nitrogen oxide is readily oxidised. For example, nitrogen dioxide is rapidly formed with oxygen, and in the presence of a charcoal catalyst the halogens, except for iodine, yield nitrosyl halides:

$$2NO + O_2 = 2NO_2$$
$$2NO + X_2 = 2NOX \qquad (X = F, Cl \text{ or } Br)$$

The reaction with the permanganate ion in acidic solution is quan-titative and can be used to estimate the gas in a mixture:

$$3MnO_4^- + 5NO + 4H^+(aq) = 3Mn^{2+} + 5NO_3^- + 2H_2O$$

Above 1 000 °C (1 273 K) nitrogen oxide decomposes into its elements. Thus burning magnesium, which is intensely hot, forms its oxide and nitride when plunged into nitrogen oxide:

$$2NO = N_2 + O_2$$
$$5Mg + N_2 + O_2 = Mg_3N_2 + 2MgO$$

Dinitrogen trioxide

This highly unstable compound is obtained as a blue liquid when equimolar quantities of nitrogen oxide and dinitrogen tetraoxide react together at −20 °C (253 K):

$$2NO + N_2O_4 \rightleftharpoons 2N_2O_3$$

At higher temperatures extensive dissociation occurs; for example, at room temperature, only about 10 per cent of the trioxide exists in the equilibrium mixture.

Reaction with water or alkali yields respectively nitrous acid, HNO_2, or the nitrite ion, NO_2^-; thus dinitrogen trioxide is the anhydride of nitrous acid.

$$N_2O_3 + H_2O = 2HNO_2$$
$$N_2O_3 + 2HO^- = 2NO_2^- + H_2O$$

Nitrogen dioxide and dinitrogen tetraoxide

Nitrogen dioxide is prepared in the laboratory by heating a nitrate. The lead salt is commonly used because it is anhydrous:

$$2Pb(NO_3)_2 = 2PbO + 4NO_2 + O_2$$

Nitrogen dioxide and oxygen are separated by passing the gases through a cooled U-tube. Nitrogen dioxide dimerises to dinitrogen tetraoxide (see below) and condenses to a yellow liquid. Alternatively, nitrogen dioxide can be obtained by the reduction of concentrated nitric acid by many metals, e.g.

$$Cu + 4HNO_3 = Cu(NO_3)_2 + 2NO_2 + 2H_2O$$

Nitrogen dioxide is a toxic brown gas with an unpleasant smell. The molecule is angular, with delocalised π bonding. It is paramagnetic and possesses one unpaired electron which is localised mainly on the nitrogen atom.

O=N=O   bond angle = 134°

Dinitrogen tetraoxide, when pure, is a colourless liquid and has a boiling temperature of 21 °C (294 K). It is diamagnetic and therefore possesses no unpaired electrons. The molecule contains a weak N—N bond which is formed by the pairing of odd electrons on two nitrogen dioxide molecules, i.e.

The dioxide and tetraoxide exist in a temperature-dependent equilibrium:

$$N_2O_4 \rightleftharpoons 2NO_2 \qquad \Delta H^{\ominus} = +58.1 \text{ kJ mol}^{-1}$$

Low temperatures favour the tetraoxide, and high temperatures, in excess of 250 °C (523 K), cause nitrogen dioxide to dissociate into nitrogen oxide and oxygen. These changes are summarised thus:

$$N_2O_4 \rightleftharpoons 2NO_2 \rightleftharpoons 2NO + O_2$$

dissociation begins at
$-11 \, °C$ (262 K) and is
complete at 240 °C (513 K)

dissociation begins at
250 °C (523 K) and is
complete at 600 °C (873 K)

Liquid dinitrogen tetraoxide has been extensively studied as a non-aqueous solvent. It ionises to a very small extent and is therefore a weak conductor of electricity:

$$N_2O_4(l) \rightleftharpoons NO^+ + NO_3^-$$

Nitrogen dioxide is very reactive. It is a mixed anhydride and dissolves in water at 0 °C (273 K) to form a mixture of nitric and nitrous acids:

$$2NO_2 + H_2O = HNO_3 + HNO_2$$

oxidation number of N $\quad +4 \qquad\qquad +5 \qquad +3$

At room temperature nitrous acid disproportionates rapidly, and the overall reaction is:

$$3NO_2 + H_2O = 2HNO_3 + NO$$

In the presence of air nitrogen oxide is oxidised to nitrogen dioxide, which reacts with further water to give nitric acid as the ultimate product.

With alkalis, nitrogen dioxide forms a mixture of nitrite ions and nitrate ions:

$$2NO_2 + 2HO^- = NO_2^- + NO_3^- + H_2O$$

Nitrogen dioxide is a powerful oxidising agent, and heated elements such as magnesium, iron, copper, carbon, phosphorus and sulphur burn in the gas to produce their oxides and nitrogen. Most other reducing agents convert it to nitrogen oxide, e.g.

$$NO_2 + H_2S = NO + S + H_2O$$
$$NO_2 + SO_2 + H_2O = NO + H_2SO_4$$

Powerful oxidants, such as the permanganate ion in acidic solution, oxidise nitrogen dioxide to the nitrate ion:

$$MnO_4^- + 5NO_2 + H_2O = Mn^{2+} + 5NO_3^- + 2H^+(aq)$$

Dinitrogen pentaoxide

This compound is obtained as a white crystalline solid by dehydrating nitric acid with phosphorus(V) oxide at low temperatures:

$$4HNO_3 + P_4O_{10} = 2N_2O_5 + 4HPO_3$$

In the crystalline state it is ionic, i.e. $NO_2^+ NO_3^-$, but N_2O_5 molecules exist in the vapour phase. Above 0 °C (273 K) it decomposes:

$$2N_2O_5 = 2N_2O_4 + O_2$$

Dinitrogen pentaoxide is the anhydride of nitric acid:

$$N_2O_5 + H_2O = 2HNO_3$$

Oxides of phosphorus

Phosphorus(III) oxide

Phosphorus(III) oxide is a white solid, prepared by heating white phosphorus in a slow stream of air:

$$P_4 + 3O_2 = P_4O_6$$

Phosphorus(V) oxide, which is produced at the same time, is condensed to a solid by passing the emergent gases through a U-tube at about 150 °C (423 K). Phosphorus(III) oxide passes on and is collected in an ice-cooled receiver.

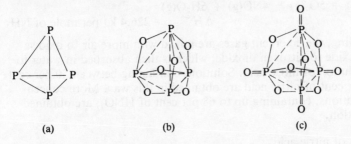

(a)   (b)   (c)

Fig. 10.2 The structural relationship between molecules of (a) P_4, (b) P_4O_6, and (c) P_4O_{10}. (Dotted lines in (b) and (c) outline the P_4 tetrahedra and do not represent bonds.)

Phosphorus(III) oxide exists as P_4O_6 molecules in the vapour phase and in solution in organic solvents (Fig. 10.2(b)). It dissolves in cold water to form phosphonic acid:

$$P_4O_6 + 6H_2O = 4H_2PHO_3$$

It is readily oxidised and is thus a reducing agent, e.g.

$$P_4O_6 + 2O_2 = P_4O_{10}$$
$$P_4O_6 + 6Cl_2 = 4POCl_3 + O_2$$

Phosphorus(V) oxide

This is the product of heating phosphorus in excess air or oxygen:

$$P_4 + 5O_2 = P_4O_{10}$$

It is a white powder. P_4O_{10} molecules (Fig. 10.2(c)) exist in the vapour phase and in one of numerous crystalline forms.

Phosphorus(V) oxide has a strong affinity for water, with which it reacts to form metaphosphoric acid, HPO_3, and orthophosphoric acid, H_3PO_4. Consequently it is used as a desiccating agent, but when exposed to the air its drying capacity is rapidly lost because a glassy layer of acids forms on the particles. Phosphorus(V) oxide is also used as a dehydrating agent.

Oxoacids of nitrogen and their salts

Nitric acid

Pure nitric acid is obtained by heating sodium nitrate or potassium nitrate with concentrated sulphuric acid:

$$NaNO_3 + H_2SO_4 = NaHSO_4 + HNO_3$$

The acid is manufactured by passing a mixture of ammonia and dry dust-free air over a platinum or platinum–rhodium catalyst at 900 °C (1 173 K). The reaction which occurs is sufficiently exothermic to maintain the catalyst at the working temperature.

$$4NH_3(g) + 5O_2(g) = 4NO(g) + 6H_2O(g)$$
$$\Delta H^{\ominus} = -226.4 \text{ kJ per mole of } NH_3$$

After cooling, the emergent gases are mixed with more air to oxidise nitrogen oxide to nitrogen dioxide, which is then absorbed in water to form a solution of nitric acid. Solutions containing between 50 per cent and 65 per cent of nitric acid are obtained in this way. More concentrated solutions, containing up to 68 per cent of HNO_3, are obtained by distillation.

Properties of nitric acid

Pure, anhydrous nitric acid is a colourless liquid of density 1.50 g cm⁻³. Above its freezing temperature, −42 °C (231 K), it dissociates into dinitrogen pentaoxide and water:

$$2HNO_3 \rightleftharpoons N_2O_5 + H_2O$$

In the presence of light, or at its boiling temperature of 83 °C (356 K), it decomposes into nitrogen dioxide and oxygen:

$$4HNO_3 = 4NO_2 + O_2 + 2H_2O$$

Nitric acid is composed of planar molecules which are linked together by hydrogen bonds:

− − − represents a hydrogen bond

----- represents a delocalised π bond

Pure nitric acid does not display any acidic properties; for example, it does not decompose carbonates, but it is a weak conductor of electricity because of self-ionisation:

$$2HNO_3 \rightleftharpoons NO_2^+ + NO_3^- + H_2O$$

Salts containing the nitryl cation are known; e.g. $NO_2^+ ClO_4^-$ and NO_2^+ NO_3^-. The nitryl cation is also formed when pure nitric acid or concentrated nitric acid is mixed with concentrated sulphuric acid, as in the nitration of benzene.

In the laboratory nitric acid is usually encountered as an aqueous solution. Concentrated nitric acid (density = 1.42 g cm^{-3}) is a constant boiling mixture (122 °C (395 K)) containing about 68 per cent of the pure acid. In dilute solution nitric acid is approximately 93 per cent ionised; therefore it is a strong acid, which possesses the usual acid properties:

$$HNO_3 + H_2O \rightleftharpoons H_3O^+ + NO_3^-$$

Aqueous nitric acid is an oxidant, a property which is derived from the nitrate ion. The possible reduction products of the nitrate ion and the relevant ionic half-equations are as follows:

(a) $\quad NO_3^- + 2H^+(aq) + \quad e^- = H_2O + NO_2$

(b) $\quad NO_3^- + 4H^+(aq) + 3e^- = 2H_2O + NO$

(c) $\quad 2NO_3^- + 10H^+(aq) + 8e^- = 5H_2O + N_2O$

(d) $\quad NO_3^- + 8H^+(aq) + 6e^- = 2H_2O + HONH_3^+$

$\qquad\qquad\qquad\qquad$ (i.e. $NH_2OH + H^+$)

(e) $\quad NO_3^- + 10H^+(aq) + 8e^- = 3H_2O + NH_4^+$

Generally, with concentrated nitric acid and weak reductants, reaction (a) predominates, but with the dilute acid and strong reductants other products are possible, as shown below.

Non-metals Often nitrogen oxide is produced, together with an oxoacid of the non-metal, e.g.

$$S + 2HNO_3 = H_2SO_4 + 2NO$$
$$4P + 10HNO_3 + H_2O = 4H_3PO_4 + 5NO + 5NO_2$$

Metals In their reactions with nitric acid, metals can be divided roughly into six categories.

(i) Calcium and magnesium are the only metals capable of liberating hydrogen from very dilute (1 per cent) nitric acid.

(ii) Metals close to, or below, hydrogen in the electrochemical series, e.g. Pb, Cu and Ag, are weak reductants and generally liberate nitrogen dioxide from concentrated nitric acid, or nitrogen oxide from the dilute acid.

(iii) Powerful reducing agents, e.g. Mg or Zn, reduce dilute nitric acid to dinitrogen oxide, the hydroxylammonium ion or the ammonium ion, depending on reaction conditions, such as temperature and acid concentration. Not surprisingly, a mixture of these products is often obtained.

(iv) Weak metals, e.g. Sn, Sb and As, reduce concentrated nitric acid to nitrogen dioxide and form their hydrated oxides (§9.7).

(v) Iron, chromium and aluminium are rendered *passive*, i.e. unreactive, by concentrated nitric acid. The passivity is due to a thin film of oxide on the surface of the metal, and until this is removed either by scraping or by means of a reducing agent the metal will not dissolve in any acid.

(vi) Noble metals, e.g. Au and Pt, are not attacked.

Cations　Iron(II) ions are oxidised to iron(III) ions (see NO). Tin(II) compounds are oxidised to tin(IV) compounds, and reduce nitric acid to the hydroxylammonium ion and the ammonium ion.

Anions　Sulphide ions and iodide ions are weak reductants and reduce the acid to nitrogen dioxide:

$$S^{2-} + 2NO_3^- + 4H^+(aq) = S + 2NO_2 + 2H_2O$$
$$2I^- + 2NO_3^- + 4H^+(aq) = I_2 + 2NO_2 + 2H_2O$$

Aqua regia

A 3 : 1 mixture of concentrated hydrochloric and nitric acids, known as 'aqua regia', dissolves many noble metals to form chloro-complexes such as $[AuCl_4]^-$ and $[PtCl_6]^{2-}$.

Ionic nitrates

All metal nitrates are soluble in water and are prepared by dissolving metals, oxides, hydroxides or carbonates in nitric acid. With the exception of those of the alkali metals, lead and ammonium, they are all hydrated. They contain the planar nitrate ion, which involves delocalised π bonding, i.e.

$$\left[\begin{array}{c} O \\ \| \\ N \\ O^- \quad O \end{array} \right]^- \quad 120°$$

Although the *hydrated* nitrates of some metals are ionic, e.g. $Cu(NO_3)_2 \cdot 3H_2O$, the *anhydrous* compounds are covalent, e.g. $Cu(NO_3)_2$. Covalent nitrates cannot be prepared by dehydration of the hydrated salts.

In contrast to its behaviour in acidic solution, the nitrate ion in neutral or alkaline solution is only a weak oxidising agent. Under these conditions, Devarda's alloy (Al 45 per cent, Cu 50 per cent, Zn 5 per cent) quantitatively reduces the nitrate ion to ammonia, and is used for estimating nitrates in the absence of ammonium salts:

$$NO_3^- + 6H_2O + 8e^- = NH_3 + 9HO^-$$

Nitrates are thermally unstable and decompose on heating in one of three ways.

(i) Nitrites are formed from the nitrates of group 1A metals except lithium, e.g.

$$2NaNO_3 = 2NaNO_2 + O_2$$

(ii) Oxides, oxygen and nitrogen dioxide are produced from the nitrates of other metals, including lithium. Some metal oxides are thermally unstable, e.g. Ag_2O and HgO, and in such cases the metal is produced:

$$2AgNO_3 = 2Ag + 2NO_2 + O_2$$

(iii) Dinitrogen oxide is formed by heating ammonium nitrate.

Nitrous acid

Nitrous acid is a weak acid ($pK_a = 3.34$). It is unstable and readily disproportionates at room temperature:

$$3HNO_2 = HNO_3 + 2NO + H_2O$$

oxidation number of N   +3   +5   +2

A pale blue solution containing the acid is obtained by adding dilute hydrochloric acid to a cold solution of a nitrite, or by dissolving dinitrogen trioxide in water.

Salts of nitrous acid contain the nitrite ion, NO_2^-, and are more stable than the acid itself. The common nitrites, i.e. $NaNO_2$ and KNO_2, are prepared by heating the corresponding nitrates either alone or with a reducing agent such as lead, or by dissolving an equimolar mixture of nitrogen oxide and nitrogen dioxide in a solution of the appropriate hydroxide:

$$NaNO_3 + Pb = NaNO_2 + PbO$$
$$NO + NO_2 + 2HO^- = 2NO_2^- + H_2O$$

In acidic solution the nitrite ion is a powerful oxidant, and oxidises iodide ions to iodine, hydrogen sulphide to sulphur, and ammonia to nitrogen. The reduction products of the nitrite ion include nitrogen oxide, dinitrogen oxide and the ammonium ion. Powerful oxidising agents, such as the permanganate ion or chlorine, oxidise the nitrite ion to the nitrate ion.

Test to distinguish between nitrites and nitrates The addition of ethanoic acid to a nitrite produces nitrous acid, which decomposes to give brown fumes of nitrogen dioxide in air:

$$CH_3COOH + NaNO_2 = CH_3COONa + HNO_2$$
$$3HNO_2 + O_2 = HNO_3 + 2NO_2 + H_2O$$

Nitrates do not react with ethanoic acid.

Oxoacids of phosphorus and their salts

Table 10.6 The common oxoacids of phosphorus.

Oxidation number of phosphorus	Formula	Name
+1	HPH_2O_2	phosphinic acid
+3	H_2PHO_3	phosphonic acid
+5	$(HPO_3)_n$	metaphosphoric acid
+5	$H_4P_2O_7$	diphosphoric acid
+5	H_3PO_4	orthophosphoric acid

Except for metaphosphoric acid, the structures of the common oxo-acids (Table 10.6) are shown below. In each molecule the phosphorus atom is surrounded by other atoms or groups to give a distorted tetrahedron.

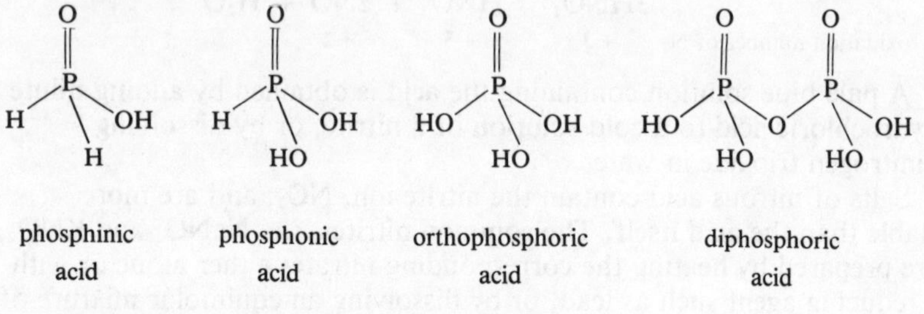

phosphinic acid   phosphonic acid   orthophosphoric acid   diphosphoric acid

The hydrogen atoms of HO groups are ionisable, but those linked directly to phosphorus are not. The former may be referred to as *acidic hydrogen atoms* and the latter as *reducing hydrogen atoms*, since the P——H bond may undergo oxidation to P——OH.

In addition to salts of the acids shown in Table 10.6, salts of other oxoacids are known but not, in many cases, the parent acids.

Phosphinic acid

The phosphinic acid molecule contains one HO group and is therefore monoprotic. The acid and its salts are powerful but often slow reductants, and reduce, for example, the sulphate ion to hydrogen sulphide.

Phosphonic acid

This compound is prepared by adding phosphorus trichloride to water at 0 °C (273 K):

$$PCl_3 + 3H_2O = H_2PHO_3 + 3HCl$$

Because it contains two HO groups, phosphonic acid is diprotic and forms two series of salts, one containing the $HPHO_3^-$ ion and the other the PHO_3^{2-} ion. The acid is a powerful reducing agent, capable of reducing copper(II) ions to copper. It is unstable, and disproportionates when heated above 200 °C (473 K):

$$2H_2PHO_3 = PH_3 + H_3PO_4 + O_2$$

Phosphonic acid forms esters in which one or both of the acidic hydrogen atoms are replaced by alkyl or aryl groups. Triesters of formula $P(OR)_3$ are also known, which contain three P——O bonds and no P——H bond. In this respect the triesters are related to phosphorus trihalides.

Orthophosphoric acid (phosphoric acid)

This is the commonest acid of phosphorus, and is prepared by oxidising red phosphorus with nitric acid or by adding phosphorus(V) oxide to hot water. Orthophosphoric acid is a weak triprotic acid:

$$H_3PO_4 + H_2O \rightleftharpoons H_3O^+ + H_2PO_4^- \qquad pK_1 = 2.15$$
$$H_2PO_4^- + H_2O \rightleftharpoons H_3O^+ + HPO_4^{2-} \qquad pK_2 = 7.21$$
$$HPO_4^{2-} + H_2O \rightleftharpoons H_3O^+ + PO_4^{3-} \qquad pK_3 = 12.36$$

Phosphoric acid is usually sold as 'syrupy phosphoric acid', an 85 per cent aqueous solution which has the consistency of syrup resulting from extensive hydrogen bonding. The acid is rather unreactive and is difficult to reduce.

Salts containing the PO_4^{3-} and HPO_4^{2-} ions are insoluble, except for those of the alkali metals and ammonium, but those containing the $H_2PO_4^-$ ion tend to be more soluble. For example, $Ca_3(PO_4)_2$ and $CaHPO_4$ are insoluble, but $Ca(H_2PO_4)_2$ is soluble. Orthophosphates are alkaline in solution because of salt hydrolysis.

Condensed acids of phosphorus and their anions

Phosphorus forms a number of condensed (i.e. polymeric) acids and anions containing ring or chain structures based on a skeleton of alternating phosphorus and oxygen atoms. Diphosphoric acid, $H_4P_2O_7$, is prepared by the partial dehydration of orthophosphoric acid at 200–300 °C (473–573 K):

$$2H_3PO_4 = H_4P_2O_7 + H_2O$$

Although it is a tetraprotic acid, only two series of salts are readily obtained, namely those containing $H_2P_2O_7^{2-}$ and $P_2O_7^{4-}$ anions. These salts are prepared by heating orthophosphates:

$$2NaH_2PO_4 = Na_2H_2P_2O_7 + H_2O$$
$$2Na_2HPO_4 = Na_4P_2O_7 + H_2O$$

Prolonged heating of orthophosphoric acid produces a glassy solid, called metaphosphoric acid, which is a mixture of condensed acids of general formula $(HPO_3)_n$.

$$n H_3PO_4 \underset{\text{hot water}}{\overset{\text{heat}}{\rightleftharpoons}} (HPO_3)_n + n H_2O$$

The acids and anions are cyclic when n is equal to 3 or 4, but have chain structures at higher n values. Sodium cyclo-triphosphate, $Na_3(PO_3)_3$, is made by heating NaH_2PO_4 to red heat:

$$3NaH_2PO_4 = Na_3(PO_3)_3 + 3H_2O$$

It contains the following anion:

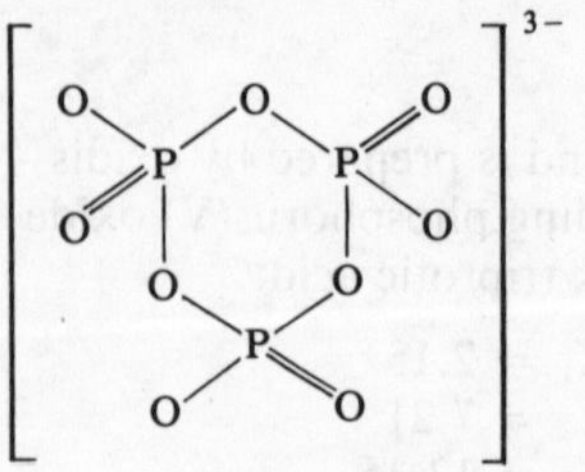

Condensed phosphates, such as metaphosphates, form soluble complexes with many metal ions and are used for water softening. One particular salt, 'sodium hexametaphosphate' or 'Calgon', is widely used in industry and domestic washing powders for this purpose.

10.6 Compounds of arsenic, antimony and bismuth

Hydrides

The known hydrides are as follows: arsine, AsH_3, stibine, SbH_3, bismuthine, BiH_3, and the very unstable diarsane, As_2H_4. Arsine and stibine are prepared by reducing the respective trichlorides with lithium tetrahydridoaluminate(III), or by reducing an arsenic or antimony compound with zinc and hydrochloric acid:

$$4AsCl_3 + 3Li[AlH_4] = 4AsH_3 + 3LiCl + 3AlCl_3$$
$$SbCl_3 + 3Zn + 3HCl = SbH_3 + 3ZnCl_2$$

Bismuthine is reportedly formed by dissolving a magnesium−bismuth alloy in a dilute acid.

The hydrides become decreasingly stable from arsine to bismuthine. Like ammonia, they are composed of pyramidal molecules, but show no tendency to form ions of the type NH_4^+.

Halides

Each element forms four trihalides, i.e. MX_3, where X = F, Cl, Br or I. They are prepared by direct combination of the elements with a deficiency of the halogen to minimise pentahalide formation.

Bismuth trifluoride is essentially ionic, but the other trihalides are covalent. Arsenic trihalides resemble those of phosphorus, except that the reaction with water is reversible, i.e.

$$4AsX_3 + 6H_2O \rightleftharpoons As_4O_6(aq) + 12HX$$

Antimony and bismuth trihalides, except for the fluorides, are also reversibly hydrolysed by water, to give white insoluble basic salts, e.g.

$$SbCl_3 + H_2O \rightleftharpoons SbClO + 2HCl$$
antimony chloride oxide

Bismuth trichloride similarly forms bismuth chloride oxide, BiClO.

Many of the trihalides act as Lewis acids towards halide ions, forming complexes such as $[AsCl_4]^-$, $[SbCl_5]^{2-}$ and $[BiCl_6]^{3-}$.

The known pentahalides, i.e. AsF_5, SbF_5, $SbCl_5$ and BiF_5, are prepared by reacting the elements or the trihalides with an excess of the appropriate halogen. The pentafluorides of arsenic and antimony are thermally stable, but the others dissociate into the trihalide and the halogen on heating. Antimony pentachloride is a powerful chlorinating agent (i.e. it readily introduces chlorine into other compounds) and bismuth pentafluoride is a fluorinating agent.

The pentahalides are vigorously hydrolysed by water, and those of arsenic and antimony form complexes such as $[AsF_6]^-$, $[SbCl_6]^-$ and $[SbF_6]^-$ by acting as Lewis acids.

Oxides

The trivalent oxides are prepared by direct combination of the elements (Table 10.4). Arsenic(III) oxide and antimony(III) oxide are similar in structure to phosphorus(III) oxide and are thus formulated as As_4O_6 and Sb_4O_6 respectively. Because bismuth(III) oxide contains no discrete molecules, it is represented by the stoicheiometric formula, Bi_2O_3.

Arsenic(III) oxide is predominantly acidic, and dissolves in alkalis to form the arsenite ion:

$$As_4O_6 + 12HO^- = 4AsO_3^{3-} + 6H_2O$$

Antimony(III) oxide is distinctly amphoteric, dissolving in alkalis to form the antimonite ion, SbO_3^{3-}, and in concentrated acids to give antimony salts, e.g. $Sb_2(SO_4)_3$. Bismuth(III) oxide, like the hydroxide, $Bi(OH)_3$, is basic.

The pentavalent oxides are represented by their stoicheiometric formulae, i.e. As_2O_5, Sb_2O_5 and Bi_2O_5, because their structures are unknown. Arsenic(V) oxide and antimony(V) oxide are prepared by oxidising the elements with concentrated nitric acid and dehydrating the products. Bismuth(V) oxide, which exists only in an impure state, is prepared by oxidising bismuth(III) oxide with peroxodisulphate ions, followed by acidification.

All these oxides are acidic. They readily decompose into the trivalent oxides and oxygen on heating.

Oxoacids and their salts

The species present in acidic aqueous solutions of arsenic(III) oxide appears to be the hydrated oxide, i.e. $As_4O_6(aq)$. Solutions of arsenic(III) oxide and arsenites, which contain the AsO_3^{3-} ion, are reductants and are readily oxidised to the arsenate ion, AsO_4^{3-}, by a variety of oxidants, such as permanganates, dichromates, halogens and iron(III) salts. Antimony(III) oxide, similarly, does not form an oxo-acid, but salts containing the antimonite ion, SbO_3^{3-}, are known. In contrast to arsenic, neither the oxide nor the anion displays reducing properties. Bismuth does not form oxoanions or an oxoacid in the trivalent state.

Arsenic acid, H_3AsO_4, is a weak triprotic acid. It is prepared by dissolving arsenic(V) oxide in water, or by oxidising arsenic with nitric acid (Table 10.4). Both the acid and its salts (arsenates) are oxidising agents. Aqueous solutions of antimony(V) oxide are acidic, but the nature of the species present is uncertain. The hexahydroxo-antimonate(V) ion, $[Sb(OH)_6]^-$, is formed by dissolving antimony(V) oxide in alkalis. Bismuthates containing pentavalent bismuth are known in the impure state. They are powerful oxidants, e.g. sodium bismuthate, $NaBiO_3$, oxidises manganese(II) ions to permanganate ions.

Chapter 11

Group 6B

Group 6B comprises the elements oxygen, sulphur, selenium, tellurium and polonium. Oxygen, the head element, differs from the other members of the group, mainly because of its inability to use d orbitals in bonding. Some important properties of the elements are given in Table 11.1.

Table 11.1 Some properties of the elements of group 6B.

	Oxygen	Sulphur	Selenium	Tellurium	Polonium
character	non-metal	non-metal	non-metal	non-metal	metal
allotropes	oxygen, ozone	α and β	α, β and metallic	—	—
atomic number	8	16	34	52	84
relative atomic mass	15.999 4	32.06	78.96	127.60	210†
outer electronic configuration	$2s^2 2p^4$	$3s^2 3p^4$	$4s^2 4p^4$	$5s^2 5p^4$	$6s^2 6p^4$
valencies	2	2, 4, 6	2, 4, 6	2, 4, 6	2, 4, 6(?)
melting temperature/°C	−218	113(α), 119(β)	217 (metallic)	450	254
boiling temperature/°C	−183	445	685	990	960

† Mass number of the most stable isotope.

236

11.1 Occurrence and isolation of the elements

Oxygen

Oxygen accounts for approximately 50 per cent of the earth's crust. The atmosphere and water contain 23 per cent and 89 per cent by mass of oxygen respectively, and most of the world's rocks contain combined oxygen.

In the laboratory, oxygen can be prepared by one of the following methods.

(i) The decomposition of hydrogen peroxide, either catalytically or by oxidation with the permanganate ion:

$$2H_2O_2 = 2H_2O + O_2 \quad \text{(MnO}_2 \text{ catalyst)}$$
$$2MnO_4^- + 5H_2O_2 + 6H^+(aq) = 2Mn^{2+} + 5O_2 + 8H_2O$$

(ii) The thermal decomposition of some oxoanions, usually in salts of the alkali metals, e.g.

$$2NO_3^- = 2NO_2^- + O_2$$
$$2ClO_3^- = 2Cl^- + 3O_2 \quad \text{(MnO}_2 \text{ catalyst)}$$

(iii) The thermal decomposition of certain metallic oxides, e.g.

$$2HgO = 2Hg + O_2$$
$$2BaO_2 = 2BaO + O_2$$

(iv) The electrolysis of solutions of acids or alkalis. Oxygen is liberated at the anode.

Industrially, oxygen is obtained by the fractional distillation of liquefied air.

Sulphur

Large quantities of sulphur are obtained from underground deposits of the element in the USA and other parts of the world. The sulphur is extracted by the *Frasch process*, which involves sinking three concentric tubes to the deposits. Superheated water is pumped down the outer tube to melt the sulphur, and when hot compressed air is injected down the central tube molten sulphur is forced up the remaining tube.

Sulphur is also produced in vast quantities from hydrogen sulphide by partial combustion or by reaction with sulphur dioxide:

$$2H_2S + O_2 = 2S + 2H_2O$$
$$2H_2S + SO_2 = 3S + 2H_2O$$

The hydrogen sulphide is obtained from natural hydrocarbon gases – some contain up to 30 per cent of H_2S – or from the sulphur compounds present in crude oil.

The numerous metallic sulphides and sulphates that occur in nature, e.g. ZnS, PbS, FeS_2 and $CaSO_4$, are not important as sources of elemental sulphur.

Selenium, tellurium and polonium

Many naturally occurring metal sulphide ores contain small quantities of selenides and tellurides. During the roasting process selenium dioxide and tellurium dioxide are obtained, which can be reduced to the free elements by aqueous sulphur dioxide:

$$MO_2 + 2SO_2 + 2H_2O = M + 2H_2SO_4 \qquad \text{(M = Se or Te)}$$

Traces of polonium occur in the ores of uranium and thorium as a result of radioactive decay. Gram quantities of polonium are now available by neutron bombardment of bismuth-209 in a nuclear reactor:

$$^{209}_{83}Bi + ^{1}_{0}n = ^{210}_{83}Bi + \gamma$$
$$^{210}_{83}Bi = ^{210}_{84}Po + ^{0}_{-1}e$$

11.2 The structure of the elements

Oxygen

Oxygen exhibits allotropy and exists in two forms, O_2 and O_3, with the systematic names of dioxygen and trioxygen respectively, and the trivial names (which will be used here) of oxygen and ozone. Although negligible amounts of ozone occur at sea level, it is formed from oxygen in the upper atmosphere by the action of ultraviolet light. In the laboratory it is prepared by passing an electrical discharge through oxygen. Sparking should be avoided as this generates heat and decomposes the ozone. At a potential of 20 000 V, about 10 per cent of oxygen is converted into ozone to give a mixture known as 'ozonised oxygen'. Pure ozone is obtained as a pale blue gas by the fractional distillation of liquefied ozonised oxygen.

The formation of ozone from oxygen is believed to involve partial atomisation of the latter into free atoms, which then combine with oxygen molecules:

$$O_2 \rightleftharpoons 2O; \qquad O_2 + O \rightleftharpoons O_3$$

The ozone molecule is bent and symmetrical, with delocalised π bonding between the oxygen atoms, i.e.

bond angle = 116.8°
bond length = 0.127 8 nm

Oxygen and ozone in the upper atmosphere form an equilibrium mixture. This provides an example of *dynamic allotropy*, which differs from enantiotropy (§9.2) in that equilibrium between two allotropes exists over a range of temperatures rather than at a definite transition temperature.

Under ordinary conditions ozonised oxygen is not an equilibrium mixture. Ozone is formed endothermically from oxygen ($\Delta H_f^{\ominus}[O_3]$ = + 142 kJ mol^{-1}) and thus decomposes exothermically and sometimes explosively to oxygen, particularly if heated. At room temperature the change is slow, except in the presence of catalysts such as finely divided metals or metal oxides.

Sulphur

Sulphur atoms, unlike oxygen atoms, are reluctant to form double bonds with other sulphur atoms. Instead, a sulphur atom forms two single covalent bonds, and many different solid and liquid allotropes exist with chain or ring structures containing S—S bonds. Sulphur thus displays catenation; cf. carbon.

Solid allotropes

Crystalline sulphur exhibits enantiotropy:

$$\alpha\text{-sulphur} \underset{\text{(rhombic sulphur)}}{\overset{95.6\,°C\ (368.8\ K)}{\rightleftharpoons}} \beta\text{-sulphur} \quad \text{(monoclinic sulphur)}$$

Below the transition temperature the α-form is stable. Above this temperature, and up to the melting temperature, the β-form is stable. Both α-sulphur and β-sulphur consist of cyclic S$_8$ molecules, but differ in the way that these molecules are packed together.

side view of S$_8$ molecule

Other forms of solid sulphur are known. *Colloidal sulphur* is made by carefully acidifying a solution of sodium thiosulphate (§11.5). *Flowers of sulphur*, which appears to be a mixture of α-sulphur and an amorphous form, is made by rapidly cooling sulphur vapour.

Liquid allotropes

Liquid sulphur exhibits dynamic allotropy. λ-Sulphur, obtained when the element is melted at 120 °C (393 K), consists of S$_8$ rings. At temperatures above 160 °C (433 K) the S$_8$ molecules break apart at one S—S bond to give a chain form (π-sulphur), which links together as the temperature rises further to give μ-sulphur. This is composed of long spiral chains containing as many as 100 000 sulphur atoms.

These changes account for the observation that, on heating, the viscosity of liquid sulphur at first increases and then decreases. The initial increase is due to the formation of chains which become entangled with one another; as the number of chains increases so does the viscosity.

At about 200 °C (473 K) a maximum is reached, beyond which thermal excitation overcomes the effect of entanglement.

When molten sulphur at 200 °C (473 K) is poured into cold water, *plastic sulphur* is formed. This is mainly μ-sulphur, with a proportion of α-sulphur which increases on standing.

Gaseous allotropes

The vapour above boiling sulphur ($\theta_{C,m} = 445$ °C; $T_m = 718$ K) contains S_8 molecules, but at higher temperatures dissociation occurs to give S_6, S_4 and S_2 molecules.

Selenium, tellurium and polonium

Selenium exists in α- and β-forms, which contain Se_8 molecules, and the more stable grey 'metallic' form. The metallic form is a poor conductor of electricity in the dark, but its conductivity increases on exposure to light. The effect is not permanent and is lost when the light is removed. For this reason selenium is used in photoelectric cells and light meters. Tellurium exists in one form only, which resembles grey selenium. Polonium is metallic.

11.3 Bonding and valency

The elements of this group each possess an outer $ns^2 np^4$ electronic configuration and may participate in ionic or covalent bonding.

Ionic bonding

The elements form dinegative ions by the gain of two electrons, i.e. O^{2-}, S^{2-}, Se^{2-} and Te^{2-}. Many metallic oxides are ionic and contain the oxide ion, O^{2-}, but the remaining elements form ions only in combination with the s-block elements. Consequently, most compounds of sulphur, selenium and tellurium are covalent.

Covalent bonding

By utilising their two unpaired p electrons, the elements can form either two single covalent bonds or one double bond, e.g.

There are several ways in which the elements of this group can achieve covalencies of greater than two.

(i) A covalently bound oxygen atom can form a coordinate bond by using one of its lone pairs of electrons, thus exhibiting a covalency or coordination number of three, e.g.

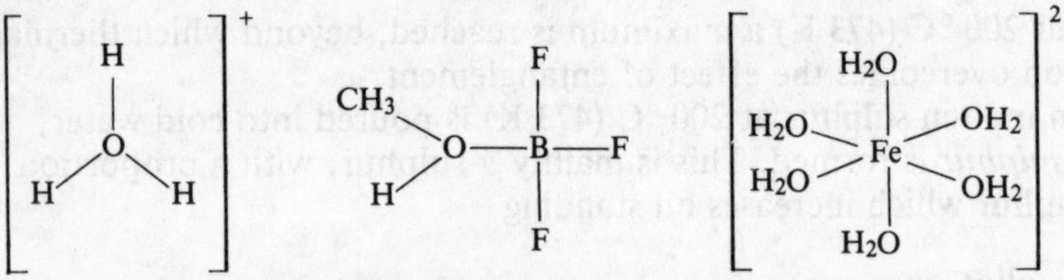

240

$$\left[\begin{array}{c} H \\ O \\ H \quad H \end{array} \right]^{+} \qquad \begin{array}{c} CH_3 \\ O-B-F \\ H \end{array} \quad F \quad F \qquad \left[\begin{array}{c} H_2O \\ H_2O \quad OH_2 \\ Fe \\ H_2O \quad OH_2 \\ H_2O \end{array} \right]^{2+}$$

Sulphur is a much weaker electron pair donor than oxygen and does not form the H_3S^+ ion. Some sulphur compounds, such as $(CH_3)_2S$ and C_2H_5SH, act as ligands through the sulphur atom and form complexes with transition elements. Selenium and tellurium are very weak electron pair donors, although some selenium compounds do function as ligands.

The donation of both electron pairs to give a coordination number of four is extremely rare, although it does occur in basic beryllium ethanoate, $Be_4O(CH_3COO)_6$.

(ii) Except for oxygen, the elements of group 6B possess vacant d orbitals in their outermost shells. By absorbing energy to promote electrons from s or p orbitals into the vacant d orbitals, these elements can participate in four and six covalent bonds as the following scheme for sulphur illustrates.

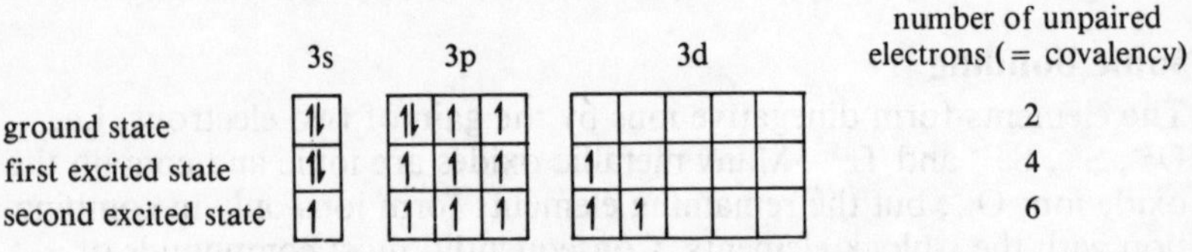

	3s	3p	3d	number of unpaired electrons (= covalency)
ground state	↑↓	↑↓ ↑ ↑		2
first excited state	↑↓	↑ ↑ ↑	↑	4
second excited state	↑	↑ ↑ ↑	↑ ↑	6

The four and six unpaired electrons of the excited states can then be used in covalent bond formation. Oxygen has no suitable d orbitals and a prohibitive amount of energy would be required for electron promotion into the third shell.

11.4 Reactions of the group 6B elements

Oxygen (dioxygen)

Oxygen combines with many metals and non-metals to form oxides. Most of the reactions take place on heating, and in some cases combustion occurs. With some elements, e.g. the majority of the s-block elements, combination with oxygen occurs readily at room temperature. When some of the less reactive metals, such as lead or iron, are finely powdered, they react exothermically with oxygen at room temperature, even though a lump of the metal is unaffected under the same conditions. These finely divided metals are said to be *pyrophoric*, and often sufficient heat is liberated during the reaction to set the powder on fire.

Acids and alkalis do not react with oxygen unless, like hydriodic acid (§12.6), they are capable of being oxidised. Many of the other reactions of oxygen are considered in other chapters of this book.

Ozone (trioxygen)

Ozone is far more reactive than oxygen and is a very powerful oxidant, especially in acidic solution. For example, it oxidises iron(II) ions, iodide ions and lead(II) sulphide:

$$2Fe^{2+} + O_3 + 2H^+(aq) = 2Fe^{3+} + O_2 + H_2O$$

oxidation number of oxygen $\qquad\qquad$ 0 $\qquad\qquad\qquad\qquad$ 0 $\quad$ -2

$$2I^- + O_3 + 2H^+(aq) = I_2 + O_2 + H_2O$$
$$PbS + 4O_3 = PbSO_4 + 4O_2$$

Alkenes react with ozone to give ozonides, although with oxygen the reaction products are epoxides.

The ozone content of ozonised oxygen can be found by titrating the iodine which is produced by the oxidation of iodide ions with a standard solution of sodium thiosulphate:

$$1 \text{ mol } O_3 \equiv 1 \text{ mol } I_2 \equiv 2 \text{ mol } Na_2S_2O_3$$

Sulphur

Most metals, particularly if heated, react with sulphur to form sulphides. With reactive metals, such as magnesium or aluminium, the reaction is exceptionally vigorous. The non-metals phosphorus, oxygen, carbon and the halogens except for iodine also combine directly with sulphur. For example, sulphur burns in air to form sulphur dioxide and a small amount of sulphur trioxide.

Oxidising acids, e.g. concentrated nitric acid or concentrated sulphuric acid, attack sulphur:

$$6HNO_3 + S = H_2SO_4 + 6NO_2 + 2H_2O$$
$$2H_2SO_4 + S = 3SO_2 + 2H_2O$$

Sulphur dissolves slowly in hot concentrated solutions of alkalis with disproportionation to produce the sulphide ion, S^{2-}, and the sulphite ion, SO_3^{2-}:

$$3S + 6HO^- = 2S^{2-} + SO_3^{2-} + 3H_2O$$

oxidation number of sulphur $\quad$ 0 $\qquad\qquad\qquad$ -2 $\quad$ $+4$

With an excess of sulphur, further reactions occur to give polysulphide ions, S_{n+1}^{2-}, and the thiosulphate ion, $S_2O_3^{2-}$:

$$S^{2-} + nS = S_{n+1}^{2-} \qquad (n \text{ has values of 1 to 8})$$
$$SO_3^{2-} + S = S_2O_3^{2-}$$

Selenium, tellurium and polonium

Some reactions of selenium and tellurium are summarised in Table 11.2.

Table 11.2 The products of some reactions of selenium and tellurium.

Reagent	Selenium	Tellurium
concentrated HNO_3 or concentrated H_2SO_4	'selenious acid'	TeO_2
halogens	selenium halides, e.g. SeF_6, $SeCl_2$, Se_2Br_2	tellurium halides, e.g. TeF_6, $TeCl_4$, TeI_4
alkalis	Se^{2-}, SeO_3^{2-} and Se_n^{2-} ions	Te^{2-}, TeO_3^{2-} and Te_n^{2-} ions
heated metals	metal selenides	metal tellurides
oxygen, when heated	SeO_2	TeO_2

Polonium is radioactive, with isotopes of fairly short half-lives, and is difficult to study because of the intense α-radiation which it emits. Most of the chemistry of polonium has been deduced from that of tellurium.

11.5 Compounds of oxygen and sulphur

Hydrogen compounds of oxygen

Water

The shape of the water molecule is discussed in §4.6 and the structure of ice is shown in Fig. 4.33.

Water is thermally very stable, and decomposition into oxygen and hydrogen becomes appreciable only above 1 000 °C (1 273 K). Pure water self-ionises to a very limited extent and is therefore only a weak conductor of electricity:

$$H_2O \rightleftharpoons H^+(aq) + HO^-$$

It is amphoteric, and acts as a Brønsted–Lowry acid or base by, respectively, donating or accepting protons.

(i) Water functions as an acid with species which are stronger bases, i.e. stronger proton acceptors, than itself, e.g.

$$NH_3 + H_2O \rightleftharpoons NH_4^+ + HO^-$$

(ii) Water acts as a base towards compounds which are stronger acids, i.e. stronger proton donors, e.g.

$$HCl + H_2O \rightleftharpoons H_3O^+ + Cl^-$$

The oxonium ion, H_3O^+, is further hydrated to form the hydrated hydrogen ion, $H^+(aq)$ (§6.3).

Thus, it is an excellent ionising solvent for molecules such as ammonia or hydrogen chloride.

Water possesses weak oxidising and weak reducing properties:

$$H_2O + e^- = \tfrac{1}{2}H_2 + HO^- \qquad E^\ominus = -0.83 \text{ V}$$
$$\tfrac{1}{2}O_2 + 2H^+(aq) + 2e^- = H_2O \qquad E^\ominus = +1.23 \text{ V}$$

Metals with standard electrode potentials which are more negative than -0.83 V can reduce water to hydrogen. In these reactions the metals are oxidised to their oxides or hydroxides. Only the more electropositive s-block elements reduce water at ordinary temperatures, but at higher temperatures metals such as magnesium, zinc or iron are able to reduce steam. Oxidising agents with standard electrode potentials more positive than $+1.23$ V can, in principle, oxidise water to oxygen, but in practice the reaction is often slow. Fluorine or the hexaaquacobalt(III) ion, however, rapidly oxidises water at room temperature (§§12.4 and 14.1).

Deuterium oxide

In ordinary water the ratio of protium to deuterium (Ch. 6) is approximately 6 000 : 1. When water is electrolysed, protium is discharged in preference to deuterium at the cathode. Consequently the final residue, after many hours of electrolysis, is rich in deuterium oxide, D_2O, and is commonly called 'heavy water'. Deuterium oxide differs from ordinary water in many of its physical properties, e.g. density = 1.103 g cm^{-3}, $\theta_{C,m} = 3.8\,°C$ ($T_m = 277.0$ K), $\theta_{C,b} = 101.4\,°C$ ($T_b = 374.6$ K), and temperature of maximum density = $11.2\,°C$ (284.4 K).

Except that it reacts more slowly, deuterium oxide has identical chemical properties to water. It is used to elucidate reaction mechanisms, and also as a moderator in nuclear reactors, since it slows down and reduces the energy of fast neutrons.

Hydrogen peroxide

An aqueous solution of hydrogen peroxide is prepared by slowly adding dilute sulphuric acid to barium peroxide, BaO_2, at $0\,°C$ (273 K):

$$BaO_2 + H_2SO_4 = BaSO_4 + H_2O_2$$

The insoluble barium sulphate is removed by filtration.

Hydrogen peroxide is manufactured by reducing an anthraquinone derivative to the corresponding anthraquinol by means of hydrogen in the presence of a palladium catalyst. The anthraquinol reacts with atmospheric oxygen to produce hydrogen peroxide and the original anthraquinone, which is then recycled:

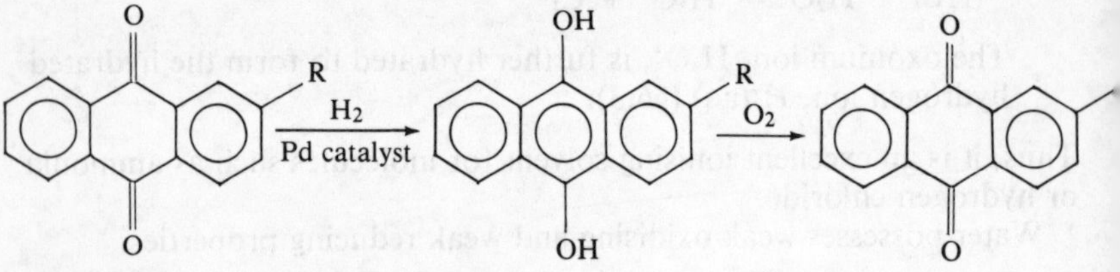

2-ethylanthraquinone (R = C_2H_5)   2-ethylanthraquinol   + H_2O_2
2-butylanthraquinone (R = C_4H_9)   2-butylanthraquinol

The anthraquinone in effect acts as a catalyst for the oxidation of hydrogen to hydrogen peroxide. A dilute solution of hydrogen peroxide is obtained by extracting the reaction mixture with water. Solutions are concentrated by fractional distillation.

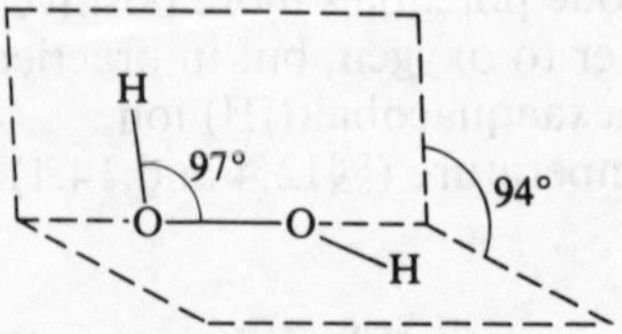

Fig. 11.1 The structure of the hydrogen peroxide molecule.

Pure hydrogen peroxide is a pale blue oily liquid, which resembles water in being extensively hydrogen bonded. The structure of the H_2O_2 molecule (Fig. 11.1) can be envisaged in terms of an open book. The O——O bond lies along the spine of the book, and the O——H bonds in the planes of the facing pages.

Hydrogen peroxide is thermodynamically unstable with respect to water and oxygen:

$$2H_2O_2 = 2H_2O + O_2 \qquad \Delta G^{\ominus} = -98 \text{ kJ mol}^{-1}$$

The decomposition is catalysed by many substances, e.g. metal ions, finely divided metals, manganese(IV) oxide, and the enzyme catalase. In the absence of such catalysts the rate of reaction is low. Some compounds, e.g. 1,2,3-propanetriol (glycerol), mineral acids and 8-hydroxy-quinoline, act as negative catalysts for the reaction and are used to stabilise hydrogen peroxide.

Hydrogen peroxide is normally encountered as aqueous solutions, which are weakly acidic because of ionisation:

$$H_2O_2 + H_2O \rightleftharpoons H_3O^+ + HO_2^- \qquad pK_a = 11.62$$
hydrogenperoxide ion

The concentration of a hydrogen peroxide solution is often expressed by the number of volumes of oxygen, at s.t.p., produced by the decomposition of one volume of the solution. For example, 1 cm³ of a '20 volume solution' (1.78 M) produces 20 cm³ of oxygen at s.t.p.

In acidic solution hydrogen peroxide functions as a weak reductant or a powerful oxidant. In the former case the oxidation product is always oxygen, e.g.

$$2MnO_4^- + 5H_2O_2 + 6H^+(aq) = 2Mn^{2+} + 5O_2 + 8H_2O$$
$$HClO + H_2O_2 = HCl + O_2 + H_2O$$

Solutions of hydrogen peroxide are often estimated by titration with a standard solution of potassium permanganate. From the equation,

$$2 \text{ mol } MnO_4^- \equiv 5 \text{ mol } H_2O_2$$

When hydrogen peroxide acts as an oxidant it is always reduced to water, e.g.

$$2I^- + H_2O_2 + 2H^+(aq) = I_2 + 2H_2O$$
$$2[Fe(H_2O)_6]^{2+} + H_2O_2 + 2H^+(aq) = 2[Fe(H_2O)_6]^{3+} + 2H_2O$$

If the six water molecules of the hexaaquairon(III) ion, $[Fe(H_2O)_6]^{3+}$, are replaced by six cyanide ions to give $[Fe(CN)_6]^{3-}$, then in alkaline solution hydrogen peroxide behaves as a *reductant* to the iron(III) complex:

$$2[Fe(CN)_6]^{3-} + H_2O_2 + 2HO^- = 2[Fe(CN)_6]^{4-} + O_2 + 2H_2O$$

hexacyanoferrate(III) ion   hexacyanoferrate(II) ion

Because hydrogen peroxide is acidic, it reacts with some bases at 0 °C (273 K) to form compounds containing the peroxide ion, O_2^{2-}, e.g.

$$Ba(OH)_2 + H_2O_2 + 6H_2O = BaO_2 \cdot 8H_2O$$
$$Na_2CO_3 + H_2O_2 = Na_2O_2 + CO_2 + H_2O$$

The most important ionic peroxides are those of the s-block elements (§7.5).

Related to hydrogen peroxide are a number of peroxoacids and their anions, which contain a covalently bonded peroxide group, —O—O—, e.g.

peroxodisulphate ion   perbenzoic acid

A blue unstable peroxide of chromium, CrO_5, is formed when hydrogen peroxide is added to a cold solution of a dichromate. This reaction is used as a test for either hydrogen peroxide or hexavalent chromium (§14.6).

Salts are known which contain hydrogen peroxide of crystallisation, instead of water of crystallisation, e.g. $Na_2CO_3 \cdot 3H_2O_2$.

Hydrogen compounds of sulphur

Hydrogen sulphide

Hydrogen sulphide is usually prepared in the laboratory by the action of dilute hydrochloric acid on iron(II) sulphide:

$$FeS + 2HCl = FeCl_2 + H_2S$$

The product so obtained is contaminated with hydrogen because iron(II) sulphide always contains a small amount of free iron. Pure hydrogen sulphide can be prepared by warming antimony(III) sulphide with concentrated hydrochloric acid, or by adding water to aluminium sulphide:

$$Sb_2S_3 + 6HCl = 2SbCl_3 + 3H_2S$$
$$Al_2S_3 + 6H_2O = 2Al(OH)_3(aq) + 3H_2S$$

Hydrogen sulphide is a colourless gas with an odour of bad eggs. It is very toxic, more so than hydrogen cyanide, but because of its strong odour it can be detected even in minute concentrations. However, hydrogen sulphide quickly kills the sense of smell and should therefore be used with extreme caution.

The hydrogen sulphide molecule has a bond angle of 93°. The electro-negativity of sulphur is not high enough to allow hydrogen bonding to occur, and as a result hydrogen sulphide shows none of the anomalous properties of water (§4.9). Because the S——H bond is weaker than the O——H bond, hydrogen sulphide is less stable than water. For example, it decomposes into sulphur and hydrogen at approximately 800 °C (1 073 K), and burns in an excess of air:

$$2H_2S + 3O_2 = 2H_2O + 2SO_2$$

It is moderately soluble in cold water to give a weakly acidic solution:

$$H_2S + H_2O \rightleftharpoons H_3O^+ + HS^- \qquad pK_1 = 7.05$$
$$HS^- + H_2O \rightleftharpoons H_3O^+ + S^{2-} \qquad pK_2 = 13.92$$

It is therefore a weak diprotic acid and forms two series of salts with alkalis, e.g.

$$H_2S + NaOH = H_2O + NaHS \qquad \text{sodium hydrogensulphide}$$
$$H_2S + 2NaOH = 2H_2O + Na_2S \qquad \text{sodium sulphide}$$

Because hydrogen sulphide is readily oxidised to sulphur by various oxidising agents, it is considered to be a good reductant, e.g.

$$X_2 + H_2S = 2HX + S \qquad \text{(X = Cl, Br or I)}$$
$$2MnO_4^- + 5H_2S + 6H^+(aq) = 2Mn^{2+} + 5S + 8H_2O$$
$$2Fe^{3+} + H_2S = 2Fe^{2+} + S + 2H^+(aq)$$

Even sulphur dioxide, which is usually regarded as a reducing agent, oxidises hydrogen sulphide, particularly in the presence of water:

$$SO_2 + 2H_2S = 3S + 2H_2O$$

Aqueous solutions of hydrogen sulphide are slowly oxidised in air:

$$2H_2S + O_2 = 2S + 2H_2O$$

Polysulphanes

When solutions of metallic sulphides are boiled with sulphur, polysulphides are obtained:

$$S^{2-} + xS = S_{(x+1)}^{2-}$$

Acidification of a solution of a metallic polysulphide gives a yellow oil which is a mixture of polysulphanes, H_2S_x, where $x = 2$ to 6, e.g.

$$Na_2S_x + 2HCl = 2NaCl + H_2S_x$$

Polysulphanes are thermodynamically unstable and decompose readily into hydrogen sulphide and sulphur:

$$H_2S_x = H_2S + (x-1)S$$

Oxides of metals

All metals form oxides, many of which are ionic. The formation of an isolated oxide ion, O^{2-}, is highly endothermic:

$$O(g) + 2e^- = O^{2-}(g) \qquad \Delta H^\ominus = +714 \text{ kJ mol}^{-1}$$

Despite this fact, many metals form stable oxides containing the oxide ion, e.g. Na_2O, CaO, Al_2O_3 and MnO_2. Ionic oxides invariably have a high lattice enthalpy, because of the strong electrostatic attraction between the small, doubly charged oxide ions and the often multiply charged metal ions. As a result:

(i) the lattice enthalpy (exothermic) is greater than the enthalpies of formation of the oxide ions and the cations. Metal oxides are therefore formed exothermically from their elements and are likely to be stable.

(ii) metal oxides are generally insoluble in water. However, most of the oxides of the s-block elements are soluble, because the low surface charge density of the cations leads to relatively low lattice enthalpies. (The lattice enthalpies are none the less high enough to ensure that the oxides are stable.)

Basic and acidic properties of metal oxides

The oxide ion readily donates one or two electron pairs and therefore functions as a strong Lewis base, e.g.

$$O^{2-} + 2H^+(aq) = H_2O$$
$$O^{2-} + SO_3 = SO_4^{2-}$$

The first example forms the basis of neutralisation reactions in which an acid reacts with an ionic oxide to form a salt and water.

The oxide ion also acts as a Brønsted−Lowry base in removing protons from other compounds. For example, when soluble oxides are dissolved in water the following reaction occurs:

$$O^{2-} + H_2O = 2HO^-$$

The strength of an oxide as a base depends on the magnitude of the attraction between the oxide ions and the metal ions. If the attraction is strong then the electron density of the oxide ion is lowered as a result of distortion by the metal ion. This reduces the electron donating ability of the oxide ion and so decreases its strength as a base. The oxides of metals within a particular group of the periodic table become increasingly basic from top to bottom of the group as the surface charge density of the metal ion decreases and the oxide ion becomes less distorted. For similar reasons, the lower the charge on the metal ion, the more basic is the oxide. For example, the oxides of group 1A metals are more basic than the corresponding oxides of group 2A elements, and iron(II) oxide, FeO, is a stronger base than iron(III) oxide, Fe_2O_3.

Metal ions with high surface charge densities, e.g. Be^{2+}, Zn^{2+}, Al^{3+} and Sn^{4+}, extensively distort and lower the electron density of oxide ions, with the result that an appreciable degree of covalent character is present in the amphoteric oxides BeO, ZnO, Al_2O_3 and SnO_2. These compounds are weak bases because of the relatively low electron density on the oxide ion. Their acidic properties result from the strong attraction that the small, highly charged cation has for bases such as the hydroxide ion. For example, with aluminium oxide, the oxide ions may react with hydrogen ions, or the Al^{3+} ion may coordinate with hydroxide ions:

$$Al_2O_3 + 6H^+(aq) + 9H_2O = 2[Al(H_2O)_6]^{3+}$$

i.e.

$$O^{2-} + 2H^+(aq) = H_2O$$
$$Al_2O_3 + 6HO^- + 3H_2O = 2[Al(OH)_6]^{3-}$$

i.e.

$$Al^{3+} + 6HO^- = [Al(OH)_6]^{3-}$$

In very high valency states some transition elements form covalent oxides, e.g. CrO_3 and Mn_2O_7. Let us consider what would happen if chromium(VI) oxide were ionic, i.e. $Cr^{6+}(O^{2-})_3$. The Cr^{6+} ion, because of its very high surface charge density, would extensively distort the oxide ions to produce covalent bonds, i.e.

hypothetical ionic structure of CrO_3

extreme distortion of O^{2-} by Cr^{6+} leads to

polar covalent bonding between Cr and O

Since there are no oxide ions present in these covalent oxides they do not function as bases. Instead, they behave as acids by accepting electrons from bases on to the *metal* atom.

Thus, we see that as the valency of a metal increases, its oxides become increasingly covalent. This trend is accompanied by a decline in basic properties and an increase in acidic character. The oxides of metals in low valency states (1 and 2) are usually basic, while in high valency states (6 and 7) the oxides are acidic. Most (but not all) amphoteric oxides contain metals in the intermediate valency states, i.e. 3, 4 or 5, e.g.

valency state of the metal	2	3	4	6	7
	CrO(b)	Cr_2O_3(am)	—	CrO_3(ac)	—
	MnO(b)	Mn_2O_3(b)	MnO_2(am)	—	Mn_2O_7(ac)

increasingly covalent and acidic

$\longrightarrow$

decreasingly ionic and basic

(b) = basic, (am) = amphoteric, (ac) = acidic

Exceptions to this generalisation occur with metals which produce small ions, e.g. beryllium and zinc, or with weak metals, such as tin, which show some non-metallic character. There is no sharp dividing line between the different types of oxide. Rather, there is a spectrum ranging from basic oxides at one extreme to acidic oxides at the other, with amphoteric oxides lying in the middle.

Some metals form oxides, known as *mixed oxides*, which behave chemically as mixtures of oxides. Typical examples are Pb_3O_4, which behaves as $2PbO + 1PbO_2$ (§9.7), and Fe_3O_4, which behaves as $1FeO + 1Fe_2O_3$ (§14.8). Mixed oxides are not simple mixtures but definite compounds. The crystal lattice of Fe_3O_4 consists of a regular array of Fe^{2+}, Fe^{3+} and O^{2-} ions in the ratio 1 : 2 : 4, while the Pb_3O_4 lattice comprises Pb^{2+}, Pb^{4+} and O^{2-} ions in a 2 : 1 : 4 ratio.

Oxides of non-metals

All non-metals, with the exception of some noble gases, form oxides. Many are discussed in other chapters of this book, but a few generalisations can be made here.

(i) All non-metal oxides are covalent.
(ii) Most non-metal oxides form single molecules, e.g. CO, N_2O_4 and P_4O_{10}. A few, such as SiO_2, form atomic crystals (§9.6).
(iii) Non-metal oxides function as Lewis acids. Because of the high electronegativity of oxygen, the non-metal atom carries a partial positive charge and can therefore attract and accept a lone pair of electrons from a base to form a coordinate bond, e.g.

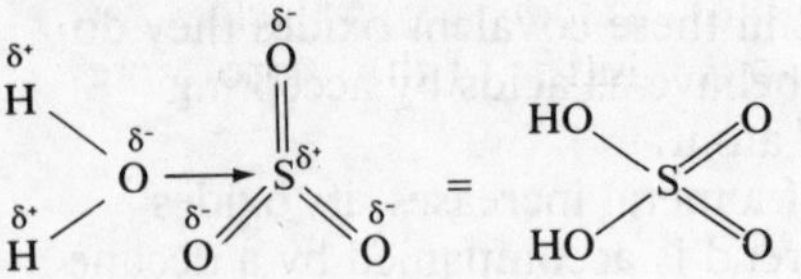

sulphuric acid

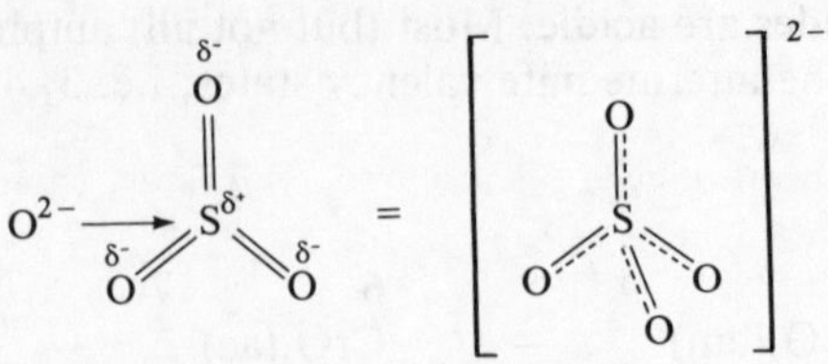

sulphate ion

The greater the number of oxygen atoms in the oxide, the higher is the positive charge on the non-metal atom and the stronger is the attraction for bases. Thus, as with metal oxides, acidic nature increases with oxygen content, e.g. sulphur trioxide, SO_3, is more acidic than sulphur dioxide, SO_2. Some non-metal oxides with a low proportion of oxygen, i.e. CO, NO and N_2O, are so feebly acidic that they are often referred to as 'neutral oxides'. They do, however, display acidic properties under extreme conditions, e.g. carbon monoxide reacts with sodium hydroxide under pressure (§9.6).

(iv) Most non-metal oxides react with water to produce acids, and are thus termed *acid anhydrides*. Certain of them give a mixture of two acids on treatment with water and are known as *mixed anhydrides*. Such reactions invariably involve disproportionation, e.g.

$$2NO_2 + H_2O = HNO_3 + HNO_2 \qquad (\S10.5)$$

The so-called neutral oxides do not give acids when dissolved in water, but they do have acids corresponding to them. Carbon monoxide, for example, can be prepared by the dehydration of methanoic acid and is therefore the anhydride of this acid. Because of its very low solubility, silica does not form an acid in water, but it does function as an acid by forming silicates with alkalis (§9.6).

Hydroxides of metals and non-metals

Metal hydroxides tend to possess a greater degree of covalency than the corresponding oxides. For example, aluminium hydroxide is essentially covalent (§8.5), while the oxide, Al_2O_3, is principally ionic. Many metals do not form hydroxides, but instead form hydrated oxides such as $SnO_2(aq)$ and $Fe_2O_3(aq)$. Most of the s-block metal hydroxides are soluble in water, but those of other metals are insoluble. They are obtained in hydrated form as precipitates, which are often gelatinous, by adding an alkali metal hydroxide to a solution of the appropriate metal ions, i.e.

$$M^{n+}(aq) + nHO^- = M(OH)_n(aq)(s)$$

The basic and acidic properties of metal hydroxides are essentially the same as those of the corresponding oxides. The basic character of the ionic s-block hydroxides stems from the presence of hydroxide ions:

$$HO^- + H^+(aq) = H_2O$$

In hydroxides which possess a high degree of covalent character, the hydroxyl group may still function as a base by accepting hydrogen ions, e.g.

$$[Al(OH)_3(H_2O)_3] + H^+(aq) \rightleftharpoons [Al(OH)_2(H_2O)_4]^+$$

Such hydroxides frequently display acidic properties too, and are thus amphoteric, e.g.

$$[Al(OH)_3(H_2O)_3] + HO^- \rightleftharpoons [Al(OH)_4(H_2O)_2]^- + H_2O$$

Non-metal hydroxides, such as hypochlorous acid, H—O—Cl, and boric acid, $B(OH)_3$, are covalent and acidic. Most non-metals, however, do not form simple hydroxides of this type, but instead give rise to *oxoacids*, which contain one or more hydroxyl groups and oxygen atoms bonded to a non-metal atom. Sulphur, for example, forms sulphuric acid and not the hydroxide, $S(OH)_6$. The oxoacid may be considered to be derived from the non-existent hydroxide by partial dehydration, i.e.

All oxoacids function as Brønsted—Lowry acids, but most can also function as bases (p. 289).

Sulphides of metals and non-metals

The sulphides of group 1A and group 2A elements are prepared by direct combination of the elements or by the action of hydrogen sulphide on the appropriate metal hydroxide. These sulphides are extensively hydrolysed in solution because of the weakly acidic nature of hydrogen sulphide:

$$S^{2-} + H_2O \rightleftharpoons HS^- + HO^-$$
$$HS^- + H_2O \rightleftharpoons H_2S + HO^-$$

Many of the remaining metal sulphides are insoluble in water and are conveniently prepared by passing hydrogen sulphide through a solution of the appropriate metal ions. An exception is iron(III) sulphide, which cannot be obtained in this way because iron(III) ions are reduced by hydrogen sulphide (§14.8).

Chromium(III) sulphide and aluminium sulphide can be prepared only by direct combination of the heated elements, because they react with water:

$$M_2S_3 + 12H_2O = 2[M(H_2O)_6]^{3+} + 3S^{2-} \qquad \text{(M = Cr or Al)}$$

The hydrated trivalent metal ions are acidic, and hydrolysis occurs with the basic sulphide ion:

$$2[M(H_2O)_6]^{3+} + 3S^{2-} = 2[M(OH)_3(H_2O)_3] + 3H_2S$$

The sulphides of group 1A and group 2A metals, except beryllium, are ionic and contain the sulphide ion, S^{2-}. The majority of transition metal sulphides resemble alloys in possessing a metallic appearance, good electrical conductivity and a variable composition, as a result of which they are often non-stoicheiometric, e.g. the composition of iron(II) sulphide varies between $Fe_{0.858}S$ and $Fe_{0.96}S$. The remaining metal sulphides, such as BeS, ZnS, CdS and Al_2S_3, are predominantly covalent.

On the basis of their precipitation from solution by hydrogen sulphide, two classes of insoluble metal sulphides can be distinguished.

(i)   Those obtained from acidic solutions, e.g. CuS (black), As_2S_3 (yellow), CdS (yellow), Sb_2S_3 (orange), SnS (brown), SnS_2 (ochre), HgS (black), PbS (black) and Bi_2S_3 (sepia).

(ii) Those obtained only from alkaline solutions, e.g. FeS (black), CoS (black), NiS (black), MnS (pink) and ZnS (white).

The solubility products of class (i) sulphides are very low, while those of class (ii) are relatively high. The concentration of sulphide ions produced by the ionisation of hydrogen sulphide is dependent on the pH of the solution:

$$H_2S + aq \rightleftharpoons 2H^+(aq) + S^{2-}$$

In acidic solution the concentration of sulphide ions is low, with the result that only class (i) sulphides will be precipitated. In alkaline conditions the sulphide ion concentration is much higher and allows the precipitation of class (ii) sulphides.

Many metal sulphides possess a distinctive colour (see above), and their precipitation by hydrogen sulphide can be used to identify the cations present in solution.

Most of the non-metals, except the noble gases, form at least one compound with sulphur. Without exception, non-metal sulphides are covalent, ranging in structure from the molecular (e.g. carbon disulphide) to the polymeric (e.g. silicon disulphide).

Oxides of sulphur

Sulphur dioxide

Sulphur dioxide is a colourless, toxic gas with a characteristic choking odour. It is formed by burning sulphur in air, although a small proportion of sulphur trioxide, which is produced simultaneously, gives the gas a white smoky appearance. In the laboratory pure sulphur dioxide is prepared by reacting a sulphite or a hydrogensulphite with dilute hydrochloric acid, or by reducing hot concentrated sulphuric acid with metals:

$$SO_3^{2-} + 2H^+(aq) = SO_2 + H_2O$$
$$HSO_3^- + H^+(aq) = SO_2 + H_2O$$
$$Cu + 2H_2SO_4 = CuSO_4 + SO_2 + 2H_2O$$

Copper is a useful metal in this respect, because it does not form hydrogen by reacting with the acid as it becomes diluted by the water produced in the reaction. Sulphuric acid is reduced not only to sulphur dioxide but also to sulphur and hydrogen sulphide, so that copper(I) sulphide, Cu_2S, and copper(II) sulphide, CuS, are also formed.

Large quantities of sulphur dioxide are manufactured for conversion into sulphuric acid.

The sulphur dioxide molecule has a bond angle of 119.5° and a bond length of 0.143 nm:

$\begin{pmatrix} x & x \end{pmatrix}$ represents a lone pair of electrons

The compound is thermally very stable, as indicated by its high free energy of formation; $\Delta G_f^{\ominus}[SO_2(g)] = -300$ kJ mol^{-1}.

Sulphur dioxide is readily oxidised and is thus a powerful reducing agent. In many cases the oxidation product is the sulphate ion, although with chlorine in the presence of a camphor catalyst sulphuryl chloride, SO_2Cl_2, is formed instead, e.g.

$$2MnO_4^- + 5SO_2 + 2H_2O = 2Mn^{2+} + 5SO_4^{2-} + 4H^+(aq)$$
$$SO_2 + Cl_2 = SO_2Cl_2$$

Sulphur trioxide

Sulphur trioxide can be prepared either by dehydrating concentrated sulphuric acid with phosphorus(V) oxide, or by heating sulphates alone or with silica, e.g.

$$P_4O_{10} + 2H_2SO_4 = 4HPO_3 + 2SO_3$$
$$Fe_2(SO_4)_3 = Fe_2O_3 + 3SO_3$$
$$CaSO_4 + SiO_2 = CaSiO_3 + SO_3$$

Industrially, large quantities of sulphur trioxide are produced for the manufacture of sulphuric acid.

In the vapour state, above 60 °C (333 K), sulphur trioxide exists as trigonal planar molecules, but in the solid state there are at least three polymeric forms, known as α-, β- and γ-sulphur trioxide.

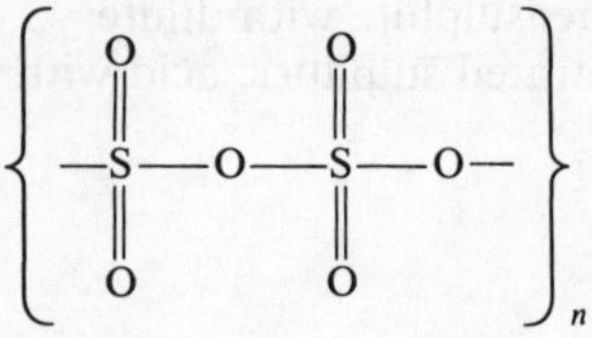

α-Sulphur trioxide is believed to consist of cross-linked chains made up of alternating sulphur and oxygen atoms.

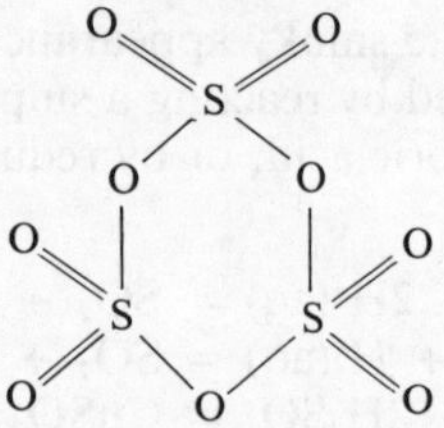

Sulphur trioxide is extremely reactive and strongly acidic. It combines exothermically with water, to give sulphuric acid, and with basic oxides to form sulphates, e.g.

$$SO_3(g) + H_2O(l) = H_2SO_4(l) \qquad \Delta H^\ominus = -130 \text{ kJ mol}^{-1}$$
$$SO_3(g) + MgO(s) = MgSO_4(s) \qquad \Delta H^\ominus = -281 \text{ kJ mol}^{-1}$$

Recent investigations indicate that the reaction between sulphur trioxide and water involves the following intermediate:

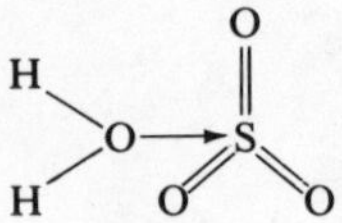

Oxoacids of sulphur and their salts

'Sulphurous acid' and sulphites

Sulphur dioxide dissolves in water to give an acidic solution which has long been called 'sulphurous acid' ('H_2SO_3'). However, there is no evidence for the existence of H_2SO_3 molecules, and solutions of sulphur dioxide are believed to contain hydrated molecules, i.e. $SO_2(aq)$, which ionise:

$$SO_2(aq) + H_2O \rightleftharpoons H^+(aq) + HSO_3^- \qquad pK_1 = 1.92$$
$$HSO_3^- + aq \rightleftharpoons H^+(aq) + SO_3^{2-} \qquad pK_2 = 7.21$$

Thus, sulphur dioxide behaves in solution as a weak diprotic acid and forms two series of salts, one containing the sulphite ion, SO_3^{2-}, and the other the hydrogensulphite ion, HSO_3^-. The common alkali metal salts are prepared by passing sulphur dioxide into solutions of alkalis, e.g.

$$2NaOH + SO_2 = Na_2SO_3 + H_2O \qquad \text{(with an excess of alkali)}$$
$$NaOH + SO_2 = NaHSO_3 \qquad \text{(with an excess of } SO_2\text{)}$$

Hydrogensulphites eliminate water when heated to produce the disulphite ion, $S_2O_5^{2-}$:

$$2HSO_3^- \underset{\text{add } H_2O}{\overset{\text{heat}}{\rightleftharpoons}} S_2O_5^{2-} + H_2O$$

All sulphites decompose into sulphur dioxide when treated with strong non-oxidising acids, i.e.

$$SO_3^{2-} + 2H^+(aq) = SO_2 + H_2O$$
$$HSO_3^- + H^+(aq) = SO_2 + H_2O$$

Acidic or alkaline solutions of sulphites or hydrogensulphites are powerful reductants. Although in alkaline solution the reducing properties are due to the sulphite ion, in acidic solution they arise from the presence of sulphur dioxide:

$$SO_4^{2-} + 4H^+(aq) + 2e^- = SO_2(aq) + 2H_2O \qquad E^{\ominus} = +0.17 \text{ V}$$
$$SO_4^{2-} + H_2O + 2e^- = SO_3^{2-} + 2HO^- \qquad E^{\ominus} = -0.93 \text{ V}$$

The standard electrode potentials indicate that the sulphites are stronger reductants in alkaline solution than sulphur dioxide is in acidic solution, but the equations show that the oxidation product in both cases is the sulphate ion, e.g.

$$2Fe^{3+} + SO_3^{2-} + H_2O = 2Fe^{2+} + SO_4^{2-} + 2H^+(aq)$$
$$Cr_2O_7^{2-} + 3SO_2 + 2H^+(aq) = 2Cr^{3+} + 3SO_4^{2-} + H_2O$$

The last reaction is accompanied by a colour change from orange ($Cr_2O_7^{2-}$ ion) to green (complex chromium(III) ion) and is used as a test for sulphur dioxide. The test is performed by directing the gas on to a filter paper soaked in an acidified dichromate solution.

Sulphur dioxide and the sulphites act as oxidants towards more powerful reducing agents, e.g.

$$2H_2S + SO_2 = 3S + 2H_2O$$
$$Zn + 2SO_3^{2-} + 4H^+(aq) = Zn^{2+} + S_2O_4^{2-} + 2H_2O$$
$$\text{dithionite ion}$$

$$S + SO_3^{2-} = S_2O_3^{2-} \quad \text{thiosulphate ion}$$
$$\text{oxidation number of sulphur} \qquad 0 \qquad +4 \qquad +2$$

White barium sulphite is precipitated from neutral solutions of sulphites by the addition of barium chloride. Unlike barium sulphate, the sulphite is soluble in hydrochloric acid, a property which enables sulphites to be distinguished from sulphates:

$$BaSO_3 + 2H^+(aq) = Ba^{2+} + SO_2 + H_2O$$

Sulphuric acid

The contact process

The *contact process*, which is used to manufacture huge quantities of sulphuric acid, involves the catalytic oxidation of sulphur dioxide to sulphur trioxide. Sulphur dioxide is produced mainly by the controlled combustion of hydrogen sulphide extracted from natural gas or petroleum:

$$2H_2S + 3O_2 = 2SO_2 + 2H_2O$$

It is also available as a by-product of some metal extraction processes in which a metal sulphide ore is roasted in air, e.g.

$$2ZnS + 3O_2 = 2ZnO + 2SO_2$$

Impurities, such as arsenic(III) oxide, poison the catalyst and are removed by washing the gas with water and passing it through an electric field. (Solid particles are electrostatically precipitated.) The purified sulphur dioxide is then mixed with a slight excess of air and passed into the converter which contains the catalyst. Here, the oxidation of sulphur dioxide occurs:

$$SO_2(g) + \tfrac{1}{2}O_2(g) \rightleftharpoons SO_3(g) \qquad \Delta H^{\ominus} = -98 \text{ kJ mol}^{-1}$$

Platinum is an effective catalyst for the reaction but suffers from the disadvantages that it is expensive and easily poisoned. A 'promoted' vanadium catalyst is used instead, comprising an alkali metal sulphate and either vanadium(V) oxide, V_2O_5, or a vanadate on an inert support of silica.

To maximise the yield of sulphur trioxide in the reversible reaction a low temperature is required. However, the efficiency of the catalyst is temperature dependent. Above or below the optimum temperature of approximately 330 °C (603 K) the efficiency falls dramatically. This ideal temperature is difficult to maintain because, as the oxidation reaction proceeds, sufficient heat is liberated to raise the temperature of the catalyst by as much as 200 °C (200 K). To overcome this problem several beds of catalyst are employed, the first being at about 440 °C (713 K) and the final one close to the optimum temperature.

Since there is a decrease in volume as the reaction proceeds from left to right, an increase in pressure will increase the yield of sulphur trioxide. However, the efficiency of the catalyst is such that almost complete conversion of sulphur dioxide into sulphur trioxide can be achieved at ordinary pressures, so that it is unnecessary to use expensive pressure vessels.

Sulphur trioxide vapour reacts with pure water to form a mist of sulphuric acid which is slow to settle. However, it combines readily with the 2 per cent of water in 98 per cent sulphuric acid without forming a mist. The cooled vapour from the converter is therefore absorbed in this medium, to which water is added continuously to maintain the concentration at 98 per cent. If no water is added, sulphur trioxide reacts with sulphuric acid to give disulphuric acid, $H_2S_2O_7$, which forms sulphuric acid on subsequent dilution with water:

$$SO_3 + H_2SO_4 = H_2S_2O_7$$
$$H_2S_2O_7 + H_2O = 2H_2SO_4$$

Physical properties of sulphuric acid

Pure sulphuric acid is a colourless, viscous liquid with a density of $1.84 \, g \, cm^{-3}$ and a freezing temperature of $10 \, °C$ (283 K). At its boiling temperature, $290 \, °C$ (563 K), sulphuric acid decomposes into sulphur trioxide and water. 'Concentrated sulphuric acid' is a constant boiling mixture containing approximately 98 per cent of the acid. The high viscosity and high boiling temperature of sulphuric acid are attributed to the presence of extensive hydrogen bonding between neighbouring molecules:

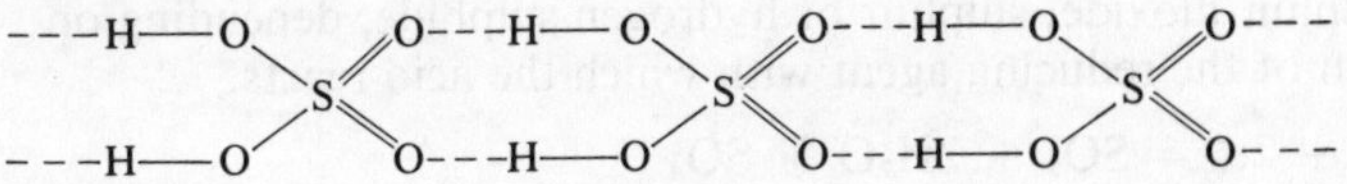

Acidic properties of sulphuric acid

Pure sulphuric acid is a covalent compound which self-ionises to a very small extent:

$$2H_2SO_4 \rightleftharpoons H_3SO_4^+ + HSO_4^-$$

In dilute aqueous solution it is extensively ionised and behaves as a diprotic acid:

$$H_2SO_4 + H_2O \rightleftharpoons H_3O^+ + HSO_4^-$$
$$HSO_4^- + H_2O \rightleftharpoons H_3O^+ + SO_4^{2-}$$

The first ionisation stage is virtually complete, i.e. sulphuric acid is a strong acid, but the ionisation of the hydrogensulphate ion, HSO_4^-, is incomplete; $pK_2 = 1.92$. A dilute solution of sulphuric acid (approximately 2 M) therefore contains hydrogen ions and hydrogensulphate ions, together with a small proportion of sulphate ions. Dilute sulphuric acid possesses typical acidic properties, e.g. it forms salts with bases, liberates carbon dioxide from carbonates, and reacts with metals above hydrogen in the electrochemical series to produce hydrogen.

The affinity of sulphuric acid for water

When concentrated sulphuric acid is diluted with water a large amount of heat is evolved as the ions formed become hydrated. The concentrated acid therefore has a strong affinity for water and is used as a drying agent. It is also used as a *dehydrating agent*, i.e. an acid catalyst for the elimination of water. The uses of concentrated sulphuric acid include:

(i)   the drying of gases, such as chlorine, oxygen and sulphur dioxide;
(ii) the removal of water of crystallisation from hydrated salts;
(iii) the removal of hydrogen and oxygen in the form of water from
      compounds which contain no water, e.g.

$$(COOH)_2 \xrightarrow{-H_2O} CO + CO_2$$

$$C_2H_5OH \xrightarrow{-H_2O} C_2H_4$$

$$C_6H_{12}O_6 \xrightarrow{-6H_2O} 6C$$
$$\text{a carbohydrate}$$

Oxidising properties of sulphuric acid

Hot concentrated sulphuric acid is a weak oxidising agent, but this
property is rapidly lost on dilution. The reduction product of the acid
may be sulphur dioxide, sulphur or hydrogen sulphide, depending on
the strength of the reducing agent with which the acid reacts.

$$2H_2SO_4 + 2e^- = SO_2 + 2H_2O + SO_4^{2-}$$
$$4H_2SO_4 + 6e^- = S + 4H_2O + 3SO_4^{2-}$$
$$5H_2SO_4 + 8e^- = H_2S + 4H_2O + 4SO_4^{2-}$$

The sulphate ion is not a reduction product, but originates from
sulphuric acid molecules which act as proton suppliers.

(i)   Non-metals or metals low in the electrochemical series are weak
      reductants and reduce sulphuric acid to sulphur dioxide, e.g.

$$C + 2H_2SO_4 = CO_2 + 2SO_2 + 2H_2O$$
$$Cu + 2H_2SO_4 = CuSO_4 + SO_2 + 2H_2O$$

(ii) Metals towards the top of the electrochemical series are powerful
      reductants and reduce the acid to sulphur or hydrogen sulphide,
      e.g.

$$4Mg + 5H_2SO_4 = 4MgSO_4 + H_2S + 4H_2O$$
$$3Zn + 4H_2SO_4 = 3ZnSO_4 + S + 4H_2O$$

(iii) Hydrogen bromide and hydrogen iodide reduce sulphuric acid
      (§12.6).

Displacement reactions of sulphuric acid

Sulphuric acid has a low volatility and can displace more volatile acids
from their salts. For example, when concentrated sulphuric acid is
added to a crystalline ionic chloride at room temperature the following
equilibrium is established:

$$Cl^- + H_2SO_4 \rightleftharpoons HSO_4^- + HCl$$

If the gaseous hydrogen chloride is allowed to escape, the equilibrium is disturbed towards the right, i.e. hydrochloric acid is displaced from its salts by a less volatile acid. (The sulphate ion, SO_4^{2-}, is formed only at much higher temperatures; see below.)

A similar reaction occurs with nitrates:

$$NO_3^- + H_2SO_4 \rightleftharpoons HSO_4^- + HNO_3$$

except that nitric acid is less volatile than hydrogen chloride and is lost from the equilibrium mixture only on heating. The reaction between sulphuric acid and ionic bromides and iodides is discussed in §12.6.

Reactions of sulphuric acid with organic compounds

Sulphuric acid reacts with many organic compounds, including alkenes, alkynes, arenes and alcohols.

Disulphuric acid

Sulphur trioxide dissolves in pure sulphuric acid. In equimolar proportions the product is disulphuric acid, $H_2S_2O_7$, commonly called 'oleum' or 'fuming sulphuric acid':

$$SO_3 + H_2SO_4 = H_2S_2O_7$$

At higher mole ratios of sulphur trioxide the acids $H_2S_3O_{10}$ and $H_2S_4O_{13}$ are believed to be formed. Small quantities of disulphuric acid are present in pure sulphuric acid as a result of the equilibrium:

$$2H_2SO_4 \rightleftharpoons H_2O + H_2S_2O_7$$

The reverse reaction occurs when disulphuric acid is added to water. Disulphuric acid is used as a sulphonating agent in organic chemistry.

Salts of sulphuric acid

Sulphuric acid is diprotic and forms two series of salts. Sulphates contain the tetrahedral SO_4^{2-} ion, and hydrogensulphates (formerly 'bisulphates') contain the HSO_4^- ion which, like the acid, has a distorted tetrahedral structure:

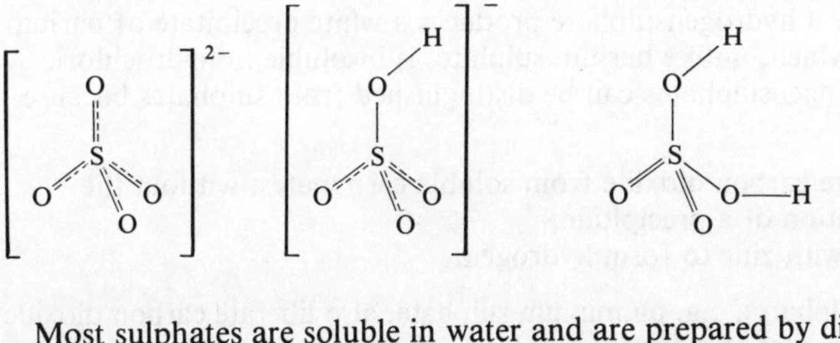

Most sulphates are soluble in water and are prepared by dissolving a metal or its oxide, hydroxide or carbonate in sulphuric acid. Insoluble sulphates, i.e. those of calcium, strontium, barium, lead and mercury(I), are prepared by metathesis, e.g.

$$BaCl_2 + H_2SO_4 = BaSO_4(s) + 2HCl$$

Many of the soluble metal sulphates are hydrated, e.g. $NiSO_4 \cdot 6H_2O$, with the water molecules coordinated to the cation. However, in some cases, e.g. $CuSO_4 \cdot 5H_2O$ and $FeSO_4 \cdot 7H_2O$, water molecules are also attached to the sulphate ion by hydrogen bonds (Fig. 4.34).

The only common hydrogensulphates are those of the alkali metals, and ammonium hydrogensulphate. The crystalline salts can be prepared by:

(i)   reacting an alkali and sulphuric acid together in equimolar proportions, followed by evaporation, e.g.

$$NaOH + H_2SO_4 = NaHSO_4 + H_2O$$

(ii) the evaporation of a solution containing equimolar quantities of a sulphate and sulphuric acid, e.g.

$$Na_2SO_4 + H_2SO_4 = 2NaHSO_4$$

(iii) the action of warm concentrated sulphuric acid on a chloride (see above).

Hydrogensulphates are acidic. They ionise in solution:

$$HSO_4^- + H_2O \rightleftharpoons H_3O^+ + SO_4^{2-}$$

and they displace hydrogen chloride from chlorides at temperatures above 500 °C (773 K):

$$NaHSO_4 + NaCl \rightleftharpoons Na_2SO_4 + HCl(g)$$

When heated strongly, hydrogensulphates decompose into disulphates, which themselves decompose on stronger heating, e.g.

$$2NaHSO_4 = Na_2S_2O_7 + H_2O$$
$$Na_2S_2O_7 = Na_2SO_4 + SO_3$$

Tests for sulphates   The addition of barium chloride to a solution of a sulphate or a hydrogensulphate produces a white precipitate of barium sulphate, which, unlike barium sulphite, is insoluble in hydrochloric acid. Hydrogensulphates can be distinguished from sulphates because they:

(i)   liberate carbon dioxide from soluble carbonates, without the formation of a precipitate;

(ii) react with zinc to form hydrogen.

Some sulphates, e.g. aluminium sulphate, also liberate carbon dioxide from carbonates and produce hydrogen with zinc, but a precipitate of the metal hydroxide is formed too (§8.5).

Peroxodisulphuric acid and its salts

The ammonium and alkali metal salts of peroxodisulphuric acid, $H_2S_2O_8$, are well known powerful oxidants:

$$\tfrac{1}{2}S_2O_8^{2-} + e^- = SO_4^{2-} \qquad E^{\ominus} = +2.01 \text{ V}$$

However, in the absence of a catalyst, such as the silver ion, the peroxodisulphate ion acts rather slowly. Its oxidising properties are illustrated by the conversion of the manganese(II) ion to manganese(IV) oxide, and the chromium(III) ion to the chromate ion.

Ammonium peroxodisulphate is prepared by the electrolysis of a solution of ammonium hydrogensulphate:

$$2HSO_4^- = S_2O_8^{2-} + 2H^+(aq) + 2e^-$$

Thiosulphates

Thiosulphates are prepared by boiling a solution of a sulphite with sulphur (p. 255). Sodium thiosulphate, $Na_2S_2O_3$, is commonly used in the laboratory for the volumetric analysis of iodine:

$$2S_2O_3^{2-} + I_2 = 2I^- + S_4O_6^{2-} \qquad \text{tetrathionate ion}$$

In acidic solution, the thiosulphate ion decomposes into sulphur dioxide and a yellow precipitate of sulphur. This is a disproportionation reaction:

$$S_2O_3^{2-} + 2H^+(aq) = SO_2 + S + H_2O$$

oxidation number of S   +2   +4   0

Thiosulphates are used as fixers in photography because they dissolve silver halides by forming soluble complex salts:

$$AgCl(s) + 2S_2O_3^{2-} = [Ag(S_2O_3)_2]^{3-} + Cl^-$$

Halides of sulphur

Fluorides

Sulphur reacts exothermically with fluorine to give sulphur hexafluoride, SF_6, a very stable and unreactive compound. It is unattacked by oxygen, ammonia, alkalis or many metals, even at red heat. The stability of sulphur hexafluoride is due partly to the strong S——F bond, and partly to the inability of attacking reagents to approach the sulphur atom because of steric hindrance by the six fluorine atoms in the octahedral molecule. Sulphur forms another inert fluoride, disulphur decafluoride, S_2F_{10}.

In contrast, sulphur tetrafluoride, SF_4, is an extremely reactive compound which is rapidly hydrolysed by water to sulphur dioxide and hydrofluoric acid. Sulphur tetrafluoride is used for selectively fluorinating certain groups in organic molecules, e.g.

$$\text{>C=O} \xrightarrow{\text{SF}_4} \text{>CF}_2 \qquad -\text{COOH} \xrightarrow{\text{SF}_4} -\text{CF}_3$$

Chlorides and bromide

Sulphur forms three chlorides, S_2Cl_2, SCl_2 and SCl_4. Only the first, disulphur dichloride, is reasonably stable and important. It is an unpleasant smelling liquid, prepared by the action of chlorine on molten sulphur. In the vapour phase, disulphur dichloride has been shown to have a structure similar to that of hydrogen peroxide (Fig. 11.1) with atoms of sulphur and chlorine in place of those of oxygen and hydrogen respectively. Disulphur dichloride is highly reactive and is used as a chlorinating agent. It is also employed in the vulcanisation of rubber, a process which involves cross-linking of the hydrocarbon chains of natural rubber. Water reacts rapidly with disulphur dichloride to give a mixture of sulphur, hydrogen sulphide, sulphite ions and thiosulphate ions.

Disulphur dibromide, S_2Br_2, is the only known bromide of sulphur. To date, no iodides of sulphur have been reported.

Oxohalides of sulphur

Phosphorus pentachloride and sulphur dioxide react together to give thionyl chloride, $SOCl_2$, which is the acid chloride of the unknown sulphurous acid:

$$SO_2 + PCl_5 = SOCl_2 + POCl_3$$

It is a colourless liquid which fumes in air because of the rapid hydrolysis reaction which occurs with water vapour:

$$SOCl_2 + H_2O = SO_2 + 2HCl$$

A similar reaction occurs with liquid water and with coordinated water in hydrated metal salts. For this reason, anhydrous metal chlorides can be prepared by heating the hydrated salts with thionyl chloride, e.g.

$$CrCl_3 \cdot 6H_2O + 6SOCl_2 = CrCl_3 + 6SO_2(g) + 12HCl(g)$$

After completion of the reaction excess thionyl chloride is removed by distillation, preferably in a vacuum.

Thionyl chloride is used in organic chemistry for replacing hydroxyl groups by chlorine atoms.

Sulphur dioxide and chlorine combine together, in the presence of a catalyst such as camphor or ethanoic acid, to form sulphuryl chloride:

$$SO_2 + Cl_2 = SO_2Cl_2$$

This compound, too, is rapidly hydrolysed by water:

$$SO_2Cl_2 + 2H_2O = H_2SO_4 + 2HCl$$

and is used as a chlorinating agent.

Another oxochloride, chlorosulphuric acid, is prepared by reacting sulphur trioxide with hydrogen chloride:

$$SO_3 + HCl = HSO_3Cl$$

Both chlorosulphuric acid and sulphuryl chloride are acid chlorides of sulphuric acid, i.e. derivatives of the acid in which hydroxyl groups are replaced by chlorine atoms:

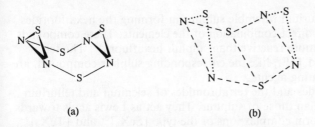

sulphuric acid   chlorosulphuric acid   sulphuryl chloride

Chlorosulphuric acid reacts explosively with water:

$$HSO_3Cl + H_2O = H_2SO_4 + HCl$$

No salts of the acid are known because with bases, e.g. sodium hydroxide, the following reaction occurs:

$$HSO_3Cl + NaOH = NaHSO_4 + HCl$$

Chlorosulphuric acid is used as a sulphonating agent in organic chemistry.

Nitrides of sulphur

Tetrasulphur tetranitride, S_4N_4, an orange coloured compound, is prepared by passing disulphur dichloride, S_2Cl_2, over solid ammonium chloride. In the tetrasulphur tetranitride molecule the four nitrogen atoms lie at the corners of a square. The four sulphur atoms are situated in pairs on opposite sides of this plane (Fig. 11.2(a)).

(a)   (b)

Fig. 11.2 The structure of tetrasulphur tetranitride, S_4N_4.

Alternatively (Fig. 11.2(b)), we can imagine an open book (cf. H_2O_2 structure) with two sulphur atoms lying at the top and bottom of the spine, and a nitrogen atom at the outer corner of each page. The two remaining sulphur atoms are located directly above the midpoints of the edges of the two facing pages.

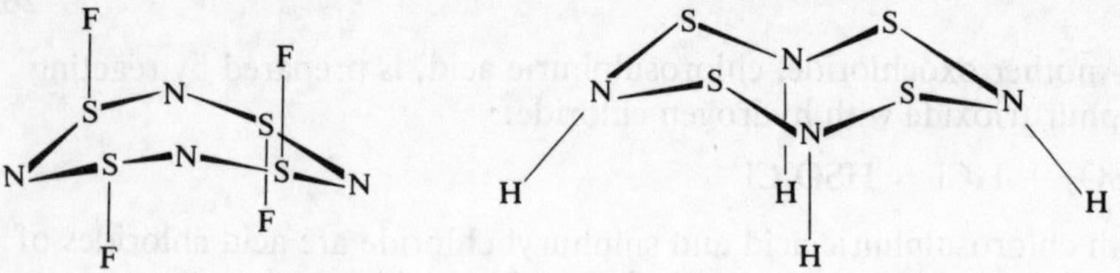

Fig. 11.3 The structures of $S_4N_4F_4$ and $H_4S_4N_4$.

Among the other known nitrogen-containing sulphur compounds are SNF_3, $H_4S_4N_4$ and $S_4N_4F_4$. The first of these has a distorted tetrahedral structure, while the other two exist as puckered eight membered rings (Fig. 11.3).

11.6 Compounds of selenium and tellurium

Hydrides

Hydrogen selenide, H_2Se, and hydrogen telluride, H_2Te, are prepared by the action of acids on metal selenides or metal tellurides respectively. They are thermally less stable than hydrogen sulphide and water, but are stronger acids. Among the group 6B hydrides there is a decrease in bond strength from O——H to Te——H, which leads to the following orders for stability and acid strength:

(i)   *stability* $H_2O > H_2S > H_2Se > H_2Te$ ($> H_2Po$)
(ii) *acid strength* $H_2O < H_2S < H_2Se < H_2Te$, but both H_2Se and H_2Te are classified as weak acids.

Hydrogen selenide and hydrogen telluride resemble hydrogen sulphide in their chemical properties, except that they are more readily oxidised.

Halides

Selenium and tellurium resemble sulphur in forming the hexafluorides SeF_6 and TeF_6 by direct combination of the elements. These compounds are considerably more reactive than sulphur hexafluoride. The tetra-fluorides SeF_4 and TeF_4, like the corresponding sulphur compound, are powerful fluorinating agents.

The tetrachlorides and the tetrabromides of selenium and tellurium are more stable than those of sulphur. They act as Lewis acids towards halide ions and form complex ions of the type $[SeX_6]^{2-}$ and $[TeX_6]^{2-}$, where X = Cl or Br. Selenium also forms chlorides and bromides with the formulae Se_2X_2 and SeX_2, and tellurium forms a dichloride, $TeCl_2$, and a dibromide, $TeBr_2$.

Except for oxygen, tellurium is the only element of group 6B to form compounds with iodine; TeI_4 and the complex ion $[TeI_6]^{2-}$ are known to exist.

Oxides and oxoacids

Selenium dioxide, SeO_2, and tellurium dioxide, TeO_2, are prepared by heating the respective elements in oxygen. Selenium dioxide is covalent with a chain-like structure,

while tellurium dioxide has an ionic character which illustrates the greater metallic nature of this element. Both dioxides are oxidising agents, and both exhibit acidic properties in reacting with alkalis to form the selenite ion or the tellurite ion; see below. Tellurium dioxide also displays basic properties.

Selenium trioxide, SeO_3, is prepared by oxidising selenium or selenium dioxide with oxygen in an electrical discharge. Tellurium trioxide, TeO_3, is formed by dehydrating orthotelluric acid. These trioxides are very powerful oxidising agents and are exclusively acidic. Selenium trioxide reacts readily with water to form selenic acid, and with alkalis to form selenates. Tellurium trioxide dissolves slowly in water to regenerate orthotelluric acid, and in alkalis to form tellurates.

Solutions of selenium dioxide and tellurium dioxide are acidic and called 'selenious acid' and 'tellurous acid' respectively. The nature of the species in solution, however, has yet to be established. Alkalis neutralise these solutions to form ions such as $HSeO_3^-$, SeO_3^{2-}, $HTeO_3^-$ and TeO_3^{2-}.

Selenic acid, H_2SeO_4, resembles sulphuric acid in being a strong diprotic acid and forming salts containing either $HSeO_4^-$ or SeO_4^{2-} ions. It is, however, a more powerful oxidising agent and less stable than sulphuric acid. Orthotelluric acid, H_6TeO_6, and its salts are prepared by oxidising tellurium or tellurium dioxide with peroxides. Despite the fact that it consists of $Te(OH)_6$ molecules, orthotelluric acid usually behaves as a weak diprotic acid, forming the ions $[H_5TeO_6]^-$ and $[H_4TeO_6]^{2-}$ with alkalis. However, the constitution of some salts, such as Ag_6TeO_6, suggests it to be a hexaprotic acid. The ions $HTeO_4^-$ and TeO_4^{2-} do not appear to exist.

Chapter 12

Group 7B

The elements of group 7B, commonly called 'halogens', are fluorine, chlorine, bromine, iodine and astatine. Fluorine, the head element of the group, differs appreciably from chlorine, bromine and iodine, which are chemically similar to one another. Some properties of these elements are shown in Table 12.1.

Table 12.1 Some properties of the elements of group 7B.

	Fluorine	Chlorine	Bromine	Iodine	Astatine
character	non-metal	non-metal	non-metal	non-metal	non-metal
allotropes	—	—	—	—	—
atomic number	9	17	35	53	85
relative atomic mass	18.998 4	34.453	79.904	126.904 5	210†
outer electronic configuration	$2s^2 2p^5$	$3s^2 3p^5$	$4s^2 4p^5$	$5s^2 5p^5$	$6s^2 6p^5$
valencies	1	1, 3, 5, 7	1, 3, 5, 7	1, 3, 5, 7	1, 3, 5, 7(?)
melting temperature/°C	− 220	− 101	− 7.2	114	302
boiling temperature/°C	− 188	− 34.7	58.8	184	not known

† Mass number of the most stable isotope.

In general discussions the symbol X is often used to represent a halogen atom. Compounds of the halogens are known as 'halides'.

12.1 Occurrence and isolation of the elements

The halogens are far too reactive to occur in the uncombined state in nature, but compounds of the halogens are reasonably abundant. Fluorspar, cryolite and apatite, CaF_2, $Na_3[AlF_6]$ and $3Ca_3(PO_4)_2 \cdot CaF_2$ respectively, are the principal sources of fluorine. Chlorides and bromides occur extensively in sea water and dried-up salt lake deposits. Iodine compounds occur in some species of seaweed, but the most important source of iodine is sodium iodate, $NaIO_3$, which constitutes up to 5 per cent of the huge deposits of Chile saltpetre (sodium nitrate) in South America.

The free halogens are usually obtained by the oxidation of halide ions, i.e.

$$2X^- = X_2 + 2e^-$$

Fluorine

Fluorine is the strongest known oxidising agent and cannot, therefore, be prepared by the chemical oxidation of fluoride ions. Fluoride ions can be oxidised only by electrolysis, which must be conducted under anhydrous conditions because water, if present, would be preferentially oxidised to oxygen. Fluorine is conveniently prepared by dissolving potassium fluoride in anhydrous liquid hydrogen fluoride to make the latter electrically conducting. With an HF to KF ratio of 2 : 1, the electrolyte melts at about 100 °C (373 K) and fluorine is liberated at the anode during electrolysis. The anode, which is constructed of graphite, is slowly attacked by fluorine and is replaced as necessary. Hydrogen is evolved at the cathode, which may be of steel or copper. The cell itself is constructed of Monel metal (a copper–nickel alloy), steel or copper. The formation of an impervious layer of the metal fluoride on the surface of the metal protects it from serious attack by the extremely reactive fluorine. Fluorine may be handled in either a metal or glass apparatus. If glass is used it must first be scrupulously dried by heating.

Chlorine

Chlorine, an important industrial chemical, is manufactured by several processes, including:

(i) the electrolysis of a concentrated solution of sodium chloride;
(ii) the oxidation of hydrogen chloride, obtained as a by-product from chlorination reactions, with atmospheric oxygen at 400 °C (673 K) in the presence of a copper(II) chloride catalyst:

$$4HCl + O_2 = 2Cl_2 + 2H_2O$$

Alternatively, the hydrogen chloride is dissolved in water and the resulting solution of hydrochloric acid is electrolysed to yield chlorine at the anode;

(iii) the electrolysis of the fused chlorides of sodium or magnesium (§7.1).

In the laboratory, chlorine is usually prepared by the oxidation of chloride ions under acidic conditions. For example, chlorine is evolved when manganese(IV) oxide, MnO_2, or lead(IV) oxide, PbO_2, is warmed with either concentrated hydrochloric acid or a mixture of an ionic chloride and concentrated sulphuric acid:

$$MO_2 + 2Cl^- + 4H^+(aq) = M^{2+} + Cl_2 + 2H_2O \quad \text{(M = Mn or Pb)}$$

Potassium permanganate oxidises concentrated hydrochloric acid to chlorine,

$$2MnO_4^- + 10Cl^- + 16H^+(aq) = 2Mn^{2+} + 5Cl_2 + 8H_2O$$

but the reaction is sometimes explosive, possibly because of the formation of unstable oxides of chlorine.

Chlorine can also be prepared in the laboratory by the action of dilute hydrochloric acid on hypochlorites such as bleaching powder, which is a complex mixture containing basic calcium hypochlorite. The reaction may be represented as

$$Ca(ClO)_2 + 2Cl^- + 4H^+(aq) = Ca^{2+} + 2Cl_2 + 2H_2O$$

Bromine

Industrially, bromine is recovered from the bromides in sea water by oxidation with chlorine at a pH of about 3.5:

$$2Br^- + Cl_2 = Br_2 + 2Cl^-$$

Bromine can be prepared in the laboratory by warming a mixture of potassium bromide, manganese(IV) oxide and concentrated sulphuric acid:

$$2Br^- + MnO_2 + 2H_2SO_4 = Br_2 + Mn^{2+} + 2SO_4^{2-} + 2H_2O$$

Iodine

Iodine is obtained commercially from the sodium iodate which remains in solution after the crystallisation of sodium nitrate from Chile saltpetre. This is treated with sulphur dioxide or sodium hydrogen-sulphite:

$$IO_3^- + 3HSO_3^- = I^- + 3HSO_4^-$$
$$IO_3^- + 5I^- + 6H^+(aq) = 3I_2 + 3H_2O$$

In the laboratory, iodine is usually prepared by warming a mixture of potassium iodide, manganese(IV) oxide and concentrated sulphuric acid:

$$2I^- + MnO_2 + 2H_2SO_4 = I_2 + Mn^{2+} + 2SO_4^{2-} + 2H_2O$$

Astatine

Astatine does not occur naturally, but is produced by bombarding bismuth isotopes with α-particles:

$$^{207}_{83}Bi + ^4_2He = ^{211}_{85}At$$

12.2 The structure of the elements

All the halogens consist of diatomic molecules, i.e. F_2, Cl_2, Br_2 and I_2, in which the two halogen atoms are joined by a single covalent bond. In solid iodine the molecules pack together in a regular manner to give a molecular crystal (Fig. 12.1).

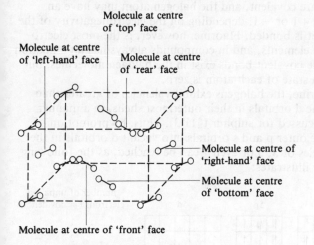

Molecule at centre of 'top' face

Molecule at centre of 'rear' face

Molecule at centre of 'left-hand' face

Molecule at centre of 'right-hand' face

Molecule at centre of 'bottom' face

Molecule at centre of 'front' face

○—○ represents an I_2 molecule

Fig. 12.1 The structure of crystalline iodine. I—I bond length = 0.354 nm. Distance between molecules = 0.43 nm = 2 × van der Waals' radius.

Fluorine is a pale yellow gas, chlorine is a pale green gas, bromine is a dark brown volatile liquid, and iodine is a black shiny solid which sublimes readily on heating to form a violet vapour.

12.3 Bonding and valency

Each element of group 7B has seven outer electrons (i.e. $ns^2\, np^5$) and can participate in ionic or covalent bonding.

Ionic bonding

Halide ions

The halogens all form mononegative halide ions, X^-, by accepting one electron into the singly filled outer p orbital. Most halides of metals in low valency states (oxidation states) are ionic, but those of metals in high valency states tend to be polar covalent.

Halogen cations

Iodine, the least electronegative of the common halogens, is present in a few compounds as a cationic species (§12.6).

Covalent bonding

A covalency of one results from the unpaired electron in an outer p orbital forming a single covalent bond. The halides of all non-metals and some metals are covalent, and the halogen atom may have an oxidation state of $+1$ or -1, depending on the electronegativity of the element to which it is bonded. Fluorine, however, is the most electronegative of all the elements, and in compounds always has an oxidation state of -1. Single covalent bonds exist in the halogen molecules, but here the oxidation state of each atom is zero.

Except for fluorine, the halogens exhibit valencies of greater than one by utilising the d orbitals in their outermost shells, in a manner similar to that discussed for sulphur (§11.3). Thus, by promotion of electrons from the outer p and s orbitals into vacant d orbitals in the same shell, valencies of 3, 5 or even 7 can be reached, as the following scheme for iodine illustrates:

	5s	5p	5d	number of unpaired electrons (= covalency)
ground state	↑↓	↑↓ ↑↓ ↑		1
first excited state	↑↓	↑↓ ↑ ↑	↑	3
second excited state	↑↓	↑ ↑ ↑	↑ ↑	5
third excited state	↑	↑ ↑ ↑	↑ ↑ ↑	7

The additional energy evolved by the formation of the extra covalent bonds usually compensates for the energy absorbed during promotion. Because there are no 2d orbitals, fluorine could achieve higher covalencies only by promotion of electrons from the second shell to vacant orbitals in the third shell. The excessive amount of energy required, however, is not offset by the energy liberated by the formation of additional covalent bonds, and fluorine is therefore restricted to a valency

Table 12.2 Examples of the various valency states of the halogens.

Valency	Oxidation state	Fluorine	Chlorine	Bromine	Iodine
1	-1	HF, F$^-$	HCl, Cl$^-$	HBr, Br$^-$	HI, I$^-$
1	$+1$	—	HClO, Cl$_2$O, ClF	HBrO, Br$_2$O, BrF	HIO, ICl, IBr
3	$+3$	—	HClO$_2$, ClF$_3$	BrF$_3$	ICl$_3$
5	$+5$	—	HClO$_3$	HBrO$_3$, BrF$_5$	HIO$_3$, IF$_5$, I$_2$O$_5$
7	$+7$	—	HClO$_4$, Cl$_2$O$_7$	HBrO$_4$	HIO$_4$, IF$_7$

of one. The species in Table 12.2 illustrate the various valencies that the halogens may possess. Notice that valencies of 3, 5 or 7 occur only in combinations of the halogens with elements of higher electronegativity, usually oxygen or fluorine, and the oxidation state is always $+3$, $+5$ or $+7$.

All the halogens can show a covalency or coordination number of two by forming a single covalent bond with one atom and a coordinate bond with another, e.g. in aluminium chloride (§8.5), the bridging chlorine atoms have a covalency of two.

12.4 Reactions of the halogens

The halogens are highly reactive, but there is a decrease in reactivity from fluorine to iodine. Little is known of astatine because it is radioactive and its isotopes have short half-lives. Much of its chemistry, however, can be predicted from a knowledge of the other halogens, particularly iodine. There is evidence that astatine forms the ions At$^-$, AtO$_3^-$, At$^+$ and AtI$_2^-$, and an interhalogen compound, AtI.

Reaction with other elements

Fluorine, because of its high reactivity, is rather difficult to handle. It combines directly with all other elements except nitrogen, helium, neon and argon. In many cases the reactions occur at room temperature, but with less reactive elements, e.g. xenon, gold and platinum, heat is required.

Many elements achieve higher oxidation states in combination with fluorine than with the other halogens, as the following examples illustrate:

AgF$_2$	CoF$_3$	AsF$_5$	PtF$_6$	SF$_6$	IF$_7$
AgCl	CoCl$_2$	AsCl$_3$	PtCl$_4$	SCl$_4$	ICl$_3$

Fluorine, like oxygen, stabilises elements in high oxidation states.

Chlorine, especially when heated, combines directly with most of the common metals and non-metals, with the exception of carbon, oxygen, nitrogen, helium, neon, argon and krypton. If more than one product is possible, and chlorine is present in excess, the higher chloride is

272

usually formed, e.g. PCl₅ (not PCl₃), and FeCl₃ (not FeCl₂). Bromine and iodine are similar in many respects to chlorine except that they do not react with any of the noble gases; furthermore, iodine does not combine with boron.

The reactions of the halogens with hydrogen to produce hydrogen halides provide an excellent illustration of the decrease in reactivity from fluorine to iodine. Fluorine and hydrogen combine explosively, even at −253 °C (20 K), at which temperature fluorine is a solid and hydrogen is a liquid. Chlorine and hydrogen react very slowly at room temperature in the dark, but in the presence of sunlight or ultraviolet light an explosive free radical chain reaction occurs, cf. the reaction between chlorine and methane.

Initiation

$$Cl_2 \xrightarrow{\text{light}} 2Cl^{\cdot}$$

Chain propagation

$$H_2 + Cl^{\cdot} \rightarrow HCl + H^{\cdot}$$
$$H^{\cdot} + Cl_2 \rightarrow HCl + Cl^{\cdot}$$

Chain termination

$$H^{\cdot} + H^{\cdot} \rightarrow H_2$$
$$Cl^{\cdot} + Cl^{\cdot} \rightarrow Cl_2$$
$$H^{\cdot} + Cl^{\cdot} \rightarrow HCl$$

Chlorine and hydrogen can be made to combine non-explosively by passing them over a catalyst of activated charcoal, or by burning a jet of chlorine in hydrogen, or hydrogen in chlorine.

In the presence of ultraviolet light, bromine reacts with hydrogen by a non-explosive reversible free radical reaction. In the absence of light, but in the presence of a platinum catalyst, the two elements combine readily at 375 °C (648 K).

Hydrogen and iodine combine at about 400 °C (673 K), especially in the presence of a platinum catalyst. This reaction is a classical example of a reversible reaction. Light has no effect upon it.

Reaction with water

Fluorine is a powerful oxidant and oxidises water to oxygen:

$$2F_2 + 2H_2O = 4HF + O_2$$

Side reactions occur, resulting in the formation of small quantities of ozone, hydrogen peroxide and oxygen difluoride, OF_2. Recently, hypofluorous acid, HOF, has been identified as another product of the interaction of fluorine and water at 0 °C (273 K).

Chlorine, bromine and iodine are less powerful oxidants than fluorine and undergo disproportionation with water. Chlorine and bromine are fairly soluble in water to give solutions known as 'chlorine water' and 'bromine water' respectively. Iodine, in contrast, is sparingly soluble. Two equilibria are established in aqueous solutions of halogens, e.g.

$$Cl_2(g) + aq \rightleftharpoons Cl_2(aq)$$
$$Cl_2(aq) + H_2O \rightleftharpoons HCl + HClO \qquad K = 4.2 \times 10^{-4}$$

In the second equilibrium, hydrated chlorine molecules react with water to produce low concentrations of hydrochloric acid and hypochlorous acid, as indicated by the low value of the equilibrium constant. Similar reactions occur in aqueous solutions of bromine and iodine, but the concentrations of the corresponding acids are even lower than those obtained from chlorine. For bromine $K = 7.2 \times 10^{-9}$, and for iodine $K = 2.0 \times 10^{-13}$.

Hypochlorous acid, HClO, and hypobromous acid, HBrO, are both powerful oxidising agents, which accounts in part for the oxidising properties of chlorine water and bromine water.

Reaction with alkalis

In many respects the reactions of the halogens with alkalis resemble those with water. Thus, fluorine oxidises concentrated alkalis to oxygen:

$$2F_2 + 4HO^- = 4F^- + O_2 + 2H_2O$$

With dilute alkalis (approximately 2 per cent) oxygen difluoride is formed:

$$2F_2 + 2HO^- = 2F^- + OF_2 + H_2O$$

Chlorine, bromine and iodine are far more soluble in solutions of alkalis than they are in water alone, because the acid-forming equilibria are displaced towards the right by reaction with hydroxide ions:

$$X_2(aq) + H_2O \rightleftharpoons HX \quad + \quad HXO \qquad (X = Cl, Br \text{ or } I)$$
$$\Big\downarrow HO^- \qquad\qquad \Big\downarrow HO^-$$
$$X^- + H_2O \quad XO^- + H_2O$$

The overall disproportionation reaction is therefore as follows:

$$X_2 + 2HO^- = X^- + XO^- + H_2O$$

Hypohalite ions, XO^-, show an increasing tendency, in the order $IO^- > BrO^- > ClO^-$, to disproportionate in alkaline solution into halide and halate ions:

$$3XO^- = 2X^- + XO_3^-$$

In cold dilute alkaline solution the hypochlorite ion, ClO^-, is reasonably stable, and as a result chlorine dissolves in cold dilute solutions of alkalis to form a chloride and a hypochlorite in a 1 : 1 mole ratio:

$$Cl_2 + 2HO^- = Cl^- + ClO^- + H_2O$$

At temperatures above 75 °C (348 K) and in concentrated alkali the hypochlorite ion rapidly disproportionates, and under these conditions chlorine dissolves in alkalis to form chloride and chlorate ions:

$$3Cl_2 + 6HO^- = 5Cl^- + ClO_3^- + 3H_2O$$

The hypobromite ion, BrO^-, is stable at 0 °C (273 K), but above this temperature it rapidly disproportionates into bromide ions and the bromate ion, BrO_3^-. The hypoiodite ion, IO^-, disproportionates at all temperatures into iodide ions and the iodate ion, IO_3^-. Thus, when bromine or iodine is dissolved in aqueous alkali at room temperature the following overall reactions occur:

$$3Br_2 + 6HO^- = 5Br^- + BrO_3^- + 3H_2O$$
$$3I_2 + 6HO^- = 5I^- + IO_3^- + 3H_2O$$

The hypochlorites of sodium and calcium are particularly important. An aqueous solution of sodium hypochlorite, commonly used as a bleach or disinfectant, is produced by the electrolysis of a cold aqueous solution of sodium chloride. Hydroxide ions, which are present around the cathode after discharge of hydrogen ions, react with the chlorine evolved at the anode to give hypochlorite ions. Calcium hypochlorite, in the form of 'bleaching powder', is made by passing chlorine over solid calcium hydroxide. Bleaching powder is a mixture of a basic hypochlorite and a basic chloride, of formulae $Ca_3(OCl)_2(OH)_4$ and $Ca_2Cl_2(OH)_2 \cdot H_2O$ respectively.

Redox properties of the halogens

Electron affinities, i.e. the enthalpy changes accompanying

$$X(g) + e^- = X^-(g)$$

are unsuitable for comparing the oxidising powers of the halogens. This is partly because reactions of the halogens involve molecules, not atoms, and partly because hydrated ions are usually formed, not gaseous ions.

If we consider the more realistic change

$$X_2 + 2e^- + aq = 2X^-(aq)$$

we find that the standard electrode potential ($E^{\ominus}$) provides a reliable guide to oxidising power, for it expresses the tendency of halogen molecules to be reduced to hydrated ions in solution. On this basis the oxidising power of the halogens decreases from fluorine to iodine, as the $E^{\ominus}$ values become less positive (§5.2).

Fluorine is the most powerful oxidant of all, which explains why fluoride ions can be oxidised only by electrolysis. In aqueous solution fluorine oxidises chloride, bromide and iodide ions to the free halogens:

$$F_2 + 2X^-(aq) = 2F^-(aq) + X_2 \qquad (X = Cl, \text{ Br or I})$$

These are often called *displacement reactions*, because halogens are displaced from their salts by other halogens which are more powerful oxidising agents. Similarly, chlorine oxidises bromide and iodide ions, and bromine oxidises iodide ions. Iodine is a relatively weak oxidant and does not oxidise other halide ions, except the astatide ion, At^-. The iodide ion is, in fact, a good reductant, because it readily loses its electron to form iodine.

Fluorine is seldom used as an oxidant because it is difficult to handle and its reactions tend to be rather vigorous. Chlorine and bromine do not suffer from these drawbacks and are in common use. In aqueous solution the oxidising action of chlorine arises from chlorine molecules and hypochlorous acid:

$$\tfrac{1}{2}Cl_2 + e^- = Cl^- \qquad\qquad E^\ominus = +1.36 \text{ V}$$
$$HClO + H^+(aq) + e^- = \tfrac{1}{2}Cl_2 + H_2O \qquad E^\ominus = +1.64 \text{ V}$$

Several examples of the use of chlorine and bromine as oxidants occur throughout this book, but for convenience a few are listed below.

$$X_2 + SO_3^{2-} + H_2O = 2X^- + SO_4^{2-} + 2H^+(aq) \qquad (X = Cl \text{ or } Br)$$
$$4X_2 + S_2O_3^{2-} + 5H_2O = 8X^- + 2SO_4^{2-} + 10H^+(aq) \qquad (X = Cl \text{ or } Br)$$

Although iodine is a much weaker oxidant than the other halogens, it does oxidise hydrogen sulphide and the thiosulphate ion:

$$X_2 + H_2S = 2HX + S \qquad (X = Cl, \text{ Br or I})$$
$$I_2 + 2S_2O_3^{2-} = 2I^- + S_4O_6^{2-}$$

The latter reaction is used in the laboratory for the quantitative estimation of iodine:

$$1 \text{ mol } I_2 \equiv 2 \text{ mol } Na_2S_2O_3$$

In anhydrous conditions chlorine and, to a lesser extent, bromine may act as oxidants by removing hydrogen from certain molecules, e.g.

$$CH_4 + Cl_2 = CH_3Cl + HCl$$
$$2NH_3 + 6Cl_2 = 2NCl_3 + 6HCl$$

Iodine is a weaker oxidant in this respect, although it does oxidise ammonia. Fluorine reacts explosively with many organic compounds.

12.5 Quantitative aspects of the properties of the halogens

In this section comparisons are made by using standard enthalpy changes ($\Delta H^{\ominus}$) instead of the more rigorous standard free energy changes ($\Delta G^{\ominus}$), but this does not invalidate the conclusions that are reached in the discussion.

The length and strength of the bond in halogen molecules

	F_2	Cl_2	Br_2	I_2
bond length/nm	0.142	0.199	0.228	0.267
bond dissociation enthalpy/ kJ mol^{-1} at 298 K	158	242	193	151

The covalent bond in a halogen molecule is formed by the overlap of singly filled p orbitals in the outermost shell of the halogen atoms. From chlorine to iodine the strength of the bond decreases as the length increases. Let us consider (Fig. 12.2) the overlap of the 3p orbitals in chlorine and the 5p orbitals in iodine.

The Cl—Cl bond is shorter than the I—I bond because a 3p orbital is smaller than a 5p orbital. The bonding electrons in a chlorine molecule are highly concentrated around the internuclear axis and effectively screen the two nuclei from each other to produce a relatively

Singly filled 5p orbitals of iodine atoms

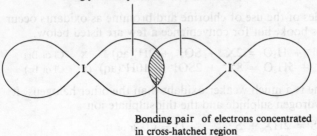

Bonding pair of electrons concentrated in cross-hatched region

Singly filled 3p orbitals of chlorine atoms

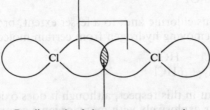

Bonding pair of electrons concentrated in cross-hatched region

Fig. 12.2 The overlap of p orbitals in chlorine and iodine molecules. The bonding electrons are localised in the overlap region between the two orbitals.

strong bond. In contrast, the bonding electrons in iodine are less concentrated in the region between the two nuclei because of the more diffuse nature of the 5p orbitals. Consequently, the bonding electrons are relatively inefficient at screening the nuclei from each other, and the I——I bond is weaker than the Cl——Cl bond. The bond in the bromine molecule is intermediate in length and strength between the bonds in molecules of chlorine and molecules of iodine.

The shortness of the bond in the fluorine molecule is due to the fact that a 2p orbital is smaller than other p orbitals, but the weakness of the F——F bond is rather unexpected, especially in view of the above discussion. The explanation is that when any two small atoms are covalently bonded together the internuclear distance is short, and the lone pairs of electrons on the atoms are particularly close to each other. As a result, there is a repulsion between these electron pairs and the bond is weakened (Fig. 12.3).

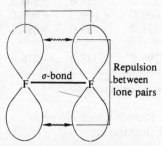

Fig. 12.3 Representation of the repulsion between two lone pairs of electrons on adjacent atoms in the F_2 molecule.

This theory is supported by the facts that the O——O bond in hydrogen peroxide (0.132 nm) and the N——N bond in hydrazine (0.146 nm) are also weak, with bond dissociation enthalpies of 146 and 163 kJ mol⁻¹ respectively. In halogen molecules other than fluorine, the lone pairs of electrons are relatively far apart and repulsion between them is unimportant.

The high reactivity of fluorine

Whenever a halogen reacts, the bond in the X_2 molecule is broken. Since the bond in a fluorine molecule is weaker than that in a chlorine molecule, it is not surprising that fluorine reacts more readily than chlorine. However, there are other factors which also need to be considered, depending on whether the compound formula is ionic or covalent, as the following calculations indicate.

Ionic compounds

Let us consider the standard enthalpies of formation ($\Delta H_f^{\ominus}$) of the sodium halides:

$$Na(s) + \tfrac{1}{2}X_2 = NaX(s) \qquad \Delta H_f^{\ominus} = ? \text{ where } X = F, Cl, Br \text{ or } I$$

By means of a Born–Haber cycle (§4.5), we can calculate the standard enthalpy of formation in each case (Table 12.3). The enthalpies of formation become decreasingly exothermic from the fluoride to the iodide, with the result that the reactions become less vigorous and the driving force for the reactions becomes weaker. We therefore observe a decrease in the reactivity of the halogens from fluorine to iodine.

Table 12.3 Standard enthalpy data for the formation of crystalline sodium halides.

Step	Standard enthalpy change/kJ mol^{-1}			
	F	Cl	Br	I
$\tfrac{1}{2}X_2 = X(g)$	$+79.1$	$+121.0$	$+112.0$	$+107.0$
$X(g) + e^- = X^-(g)$	-342.0	-358.0	-336.0	-308.0
$Na(s) = Na^+(g)$†	$+609.0$	$+609.0$	$+609.0$	$+609.0$
$Na^+(g) + X^-(g) = NaX(s)$	-902.0	-771.0	-733.0	-684.0
$\Delta H_f^{\ominus}$	-555.9	-399.0	-348.0	-276.0

† Sum of enthalpy of atomisation and first ionisation enthalpy of sodium.

The data in Table 12.3 show that the two factors which are principally responsible for the high reactivity of fluorine are:

(i) the weakness of the F——F bond;
(ii) the high lattice enthalpy of sodium fluoride, which is a consequence of the small size of the fluoride ion.

The decrease in reactivity from chlorine to iodine stems from the decreasing electron affinities of the halogens and, more importantly, from the decrease in lattice enthalpy as the size of the halide ion increases. These arguments apply also to the formation of crystalline ionic halides of other metallic elements. We can extend the arguments to the formation of ionic halides in solution by considering hydration enthalpies, i.e. $\Delta H^{\ominus}$ for the change

$$Na^+(g) + X^-(g) \xrightarrow{\ aq\ } Na^+(aq) + X^-(aq)$$

in place of lattice enthalpies.

Covalent compounds

If we consider the covalent halides of a particular element, we again find that the enthalpies of formation become decreasingly exothermic from the fluoride to the iodide. As before, the weakness of the F——F bond is an important factor, but of greater significance is the fact that fluorine forms very strong covalent bonds with most other elements.

To illustrate this point, let us consider the enthalpies of the reactions:

$$C(s) + 2X_2 = CX_4 \qquad \Delta H_f^{\ominus} = ? \text{ where } X = F, Cl, Br \text{ or } I$$

The data in Table 12.4 show that in this case the strength of the carbon–halogen bond makes the greatest contribution to the overall enthalpy change, and is primarily responsible for the fall in reactivity from fluorine to iodine.

Table 12.4 Calculated enthalpies of formation of the tetrahalomethanes.

Step	Standard enthalpy change/kJ mol^{-1}			
	F	Cl	Br	I
$2X_2 = 4X(g)$	+316.4	+484.0	+448.0	+428.0
$C(s) = C(g)$	+715.0	+715.0	+715.0	+715.0
$C(g) + 4X(g) = CX_4(g)$†	−1 936.0	−1 352.0	−1 104.0	−952.0
calculated ΔH_f	−904.6	−153.0	+59.0	+191.0

† These values are four times the negative average bond dissociation enthalpies of the bonds concerned.

Standard electrode potentials

The standard electrode potentials $(E^{\ominus})$ of the halogens provide us with a quantitative measure of their ability to act as oxidising agents by removing electrons from other species. This is because standard electrode potential is related (§7.3) to the standard free energy change $(\Delta G^{\ominus})$ accompanying the process:

$$\tfrac{1}{2}X_2 + e^- = X^-(aq)$$

$\Delta G^{\ominus}$ is in turn related to the overall enthalpy change $(\Delta H^{\ominus})$, which can be calculated from the enthalpy changes for the contributing steps (Table 12.5).

Table 12.5 Standard enthalpy changes involved in the overall process $\tfrac{1}{2}X_2 + e^- = X^-(aq)$.

Step	Standard enthalpy change/kJ mol^{-1}			
	F	Cl	Br	I
$\tfrac{1}{2}X_2 = X(g)$	+79.1	+121.0	+112.0	+107.0
$X(g) + e^- = X^-(g)$	−342.0	−358.0	−336.0	−308.0
$X^-(g) + (aq) = X^-(aq)$	−506.0	−364.0	−335.0	−293.0
∴ $\tfrac{1}{2}X_2 + e^- = X^-(aq)$	−768.9	−601.0	−559.0	−494.0
$E^{\ominus}/V$	+2.87	+1.36	+1.07	+0.54

The tendency for the halogens to act as oxidants decreases from fluorine to iodine as the overall enthalpy change becomes less exothermic and the $E^{\ominus}$ values become less positive. Despite its low electron affinity (§4.5), fluorine has the most positive $E^{\ominus}$ value and thus shows the greatest tendency to remove electrons from other species to form hydrated halide ions. Fluorine is therefore the most powerful oxidant in this group.

Electronegativity

The electronegativity of the halogens decreases from fluorine, the most electronegative element of all, to iodine:

$$x_F = 4.0 \quad x_{Cl} = 3.0 \quad x_{Br} = 2.8 \quad x_I = 2.5$$

For the halides of any given element, the difference between the electronegativity of the halogen and that of the element increases on progressing from the iodide to the fluoride. Thus, for halides of metallic elements, the bonding becomes decreasingly covalent or increasingly ionic in this order. For example, the iodides, bromides and chlorides of aluminium and tin(IV) are covalent, but their fluorides are ionic. Non-metallic elements have higher electronegativities than metals and all their halides are covalent, but the same trend is again encountered, i.e. the polarity of the bonding increases from the iodide to the fluoride of a particular element.

Because of the exceptionally high electronegativity of fluorine, hydrogen bonding occurs in anhydrous hydrogen fluoride but not in the other hydrogen halides (§4.9).

12.6 Compounds of the halogens

Almost all elements form compounds with the halogens, and for the most part these are discussed in other chapters. Here, we shall first make a few generalisations about the halides of metals and non-metals, and then consider hydrogen halides, oxoacids, interhalogens and a few other important compounds in more detail.

Metal halides

Many hydrated metal halides are prepared by dissolving the metal or its oxide, hydroxide or carbonate in the appropriate hydrohalic acid. The anhydrous halides may be obtained by heating the metal in a stream of dry halogen or hydrogen halide. Metals such as tin or iron, which exhibit two common valency states (oxidation states), generally achieve the higher state with the free halogen and the lower state with the hydrogen halide, e.g.

$$Sn + 2I_2 = SnI_4$$
$$Sn + 2HI = SnI_2 + H_2$$

Exceptions to this generalisation are:

$$Fe + I_2 = FeI_2 \quad \text{(not FeI}_3\text{)}$$
$$2Cu + I_2 = 2CuI \quad \text{(not CuI}_2\text{)}$$

The halides of noble metals, such as gold or platinum, are obtained readily only by direct combination of the elements.

Many anhydrous metal halides differ considerably from the corresponding hydrated compounds. Anhydrous aluminium chloride, for example, is covalent, but the hydrated salt, $AlCl_3 \cdot 6H_2O$, is ionic (§8.5). Anhydrous metal halides, with a few exceptions such as $BaCl_2$, cannot be prepared by heating the hydrated halides because the latter undergo hydrolysis when heated to give either a hydroxide or a basic chloride, e.g.

$$AlCl_3 \cdot 6H_2O = Al(OH)_3 + 3HCl + 3H_2O$$
$$MgCl_2 \cdot 6H_2O = MgCl(OH) + HCl + 5H_2O$$

If hydrolysis does occur on heating, the water can often be removed by refluxing the hydrated salt with reagents that react with water, e.g.

$$NiCl_2 \cdot 6H_2O + 6SOCl_2 = NiCl_2 + 6SO_2 + 12HCl$$
$$FeCl_2 \cdot 6H_2O + 6CH_3C(OCH_3)_2CH_3 = FeCl_2 + 6CH_3COCH_3 + 12CH_3OH$$
2,2-dimethoxypropane

Some anhydrous metal chlorides can be prepared by heating the metal oxide with tetrachloromethane, or by heating a mixture of the metal oxide and carbon in a stream of chlorine, e.g.

$$TiO_2 + CCl_4 = TiCl_4 + CO_2$$
$$SnO_2 + C + 2Cl_2 = SnCl_4 + CO_2$$

Ionic metal halides possess the usual properties of electrovalent compounds, i.e. they have high melting temperatures, and they conduct electricity in the fused state or in aqueous solution. In contrast, covalent metal halides have low melting temperatures and do not conduct electricity when molten. They are usually anhydrous, and react with water to produce hydrated metal ions, e.g.

$$AlCl_3 + 6H_2O = [Al(H_2O)_6]^{3+} + 3Cl^- \quad \text{(§8.5)}$$

According to Fajans' rules (§4.4), covalency is promoted by a low cationic radius or high cationic charge. Thus, from top to bottom of a periodic group, as the surface charge density of the metal ions decreases, the distortion of any given halide ion becomes less pronounced and the bonding becomes more ionic or less covalent. In group 2A, for example, the halides of beryllium are covalent, those of magnesium are ionic with some covalent characteristics, but those of calcium, strontium and barium are essentially ionic. The effect of cationic charge on halide ion distortion can be seen in the chlorides of the metallic elements of the third period, i.e. NaCl (ionic), $MgCl_2$ (ionic with some covalency) and $AlCl_3$ (covalent).

We must also remember that the ease of distortion of halide ions increases with ionic radius from fluoride to iodide. Thus, the halides of a particular metal become increasingly covalent in character from the fluoride to the iodide.

Non-metal halides

The halides of non-metals are usually prepared by direct combination of the elements, and many examples are quoted throughout this book. Multivalent elements usually reach their highest valency if an excess of the halogen is used, but a lower valency results if the halogen is deficient. The formation of the chlorides of phosphorus (§10.5) illustrates this point.

Most non-metal halides have low melting and boiling temperatures, which increase with relative molecular mass. In general, the compounds are soluble in non-polar solvents and are hydrolysed by water, e.g.

$$BI_3 + 3H_2O = H_3BO_3 + 3HI$$
$$SiCl_4 + 2H_2O = SiO_2(aq) + 4HCl$$

Tetrachloromethane is exceptional in its resistance to hydrolysis (§9.6).

Hydrogen halides

The hydrogen halides are among the most important halogen compounds. In the anhydrous state their names are:

HF hydrogen fluoride   HBr hydrogen bromide
HCl hydrogen chloride   HI   hydrogen iodide

Preparation

Direct combination

Direct combination (§12.4) is a useful means of preparing hydrogen chloride, but not the other hydrogen halides. The reaction between hydrogen and fluorine is far too violent to be of use, while the reactions between hydrogen and bromine or iodine are reversible and do not give hydrogen bromide or hydrogen iodide in the pure state.

Displacement reactions

Hydrogen chloride is displaced from mixtures of concentrated sulphuric acid and crystalline ionic chlorides at room temperature (§11.4). At higher temperatures, the hydrogensulphate which is formed reacts with further ionic chloride to give more hydrogen chloride.

Displacement can also be used for the preparation of hydrogen fluoride from ionic fluorides. Hydrogen bromide and hydrogen iodide, however, are oxidised by concentrated sulphuric acid (see below) and therefore cannot be prepared in this way.

Hydrolysis of phosphorus trihalides

Gaseous hydrogen halides are evolved when water is added dropwise to phosphorus trihalides, other than the fluoride. If the water is added in large amounts, the hydrogen halide dissolves in it and is not isolated. The method is particularly useful for preparing hydrogen bromide and hydrogen iodide, for which purpose the phosphorus trihalide is usually made *in situ*. Hydrogen bromide can be obtained by adding bromine dropwise to a paste of red phosphorus and water, while hydrogen iodide is conveniently produced by adding water dropwise to a mixture of red phosphorus and iodine:

$$2P + 3X_2 = 2PX_3$$
$$PX_3 + 3H_2O = H_2PHO_3 + 3HX \qquad \text{(X = Br or I)}$$

Any halogen vapour which escapes with the hydrogen halide is removed by passing the gases through a tube packed with moist red phosphorus.

The action of halogens on covalent hydrides

The halogens are reduced to hydrogen halides by hydrogen sulphide:

$$H_2S + X_2 = S + 2HX \qquad \text{(X = F, Cl, Br or I)}$$

Hydrogen chloride is often obtained as a by-product of the reactions between hydrocarbons and chlorine.

General properties

Table 12.6 shows that hydrogen–halogen bonds decrease in both strength and ionic character as the halogen atoms increase in size.

Table 12.6 Some properties of the hydrogen halides.

	HF	HCl	HBr	HI
$\Delta H_f^{\ominus}$/kJ mol^{-1}	−269	−92.3	−36.2	+25.9
bond dissociation enthalpy/kJ mol^{-1}	+562	+431	+366	+299
boiling temperature/°C	+20	−85	−67	−35
melting temperature/°C	−83	−115	−88	−51
% ionic character in H—X bond	43	17	13	7
pK_a (in 1 M solutions)	3.25	−7.4	−9.5	−10

In line with the decreasing bond dissociation enthalpy, the thermal stability of the hydrogen halides decreases from the fluoride to the iodide. For example, hydrogen iodide decomposes at 400 °C (673 K), while hydrogen fluoride and hydrogen chloride are quite stable at this temperature.

At room temperature the hydrogen halides are gaseous, although the fluoride is readily liquefied by cooling. The gases are colourless, but in contact with moist air white fumes are formed due to the production of droplets of the hydrohalic acid. Hydrogen bonding occurs in hydrogen fluoride and accounts for its anomalously high melting and boiling temperatures (§4.9). The effect is absent in the other hydrogen halides.

Liquid hydrogen fluoride self-ionises to a limited extent and is thus a weak conductor of electricity:

$$2HF \rightleftharpoons H_2F^+ + F^-$$

cf.

$$2H_2O \rightleftharpoons H_3O^+ + HO^-$$

Acidic properties

The hydrogen halides are extremely soluble in water; e.g. 1 volume of water dissolves approximately 500 volumes of a hydrogen halide at $0 \,°C$ (273 K) and a pressure of 1 atm (100 kPa). The high solubility is due to ionisation in water:

$$HX(g) + H_2O \rightleftharpoons H_3O^+ + X^- \qquad \text{(X = F, Cl, Br or I)}$$

Solutions of hydrogen halides are therefore acidic and are known generally as 'hydrohalic acids'. Their individual names are:

HF hydrofluoric acid   HBr hydrobromic acid
HCl hydrochloric acid   HI   hydriodic acid

Hydrochloric, hydrobromic and hydriodic acids are almost completely ionised and are therefore strong acids. The pK_a values (Table 12.6) indicate that acid strength increases as the hydrogen−halogen bonds become weaker. This is to be expected because hydrogen−halogen bonds are broken during ionisation. In contrast, hydrofluoric acid is a weak acid in dilute solution because of the great strength of the hydrogen−fluorine bond; e.g. in 0.1 M solution it is approximately 10 per cent ionised. In solutions of 5−15 M, however, hydrofluoric acid is a much stronger acid. The reason is that two equilibria exist in aqueous solutions of hydrogen fluoride:

$$HF + H_2O \rightleftharpoons H_3O^+ + F^- \qquad\qquad\qquad\qquad (1)$$
$$HF + F^- \rightleftharpoons HF_2^- \qquad\qquad K = 5.2 \text{ mol}^{-1} \text{ dm}^3 \qquad (2)$$

At high concentrations of HF, equilibrium (2) is important, since it removes fluoride ions from solution and hence displaces equilibrium (1) to the right. Thus, as the solution becomes more concentrated, there is an increase in the degree of ionisation of HF and in the hydrogen ion concentration of the solution.

Neutron diffraction measurements of the hydrogendifluoride ion, HF_2^-, suggest that the hydrogen atom lies midway between the two fluorine atoms, and that the H——F distance in the ion (0.113 nm) is considerably greater than in the HF molecule (0.092 nm). It has been proposed that the ion has a 'one electron bond' structure represented thus:

$$[F\text{-----}H\text{----}F]^-$$

The ion is *not* formed by hydrogen bonding between the HF molecule and the F^- ion.

Several stable salts containing the hydrogendifluoride ion are known, e.g. KHF_2 and NH_4HF_2. The remaining hydrohalic acids do not readily form the corresponding hydrogendihalide ions, HX_2^-, because of:

(i) the lower surface charge density of chloride, bromide and iodide ions, which causes the attraction of these ions for hydrogen halide molecules to be weak;

(ii) the low concentration of non-ionised hydrogen halide in solution.

The hydrohalic acids exhibit typical acidic properties. For example, they form salts with bases, and react with metals above hydrogen in the electrochemical series to form hydrogen. Hydrofluoric acid and moist (but not dry) hydrogen fluoride rapidly attack glass or silica to form hexafluorosilicic(IV) acid:

$$SiO_2 + 4HF = SiF_4 + 2H_2O$$
$$SiF_4 + 2HF = H_2SiF_6$$

Because hydrogen fluoride is formed when fluorine reacts with water, moist fluorine also attacks glass and silica. Dry hydrogen fluoride is usually stored in mild steel cylinders, and hydrofluoric acid in polythene bottles.

Ease of oxidation

Hydrogen iodide is easily oxidised to iodine and is thus a good reducing agent. Hydriodic acid responds to atmospheric oxygen and a variety of oxidising agents:

$$2HI = I_2 + 2H^+(aq) + 2e^-$$

Acidic solutions of iodides are also readily oxidised, a property which is used as a test for oxidising agents. A positive result is denoted by the liberation of iodine, which gives a blue-black coloration with starch.

Hydrogen bromide is more difficult to oxidise than hydrogen iodide, and is therefore a weaker reductant. For example, hydrogen bromide and ionic bromides slowly reduce concentrated sulphuric acid to sulphur dioxide:

$$2HBr + H_2SO_4 = Br_2 + SO_2 + 2H_2O$$

but hydrogen iodide and ionic iodides rapidly reduce sulphuric acid not only to sulphur dioxide but also to hydrogen sulphide:

$$8HI + H_2SO_4 = 4I_2 + H_2S + 4H_2O$$

The addition of concentrated sulphuric acid to crystalline ionic bromides thus produces a red-brown vapour of bromine and white fumes of unoxidised hydrogen bromide, together with sulphur dioxide. Ionic iodides, similarly treated, produce iodine as a black solid and violet vapour. Sulphur dioxide and hydrogen sulphide are also given off as gases, but react together to some extent to form sulphur.

Additional examples of the powerful reducing properties of hydrogen iodide include the reduction of:

(i) nitric acid to nitrous acid:

$$HNO_3 + 2HI = HNO_2 + I_2 + H_2O$$

(ii) dinitrogen oxide to the ammonium ion:

$$N_2O + 10HI = 2NH_4^+ + 2I^- + 4I_2 + H_2O$$

Hydrogen chloride is unaffected by concentrated sulphuric acid and is oxidised only by strong oxidants such as manganese(IV) oxide or potassium permanganate. Hydrogen fluoride can be oxidised only by electrolysis. There is thus a well defined increase in the ease of oxidation of hydrogen halides from the fluoride to the iodide.

Oxoacids of the halogens and their salts

Hypohalous acids

The recently discovered hypofluorous acid, HOF (§12.4), is the only known oxoacid of fluorine. No salts of this acid have yet been reported.

Low concentrations of hypohalous acids derived from chlorine, bromine and iodine are produced when these halogens are dissolved in water (§12.4). The equilibria:

$$X_2 + H_2O \rightleftharpoons HX + HXO \qquad (X = Cl, Br \text{ or } I)$$

can be displaced to the right, thereby increasing the yield of hypohalous acid, by the addition of mercury(II) oxide. This compound removes halide ions, derived from the hydrohalic acids, by forming covalent mercury(II) halides, e.g.

$$Cl_2 + H_2O \rightleftharpoons HCl + HClO$$
$$HCl \rightleftharpoons H^+(aq) + Cl^-$$
$$HgO + 2H^+(aq) + 2Cl^- = HgCl_2 + H_2O$$

overall equation: $2Cl_2 + HgO + H_2O = HgCl_2 + 2HClO$

The hypohalous acids are known only in aqueous solution and are very weak, with the following pK_a values:

HClO 7.43   HBrO 8.70   HIO 10.52

They are powerful oxidants, more so than the corresponding free halogens, e.g.

$$HClO + H^+(aq) + e^- = \tfrac{1}{2}Cl_2 + H_2O \qquad E^\ominus = +1.64 \text{ V}$$

cf.

$$\tfrac{1}{2}Cl_2 + e^- = Cl^- \qquad E^\ominus = +1.36 \text{ V}$$

The hypohalous acids are unstable. Hypochlorous acid slowly decomposes by two disproportionation reactions:

$$3HClO = 2HCl + HClO_3$$
$$2HClO = 2HCl + O_2$$

Both reactions are accelerated by light, particularly the latter, for which the hydroxides of nickel and cobalt also act as catalysts. Hypobromous and hypoiodous acid are less stable than hypochlorous acid and disproportionate rapidly, e.g.

$$3HBrO = 2HBr + HBrO_3$$

The only important salts of the hypohalous acids are the hypochlorites, which are powerful oxidants. For example, sodium hypochlorite and bleaching powder (§12.4) are used as bleaching agents and for the preparation of lead(IV) oxide. In the presence of catalysts, such as cobalt(II) or nickel(II) ions, the hypochlorite ion decomposes to yield oxygen:

$$2ClO^- = 2Cl^- + O_2$$

Halous acids

Chlorous acid, $HClO_2$, is the only known acid of this type. It is prepared by the addition of sulphuric acid to barium chlorite (see below):

$$Ba(ClO_2)_2 + H_2SO_4 = BaSO_4(s) + 2HClO_2$$

Chlorous acid is a powerful oxidant, and it rapidly disproportionates:

$$8HClO_2 = 6ClO_2 + Cl_2 + 4H_2O$$

oxidation number of Cl $\quad +3 \qquad\quad +4 \qquad 0$

Salts of chlorous acid, i.e. chlorites, are also oxidants and are prepared by reacting chlorine dioxide with either the hydroxide or peroxide of a metal, e.g.

$$2ClO_2 + 2NaOH = NaClO_2 + NaClO_3 + H_2O$$
$$2ClO_2 + BaO_2 = Ba(ClO_2)_2 + O_2$$

The salts are more stable than the parent acid and undergo disproportionation only when heated:

$$3ClO_2^- = 2ClO_3^- + Cl^-$$

oxidation number of Cl $\quad +3 \qquad +5 \qquad -1$

Sodium chlorite is used commercially as a mild bleaching agent for fibres, oils and waxes.

Halic acids

Chloric acid, $HClO_3$, bromic acid, $HBrO_3$, and iodic acid, HIO_3, are all known, but only the last named is sufficiently stable to be isolated in the pure state. Aqueous solutions of chloric acid and bromic acid are obtained by the addition of sulphuric acid to, respectively, the chlorates and bromates of barium:

$$Ba(XO_3)_2 + H_2SO_4 = BaSO_4(s) + 2HXO_3 \qquad (X = Cl\ or\ Br)$$

Iodic acid is more conveniently prepared by the oxidation of iodine with either nitric acid or chlorine:

$$3I_2 + 10HNO_3 = 6HIO_3 + 10NO + 2H_2O$$
$$I_2 + 5Cl_2 + 6H_2O = 2HIO_3 + 10HCl$$

Chloric and bromic acids are stable in dilute aqueous solution but are liable to decompose explosively if their concentrations exceed 50 per cent. In contrast, iodic acid is much more stable; for example, it can be obtained in the crystalline state, and when heated it decomposes non-explosively:

$$2HIO_3 = I_2O_5 + H_2O$$

Salts of the halic acids are readily prepared by dissolving the appropriate halogen in a hot concentrated solution of an alkali:

$$3X_2 + 6HO^- = XO_3^- + 5X^- + 3H_2O \qquad (X = Cl,\ Br\ or\ I)$$

The salts are more stable than the parent acids and decompose only when strongly heated. Potassium chlorate, for example, fuses before it decomposes into potassium perchlorate and oxygen:

$$2KClO_3 = KClO_4 + KCl + O_2$$

At higher temperatures, the perchlorate decomposes:

$$KClO_4 = KCl + 2O_2$$

Certain compounds, such as manganese(IV) oxide or lead(IV) oxide, catalyse the thermal decomposition of chlorates, so that they evolve oxygen before fusing and do not form perchlorates:

$$2KClO_3 = 2KCl + 3O_2$$

The halic acids and, in particular, their salts are used in the laboratory as powerful oxidising agents.

Perhalic acids

Perchloric acid

Pure perchloric acid is prepared by the hazardous procedure of vacuum distilling a mixture of potassium perchlorate and concentrated sulphuric acid:

$$KClO_4 + H_2SO_4 = KHSO_4 + HClO_4$$

Pure perchloric acid is extremely unstable and liable to decompose explosively. Aqueous solutions of the acid are more stable, but if organic material is present an explosive reaction is likely to occur. A crystalline hydrate of perchloric acid is known, of formula $HClO_4 \cdot H_2O$. This compound has been shown to be oxonium perchlorate, i.e. H_3O^+ ClO_4^-. Perchloric acid is almost completely ionised in aqueous solution and is regarded as the strongest known acid. Such is the strength of perchloric acid that it can force other acidic compounds to function as bases by accepting protons, e.g.

$$CH_3COOH + HClO_4 \rightleftharpoons CH_3COOH_2^+ + ClO_4^-$$

In cold dilute solution perchloric acid is a weak oxidant, but in hot concentrated solution it is a powerful and occasionally violent oxidant.

The salts of perchloric acid, in contrast to the parent acid, are reasonably stable and decompose only at high temperatures. The perchlorates of potassium, rubidium, caesium and ammonium are noteworthy for being sparingly soluble in water.

Perbromic acid

Perbromates, containing the BrO_4^- ion, have only recently been reported. They are prepared by oxidising bromates with either xenon difluoride or fluorine. Perbromic acid is reasonably stable in solution.

Periodic acids

Several weak acids containing iodine in a heptavalent state ($+7$ oxidation state) are known. Iodates are oxidised by hypochlorite ions or peroxodisulphate ions, $S_2O_8^{2-}$, to produce the best known periodic acid, orthoperiodic acid, H_5IO_6. This acid can be dehydrated on heating to form other periodic acids: diiodic acid, $H_4I_2O_9$, and periodic acid, HIO_4. The periodic acids and their salts are powerful oxidants; for example, they oxidise manganese(II) ions to permanganate ions.

Interhalogens

Interhalogens are binary compounds consisting of two halogens. Four types exist, as follows:

XX' e.g. ClF, BrF, BrCl, ICl, IBr
XX_3' e.g. ClF_3, BrF_3, IF_3, ICl_3
XX_5' e.g. BrF_5, IF_5
XX_7' e.g. IF_7

They are prepared by direct combination of the elements, and the shapes of their molecules can be predicted from the Sidgwick—Powell theory (§4.6). Except for iodine pentafluoride, IF_5, they are extremely reactive. The trifluorides of chlorine and bromine are used as fluorinating agents, and for converting metals or their oxides into fluorides.

Polyhalide ions

Polyhalide ions carry a single negative charge and comprise three or more halogen atoms. The best known example is the triiodide ion, I_3^-, which is formed by dissolving iodine in an aqueous solution of an ionic iodide:

$$I^- + I_2 \rightleftharpoons I_3^-$$

The stability of this ion is favoured by large non-distorting cations such as K^+, Rb^+, Cs^+ and $(C_2H_5)_4N^+$. Bromine and chlorine form the corresponding Br_3^- and Cl_3^- ions, but these are less stable than the triiodide ion. Other known polyhalide ions derived from a single element are I_5^-, I_7^- and I_9^-.

Mixed polyhalide ions, containing two different halogens, are prepared by reacting a finely powdered halide with the appropriate halogen or interhalogen, e.g.

$$CsI + Br_2 = Cs[IBr_2] \qquad \text{(contains } [IBr_2]^- \text{ ions)}$$
$$CsCl + ICl = Cs[ICl_2] \qquad \text{(contains } [ICl_2]^- \text{ ions)}$$
$$Cl^- + ICl_3 = [ICl_4]^-$$

The tetrachloroiodate(III) ion, $[ICl_4]^-$, has a square planar structure similar to that of xenon tetrafluoride (§4.6). Alkali metal salts of this ion are known.

Compounds containing cationic iodine

Iodine is not a metal, but it does show some tendency to form cations. Simple (i.e. uncomplexed) I^+ ions do not appear to exist, but the blue I_2^+ ion is produced by the oxidation of iodine molecules when iodine is dissolved in 60 per cent oleum.

Complexes in which the I^+ ion is stabilised by coordination with two ligands are reasonably stable. Pyridine (py) appears to be one of the best ligands for this purpose. Compounds containing the linear $[Ipy_2]^+$ complex ion, i.e.

$$\text{or} \qquad [C_5H_5N \rightarrow I \leftarrow NC_5H_5]^+$$

are prepared by adding a silver salt to a solution of iodine and pyridine in trichloromethane:

$$AgX + I_2 + 2py = [Ipy_2]X + AgI(s)$$

After filtering off the silver iodide, the compound $[Ipy_2]X$ is precipitated from the filtrate by the addition of petroleum ether.

Electrolysis of solutions of iodine–pyridine complexes, e.g. $[Ipy_2]NO_3$, yield iodine at the cathode, thus proving the existence of cationic iodine.

Complexes that contain I^{3+} ions stabilised by coordination are also believed to exist, e.g. $[I(CH_3COO)_3]$.

12.7 Summary of the properties of fluorine and its compounds

References have already been made to the fact that fluorine and its compounds differ significantly from the other halogens and their compounds. Some of the important differences are summarised below.

(i)   The bond in the fluorine molecule is weak, but fluorine forms exceptionally strong bonds with most other elements.
(ii) Fluorine has a limited covalency.
(iii) Fluorine is the most powerful oxidant and can be prepared only by electrolysis.
(iv) Hydrogen bonding occurs in hydrogen fluoride, but not the other hydrogen halides.
(v)   Hydrofluoric acid is a weak acid in dilute solution, but becomes stronger with increasing concentration. The remaining hydrohalic acids are strong at all concentrations.
(vi) Differences exist between the solubilities in water of some metal fluorides and the corresponding chlorides, bromides and iodides, e.g.
  (1) CaF_2 is insoluble, but $CaCl_2$, $CaBr_2$ and CaI_2 are soluble. This is due to the high lattice enthalpy of the fluoride;
  (2) AgF is soluble, but AgCl, AgBr and AgI are insoluble. In this case the high hydration enthalpy of the fluoride ion provides sufficient energy for the AgF lattice to be broken down.

12.8 Stabilisation of high oxidation states by fluorine or oxygen

Fluorine, like oxygen, is able to stabilise high oxidation states in a way that other elements cannot. There is no single reason for this property, and we must discuss ionic and covalent species separately.

Ionic species   In general, an ionic compound is stable if its lattice enthalpy exceeds the enthalpy required to form isolated ions from its constituent elements. The fluoride and oxide ions are relatively small, which tends to encourage high lattice enthalpies, and in certain cases (e.g. CoF_3 and MnO_2) the lattice enthalpy of a fluoride or an oxide is high enough to compensate for the large amount of energy required for the formation of high valency cations.

Covalent species   Three factors contribute to the stability of such species as SF_6, $Cr_2O_7^{2-}$ and MnO_4^-.

(i) The small size of fluorine and oxygen atoms. Because of this, they can pack easily around a central atom so that strong covalent bonds can be formed.

(ii) Both fluorine and oxygen form particularly strong bonds with many elements. The large amount of energy released during the formation of such bonds is in excess of that required to atomise the elements and raise the atoms to highly excited states.

(iii) The electronegativity of fluorine and oxygen. An atom in a high oxidation state has a great affinity for electrons and will attempt to gain electrons from the nearest available source, such as the atoms to which it is bonded. However, if it is joined to an atom of fluorine or oxygen, the high electronegativity of the latter prevents electron transfer.

12.9 Pseudohalogens

Pseudohalogens are compounds which bear some resemblance to the halogens. Their molecules consist of four or more atoms, and they give rise to mononegative *pseudohalide* ions. The most important pseudohalogens and their associated anions are as follows:

Pseudohalogen		Pseudohalide ion	
$(CN)_2$	cyanogen	CN^-	cyanide ion
$(OCN)_2$	oxocyanogen	OCN^-	cyanate ion
$(SCN)_2$	thiocyanogen	SCN^-	thiocyanate ion
—		N_3^-	azide ion

The pseudohalogen corresponding to the azide ion is unknown.

The pseudohalogens are volatile compounds consisting of symmetrical molecules, e.g.

$$N\equiv C-C\equiv N \qquad N\equiv C-S-S-C\equiv N$$

Like the halogens, the pseudohalogens can be prepared by oxidation of their associated anions, e.g.

$$4CN^- + 2Cu^{2+} = 2CuCN(s) + (CN)_2$$

cf.

$$4I^- + 2Cu^{2+} = 2CuI(s) + I_2$$
$$2SCN^- + MnO_2 + 4H^+(aq) = Mn^{2+} + (SCN)_2 + 2H_2O$$

cf.

$$2Cl^- + MnO_2 + 4H^+(aq) = Mn^{2+} + Cl_2 + 2H_2O$$

Although cyanogen is reasonably stable at room temperature, it polymerises to $(CN)_n$ on heating. Oxocyanogen and thiocyanogen are difficult to prepare because they either decompose or polymerise.

Cyanogen, at least, resembles the halogens in undergoing disproportionation in basic solution:

$$(CN)_2 + 2HO^- = CN^- + OCN^- + H_2O$$

cf.

$$Cl_2 + 2HO^- = Cl^- + ClO^- + H_2O$$

Acids which compare with the hydrohalic acids, HX, are known. They are:

HCN   hydrocyanic acid
HOCN   cyanic acid
HSCN   thiocyanic acid
HN_3 hydrazoic acid

However, they are all very weak acids and, apart from hydrocyanic acid, are highly unstable. Pure hydrazoic acid, for example, is liable to decompose explosively, and cyanic acid decomposes rapidly into carbon dioxide and ammonia in aqueous solution. Both HCN and HOCN polymerise in the pure state; the former may do so explosively.

Similarities also exist among metal salts. For example, the pseudohalide salts of mercury(I), lead(II) and silver are sparingly soluble in water, as are the corresponding halides. In crystalline salts the cyanide ion rotates, and thus acts as a spherical anion of radius 0.192 nm, a value which corresponds closely to that of the chloride ion, 0.181 nm. Consequently, some ionic chlorides and ionic cyanides, e.g. NaCl and NaCN, are isostructural.

Many of the pseudohalide ions form complexes with metal ions. The cyanate ion is perhaps an exception because, unlike the other pseudohalide ions, it decomposes in solution:

$$OCN^- + 2H_2O = NH_3 + HCO_3^-$$

In general, the pseudohalide ions form complexes with metal ions far more readily than do the halide ions. The cyanide ion is particularly outstanding in forming a large number of such complexes. Some of them, e.g. $[Fe(CN)_6]^{4-}$, are notable for their high stability.

Although the halogens readily form covalent compounds with non-metals, the same cannot be said of the pseudohalogens. There are relatively few covalent compounds containing, for example, SCN or OCN groups. Organic nitriles, RCN, are well known, but otherwise there are few examples of covalent pseudohalogen compounds. The cyanogen halides, FCN, ClCN, BrCN and ICN, are all known, as are interpseudohalogen-type compounds involving CN, e.g. N_3——CN and NCS——CN.

Chapter 13

The noble gases

The noble gases are helium, neon, argon, krypton, xenon and radon. Some important properties of these elements are set out in Table 13.1.

Table 13.1 Some properties of the noble gases.

	Helium	Neon	Argon	Krypton	Xenon	Radon
character	non-metal	non-metal	non-metal	non-metal	non-metal	non-m
atomic number	2	10	18	36	54	86
relative atomic mass	4.002 60	20.179	39.948	83.80	131.30	(222)†
outer electronic configuration	$1s^2$	$2s^22p^6$	$3s^23p^6$	$4s^24p^6$	$5s^25p^6$	$6s^26p^6$
valencies	none	none	none	2	2, 4, 6, 8	?
melting temperature/°C	−270	−249	−189	−157	−112	−71
boiling temperature/°C	−269	−246	−186	−152	−108	−61.8
volume per cent in dry air	5.2×10^{-4}	1.8×10^{-3}	0.93	1.1×10^{-4}	9×10^{-6}	6×1

† Mass number of the most stable isotope.

13.1 Occurrence and isolation of the elements

The noble gases are minor constituents of the atmosphere (Table 13.1). Neon, argon, krypton and xenon are obtained by the fractional distillation of liquefied air. The principal source of helium is natural hydrocarbon gas from the USA and Canada, which contains up to 8 per cent of the element. Helium is obtained by cooling the natural gas to −196 °C (77 K). At this temperature the only remaining gas is helium, which can be pumped off. The helium originates from α-particles emitted during the radioactive decay of uranium and thorium minerals present in the rocks. The α-particles remove electrons from the surrounding rocks and become helium atoms. Radon is produced by the radioactive decay of radium, and is obtained by pumping off the gas from above aqueous solutions of radium salts:

$$^{226}_{88}\text{Ra} = {}^{222}_{86}\text{Rn} + {}^{4}_{2}\text{He}$$

13.2 The structure of the elements

The noble gases are monoatomic in all physical states. The structure of solid radon is unknown, but the other noble gases, except helium, all crystallise in a cubic close packed structure (Fig. 13.1). Helium can be solidified only under pressures greater than 25 atm (2 500 kPa), to form what appears to be a hexagonal close packed structure.

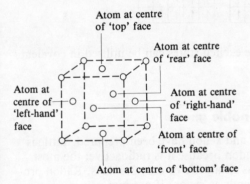

Atom at centre of 'top' face

Atom at centre of 'rear' face

Atom at centre of 'left-hand' face

Atom at centre of 'right-hand' face

Atom at centre of 'front' face

Atom at centre of 'bottom' face

○ represents an argon atom

Fig. 13.1 The structure of crystalline argon.

Weak van der Waals' forces of attraction exist between the atoms of noble gases. The melting and boiling temperatures increase from helium to radon as these forces increase in magnitude. The van der Waals' forces are weakest in helium. Because of this, and the small radius of its atoms, helium closely approaches an ideal gas in its behaviour.

13.3 Bonding and valency

The noble gases have very high ionisation enthalpies, and it is difficult for the outer electrons of their atoms to be used in forming chemical bonds. In view of this it is perhaps not surprising that the noble gases are characterised by a lack of chemical reactivity. The fact that they exist as individual atoms is an indication of this property. Ionisation enthalpies decrease with increasing atomic radius, because the outer electrons are less firmly held by the nucleus, and the heavier noble gases can enter into chemical bond formation. Krypton, xenon and, presumably, radon form compounds, but helium, neon and argon do not. Xenon in particular forms numerous compounds. By absorbing energy to promote electrons from 5s or 5p orbitals into the vacant 5d orbitals, this element can participate in two, four, six or eight covalent bonds as the following scheme illustrates:

	5s	5p	5d	number of unpaired electrons (= covalency)
ground state	↑↓	↑↓ ↑↓ ↑↓		0
first excited state	↑↓	↑↓ ↑↓ ↑	↑	2
second excited state	↑↓	↑↓ ↑ ↑	↑ ↑	4
third excited state	↑↓	↑ ↑ ↑	↑ ↑ ↑	6
fourth excited state	↑	↑ ↑ ↑	↑ ↑ ↑ ↑	8

The unpaired electrons of the excited states can be utilised in covalent bond formation.

13.4 Compounds of the noble gases

Only compounds of krypton and xenon have been prepared. Little is known of the chemistry of radon because it is radioactive; the most stable isotope, radon-222, has a half-life of only 3.8 days. Radon probably forms as many compounds as xenon, if not more.

Xenon

In 1962, N. Bartlett mixed xenon with platinum(VI) fluoride, PtF_6, and isolated red crystals of the first noble gas compound. This substance was at first thought to be xenon hexafluoroplatinate(V), $Xe[PtF_6]$, but the structure is now known to be more complex than this. Since that date several compounds of xenon with fluorine and oxygen, and one compound with chlorine, have been characterised. Xenon reacts directly with fluorine and chlorine: the oxygen compounds are obtained from the fluorides.

Fluorine and chlorine compounds

Xenon difluoride, XeF_2, a powerful oxidant, is prepared by heating xenon with a deficiency of fluorine to 400 °C (673 K). The molecule is linear.

Xenon tetrafluoride, XeF_4, is obtained as colourless crystals by heating a mixture of fluorine and xenon in the ratio 5 : 1 to 400 °C

(673 K) under a pressure of 6 atm (600 kPa). The molecule is square planar (§4.6). The compound disproportionates in water:

$$6XeF_4 + 12H_2O = 2XeO_3 + 4Xe + 3O_2 + 24HF$$

Xenon hexafluoride, XeF_6, is obtained by heating xenon with a large excess of fluorine to 250 °C (523 K) under a pressure of 50 atm (5 000 kPa). There are seven electron pairs around the xenon atom, of which six are Xe——F bonds while the seventh is a lone pair. As a result, the molecule has a distorted octahedral structure. The compound is exceptionally reactive. It attacks silica and undergoes a two stage hydrolysis with water:

$$2XeF_6 + SiO_2 = SiF_4 + 2XeOF_4$$
$$XeF_6 + H_2O = 2HF + XeOF_4$$
$$XeOF_4 + 2H_2O = XeO_3 + 4HF$$

Xenon hexafluoride functions as a Lewis acid towards fluoride ions, and forms the heptafluoroxenate(VI) ion, $[XeF_7]^-$, and octafluoro-xenate(VI) ion, $[XeF_8]^{2-}$.

The fluorides of xenon are powerful fluorinating agents. Xenon difluoride, for example, converts benzene to fluorobenzene.

Xenon dichloride, $XeCl_2$, is prepared by subjecting a mixture of xenon and chlorine to microwave radiation.

Oxygen compounds

Xenon trioxide, XeO_3, dissolves in aqueous alkalis to form the xenate(VI) ion, which slowly disproportionates into the xenate(VIII) ion:

$$XeO_3 + HO^- = HXeO_4^-$$
$$2HXeO_4^- + 2HO^- = XeO_6^{4-} + Xe + O_2 + 2H_2O$$

Stable salts containing the xenate(VIII) ion are known, e.g. $Na_4XeO_6 \cdot 8H_2O$. The xenate(VIII) ion is a powerful oxidant, e.g. it oxidises the manganese(II) ion to the permanganate ion in acidic solution.

Xenon also forms a tetraoxide, XeO_4, which is an explosive gas.

Krypton

The characterised compounds of krypton include the difluoride, KrF_2, and the addition compound $KrF_2 \cdot 2SbF_5$. Krypton difluoride is prepared by passing an electric discharge through a mixture of krypton and fluorine.

13.5 Uses of the noble gases

Helium

Mixtures of oxygen and helium are used for respiration purposes in deep sea diving. When air is breathed under pressure more nitrogen dissolves in the blood than at ordinary pressures. This is not serious, except that when the pressure returns to normal the excess nitrogen is liberated from the blood to cause a potentially fatal condition called 'the bends'. Helium is not appreciably soluble in blood, and can safely be substituted for nitrogen and breathed under pressure.

Meteorological balloons and airships are often filled with helium in place of hydrogen, which is dangerously flammable. Liquid helium is used in *cryogenics*, which is the study of phenomena at temperatures close to absolute zero.

Neon

Neon is widely used in 'neon tube' advertising signs, which consist of a glass tube containing the gas at a low pressure. When an electric discharge is passed, the familiar red glow (the emission spectrum of neon) appears.

Argon

Electric light bulbs are usually filled with argon to minimise evaporation of the hot tungsten filament. Argon is also used to provide an inert atmosphere for heated metals to prevent them from being attacked by air in, for example, the extraction and working of titanium (§14.4) and argon arc welding.

Krypton, xenon and radon

Krypton and xenon are expensive, but are used to a limited extent for filling high intensity light bulbs, such as those used in cinema projectors. Radon is seldom used commercially.

Chapter 14

d-Block transition elements

14.1 General characteristics

Transition elements are defined strictly as those which have partially filled d or f orbitals. A slightly broader definition, which is commonly adopted, includes those elements that have partially filled d or f orbitals in any of their common valency states.

This broad definition embraces some 56 of the elements lying between scandium ($Z = 21$) and lawrencium ($Z = 103$). They are subdivided into:

(i)   the main transition elements (those of the d-block); and
(ii) the inner transition elements (those of the f-block).

The main transition elements fall into three series. The nine elements scandium to copper, whose atoms or ions possess partially filled 3d orbitals, comprise the first series transition elements. Zinc, with the configuration $3d^{10} 4s^2$, forms no compounds involving 3d electrons, and is therefore not a transition element. The second transition series (the nine elements yttrium to silver) are characterised by partially filled 4d orbitals in their atoms or ions. Like zinc, cadmium (configuration $4d^{10} 5s^2$) is non-transitional in character. The third transition series, arising from the filling of 5d orbitals, includes the nine elements from lanthanum to gold; mercury (configuration $5d^{10} 6s^2$) is excluded.

The inner transition elements fall into two categories, namely *lanthanoids* and *actinoids*. The lanthanoids comprise the 14 elements having partially filled 4f orbitals, i.e. the elements cerium to lutecium, although lanthanum is commonly included because of its similarity. The actinoids, which have partially filled 5f orbitals, comprise the radioactive elements (mostly man-made) thorium to lawrencium; actinium may also be included for convenience.

Table 14.1 The outer electronic configurations of the first series transition elements and their ions.

Element	Outer electronic configuration of atoms	Outer electronic configuration of ions	
scandium	$3d^14s^2$		$Sc^{3+}\ 3d^0$
titanium	$3d^24s^2$	$Ti^{2+}\ 3d^2$	$Ti^{3+}\ 3d^1$
vanadium	$3d^34s^2$	$V^{2+}\ 3d^3$	$V^{3+}\ 3d^2$
chromium	$3d^54s^1$	$Cr^{2+}\ 3d^4$	$Cr^{3+}\ 3d^3$
manganese	$3d^54s^2$	$Mn^{2+}\ 3d^5$	$Mn^{3+}\ 3d^4$
iron	$3d^64s^2$	$Fe^{2+}\ 3d^6$	$Fe^{3+}\ 3d^5$
cobalt	$3d^74s^2$	$Co^{2+}\ 3d^7$	$Co^{3+}\ 3d^6$
nickel	$3d^84s^2$	$Ni^{2+}\ 3d^8$	
copper	$3d^{10}4s^1$	$Cu^+\ 3d^{10}$	$Cu^{2+}\ 3d^9$
zinc	$3d^{10}4s^2$	$Zn^{2+}\ 3d^{10}$	

Notes
(i) The configurations given are those outside an argon noble gas core.
(ii) Zinc is included to show its non-transitional configuration.

We shall concentrate on the first series transition elements. The outer electronic configurations of the atoms and some ions of these elements are given in Table 14.1. The more detailed configurations (Table 2.4) accord with Hund's rules (§2.4). In an isolated atom or ion the five 3d orbitals are degenerate; thus, each of these orbitals is singly occupied by an electron before spin pairing occurs.

Features of the first series transition elements and their ions

The transition elements have the following general features in common:

(i)   they are all metals, showing many similarities in their physical properties;
(ii) they form complexes;
(iii) their complexes are often coloured;
(iv) they show a variety of valency states (oxidation states);
(v)   both metals and ions often exhibit catalytic activity;
(vi) their ions are often paramagnetic.

Metallic properties
All are dense, hard, lustrous, strong metals with high melting and boiling temperatures. They are good conductors of heat and electricity. The

metallic bonding (§4.7), which involves both 4s and 3d electrons, undoubtedly accounts for many of these properties. The ready formation of alloys is also a feature of the elements.

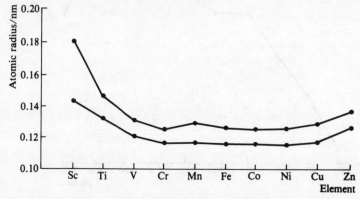

Fig. 14.1 Atomic and metallic radii of the first series transition elements. The upper curve shows metallic radius and the lower curve atomic radius, i.e. covalent bond radius.

Atomic and metallic radii (§3.4) all show a general decrease on passing from scandium to copper (Fig. 14.1). Initially, the radius decreases steeply, but levels out after vanadium. Electrons in 3d orbitals are poor *screeners*, i.e. they shield 4s electrons from the nuclear charge in a highly inefficient manner. A decrease in atomic radius is therefore to be expected on passing from scandium to copper, since the increase in nuclear charge will have a greater effect than the addition of an electron. The flattening of the graph after vanadium could be due to there being a certain minimum volume that atoms may occupy efficiently. The change in density (Fig. 14.2) is explained by the decreasing volume and increasing atomic mass on passing from scandium to copper. The small variation in metallic radius for the elements (particularly vanadium to copper) explains, at least partly, the ease of alloy formation.

Complex formation

Although the formation of complexes is an important property of transition elements, it is not exclusive to them, for certain non-transition elements, e.g. aluminium and zinc, also form complexes. Complexes contain a central metal atom or ion linked to one or more ligands (§4.3). If the species carries an overall charge it is often termed a *complex ion*.

The bonding in complexes is essentially dative in character, with the ligands acting as electron pair donors. Consider the complex ion $[Co(NH_3)_6]^{3+}$. This comprises a Co^{3+} ion surrounded by six ammonia ligands, each nitrogen atom donating its lone pair of electrons to the metal ion. Because ammonia molecules are coordinated to the Co^{3+} ion, we say that the Co^{3+} ion is 'complexed by ammonia'.

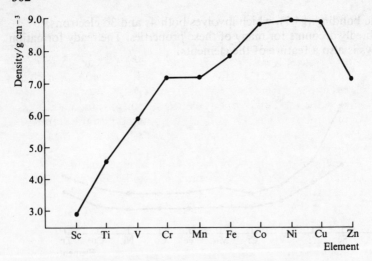

Fig. 14.2 Densities of the first series transition elements.

Water, also, acts as a ligand by utilising one of the lone pairs on the oxygen atom. Aqueous solutions of simple salts (such as sulphates) contain metal ions complexed with water molecules. For example, a solution of iron(II) sulphate contains the hydrated ions $[Fe(H_2O)_6]^{2+}$, in which the six water molecules are coordinated to an Fe^{2+} ion. These hydrated or complex ions usually persist in the crystalline salts, e.g. $FeSO_4 \cdot 7H_2O$ crystals contain $[Fe(H_2O)_6]^{2+}$ complex ions.

The number of coordinate bonds formed by the central metal atom or ion is known as its *coordination number*. The usual coordination numbers are 2, 4 and 6, with 6 by far the most common.

Chelating ligands

Some ligands, e.g. ethylenediamine (Fig. 14.3), possess two or even more atoms that can bond to the central metal.

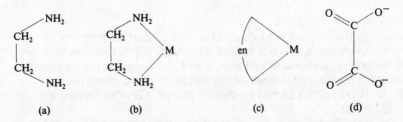

Fig. 14.3 (a) Ethylenediamine molecule (commonly abbreviated 'en'). (b) Mode of attachment to metal M; note ring structure. (c) Abbreviated representation of (b). (d) The ethanedioate ion: this may act in a similar manner to (a).

The formation of ring structures by coordination is termed *chelation*, and the ligand a *chelating ligand*. The compounds formed are *chelate compounds*. Ligands coordinating through two atoms are termed *bidentate* (meaning 'two teeth'); those using three atoms are *tridentate*, and so on. Simple ligands, e.g. H_2O, Cl^- and NH_3, are *monodentate*.

As a ligand, ethylenediamine is essentially equivalent to two molecules of ammonia, in the sense that each molecule of ethylenediamine forms two coordinate bonds. Thus, the coordination number in the complex $[Co(en)_3]^{3+}$ is not three but six, because the cobalt(III) ion forms six coordinate bonds.

Complexes which contain one or more chelate ring structures are more stable than those derived from monodentate ligands only. This is known as the *chelate effect*. Complexes with five membered chelate ring structures are the most stable.

The main reason for the enhanced stability of chelate complexes compared with non-chelate complexes appears to be one of entropy or disorder. Consider a reaction in which six water molecules are replaced by six other monodentate ligands (L), i.e.

$$[M(H_2O)_6]^{2+} + 6L = [ML_6]^{2+} + 6H_2O$$

The total number of molecules and ions before and after the reaction is the same, therefore the entropy change is small. However, in the case of a bidentate ligand (B), three ligand molecules replace six water molecules:

$$[M(H_2O)_6]^{2+} + 3B = [MB_3]^{2+} + 6H_2O$$

Substitution by a chelating ligand therefore increases the number of molecules and hence the entropy or disorder. It is this increase in entropy which largely accounts for the enhanced stability of chelate complexes.

Another reason is that a chelating ligand is attached to a metal ion by more than one bond. If one of these bonds breaks, the detached end of the ligand cannot move far away from the ion because it is still attached elsewhere. Consequently, the broken bond is likely to be re-formed.

Charge on complexes

The charge on a complex ion is delocalised over the whole of the complex. The charge is the algebraic sum of that on the central ion and the total charge carried by the ligands. When all the ligands are neutral, the overall charge of the complex ion is simply that carried by the central ion; hence complex cations arise, e.g. $[Co(NH_3)_6]^{3+}$. With anionic ligands, complex anions or cations may result. For example, $[Fe(CN)_6]^{4-}$ comprises six cyanide ligands, CN^- (total charge -6), complexed to one Fe^{2+} ion (charge $+2$). The overall charge is therefore -4. However, $[CrCl_2(H_2O)_4]^+$ comprises a central Cr^{3+} ion, complexed with two chloride ions (total charge -2) and four neutral water molecules. This is a complex cation (overall charge = +3 −2 = +1), despite its anionic ligands.

The overall complex charge may even be zero. This can happen when a neutral ligand, particularly carbon monoxide, forms a complex with a metal atom, e.g. $[Cr(CO)_6]$ and $[Ni(CO)_4]$. It also happens when the total charge on anionic ligands is equal and opposite to that carried by a central metal ion, e.g. $[CrCl_3(NH_3)_3]$, which represents a chromium(III) ion complexed with three ammonia molecules and three chloride ions.

Stereochemistry (shapes of complexes)

In six-coordinate complexes the ligands are arranged octahedrally about the metal, as in $[Co(NH_3)_6]^{3+}$, $[Fe(H_2O)_6]^{2+}$, etc. Figure 14.4 illustrates a convenient method of representing such complexes.

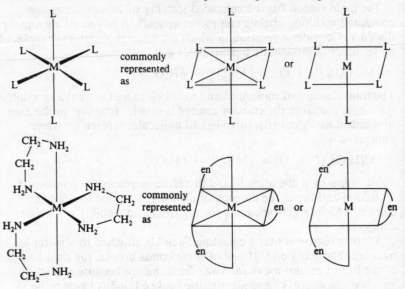

Fig. 14.4 Octahedral coordination with a monodentate ligand L and the bidentate ligand ethylenediamine.

Four-coordinate complexes are either square planar or tetrahedral. With coordination number 2, ligands and metal are collinear.

$$\left[\begin{array}{c} NC \cdots \cdots CN \\ Ni \\ NC \cdots \cdots CN \end{array} \right]^{2-} \qquad \left[\begin{array}{c} Cl \\ Co \\ Cl \quad Cl \\ Cl \end{array} \right]^{2-} \qquad [Cl \rightarrow Cu \leftarrow Cl]^-$$

square planar   tetrahedral   linear

Table 14.2 The geometry of some typical complexes.

Octahedral	Square planar	Tetrahedral	Linear
$[Ni(NH_3)_6]^{2+}$	$[Ni(CN)_4]^{2-}$	$[CoCl_4]^{2-}$	$[Cu(NH_3)_2]^+$
$[CoCl_2(NH_3)_4]^+$	$[CuCl_4]^{2-}$ (§14.11)	$[Cu(CN)_4]^{3-}$	$[CuCl_2]^-$
$[Fe(CN)_6]^{4-}$		$[Ni(CO)_4]$	$[Ag(NH_3)_2]^+$
$[Fe(CN)_5(NO)]^{2-}$			
$[Cr(CO)_6]$			

Table 14.2 shows the geometry of some typical complexes.

Isomerism

Both geometrical and optical isomerism may be encountered in transition element complexes.

Geometrical isomerism This occurs with square planar complexes of the type ML_2L_2', and octahedral complexes of the type ML_4L_2' and ML_3L_3'. The best known square planar examples occur with platinum(II) complexes, e.g.

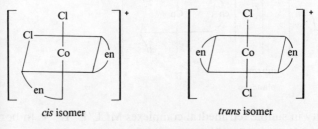

For octahedral complexes, *cis–trans* isomerism may occur with mono- and bidentate ligands, e.g.

Both have the formula $[CoCl_2(NH_3)_4]^+$

Both have the formula $[CoCl_2(en)_2]^+$

Octahedral complexes of the type ML_3L_3' exist as *facial* and *meridional* isomers, for which the abbreviations *fac* and *mer*, respectively, are used in the same way as *cis* and *trans*. Consider, for example, the isomers of formula $[CoCl_3(NH_3)_3]$.

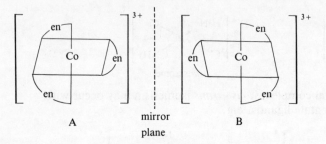

fac isomer   *mer* isomer

In the *fac* isomer, all ligands of the same type are adjacent to one another. In the *mer* isomer, two of the three identical ligands are opposite to each other, while both are adjacent to the third.

Optical isomerism   Optical isomerism occurs with complexes such as $[Co(en)_3]^{3+}$ and $[Cr(en)_3]^{3+}$, e.g.

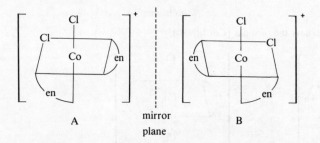

Neither A nor B possesses a centre or plane of symmetry. A is non-superimposable on B.

The *cis* (but not the *trans*) isomer of $[CoCl_2(en)_2]^+$ also shows optical activity:

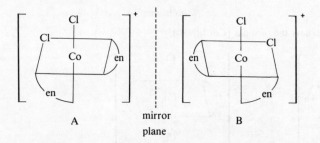

Optical activity in simple tetrahedral complexes $MLL'L''L'''$ is to be expected but has not yet been confirmed.

Ionisation isomerism Compounds which have the same composition but are composed of different ions are known as *ionisation isomers*. For example, there are two compounds of formula $Co(NH_3)_4Cl_2NO_2$. One is $[CoCl_2(NH_3)_4]^+NO_2^-$, and the other $[CoCl(NO_2)(NH_3)_4]^+Cl^-$. Although the latter gives a precipitate of silver chloride with Ag^+ ions, the former does not because it has no free Cl^- ions.

The following differently coloured complexes, each with the formula $CrCl_3 \cdot 6H_2O$, may be referred to as ionisation isomers or *hydrate isomers*:

$[Cr(H_2O)_6]^{3+}(Cl^-)_3$ $[CrCl(H_2O)_5]^{2+}(Cl^-)_2 \cdot H_2O$
    grey-blue   light green

$[CrCl_2(H_2O)_4]^+Cl^- \cdot 2H_2O$
    dark green

Coloured complex ions

Isolated transition element ions are devoid of colour, whereas complexed ions are usually coloured. For example, the pale green colour of iron(II) sulphate heptahydrate, $FeSO_4 \cdot 7H_2O$, arises from the presence in the crystal of hexaaquairon(II) ions.

The colour of complex ions is associated with partially filled d orbitals and the nature of the metal, and also with the nature of the ligands.

Nature of the metal and d orbital occupation Vacant or fully occupied d orbitals are associated with a lack of colour (Table 14.3). For a particular metal, the colour produced depends on the number of d electrons (compare Fe^{3+} with Fe^{2+}). Different metals produce differently coloured complex ions, even when those ions possess the same electronic configuration (compare Mn^{2+} with Fe^{3+}).

Table 14.3 Electronic configurations and colours of some hydrated ions, $[M(H_2O)_6]^{n+}$ (n = 2 or 3).

M	Electronic configuration	Colour	M	Electronic configuration	Colour
Sc^{3+}	$3d^0$	none	Fe^{3+}	$3d^5$	pale violet
Ti^{3+}	$3d^1$	violet	Fe^{2+}	$3d^6$	pale green
V^{3+}	$3d^2$	green	Co^{2+}	$3d^7$	pink
Cr^{3+}	$3d^3$	grey-blue	Ni^{2+}	$3d^8$	green
Mn^{3+}	$3d^4$	violet	Cu^{2+}	$3d^9$	blue
Mn^{2+}	$3d^5$	pale pink	Cu^+	$3d^{10}$	none
			Zn^{2+}	$3d^{10}$	none

Nature of the ligand Complexes undergo *substitution reactions* in which some or all of the ligands are replaced by different ligands. Aqua-complexes undergo such reactions readily, and many examples will be met. Altering the ligands around an ion often brings about a marked colour change, e.g.

$$[CuCl_4]^{2-} \xleftarrow{\text{excess HCl}} [Cu(H_2O)_6]^{2+} \xrightarrow{\text{excess NH}_3} [Cu(NH_3)_4(H_2O)_2]^{2+}$$
$$\text{yellow} \qquad\qquad\qquad \text{blue} \qquad\qquad\qquad\qquad \text{deep blue}$$

$$[CoCl_4]^{2-} \xleftarrow{\text{excess HCl}} [Co(H_2O)_6]^{2+} \xrightarrow{\text{excess NH}_3} [Co(NH_3)_6]^{2+}$$
$$\text{blue} \qquad\qquad\qquad \text{pink} \qquad\qquad\qquad\qquad \text{red-brown}$$

Crystal field theory

The five 3d orbitals of an *isolated* metal ion are degenerate, but the approach to the central ion of six ligands in the formation of a complex results in the degeneracy being partially relieved. When this happens, two of the d orbitals are raised in energy, relative to the d orbital energy of the isolated ion, while three are lowered.

In *crystal field theory* (CFT), the ligands are regarded as point charges which surround a metal ion, M^{n+}, in an octahedral manner (Fig. 14.5).

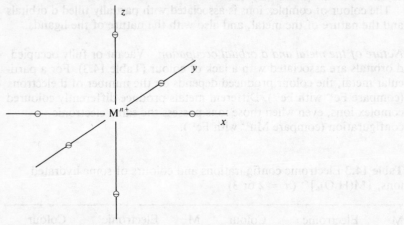

Fig. 14.5 Six negative point charges, representing the ligands, arranged octahedrally around a central ion, M^{n+}.

The interaction between the cation and the ligands is regarded as purely electrostatic (cf. an ionic crystal).

The negative point charges of the ligands repel d electrons on the metal ion and hence increase their energy (Fig. 14.6). The energy of each orbital concentrated along the x, y and z axes (i.e. $d_{x^2-y^2}$ and d_{z^2}) is increased by the same amount. Similarly, orbitals concentrated between the axes (i.e. d_{xz}, d_{yz} and d_{xy}) are also raised in energy to the same

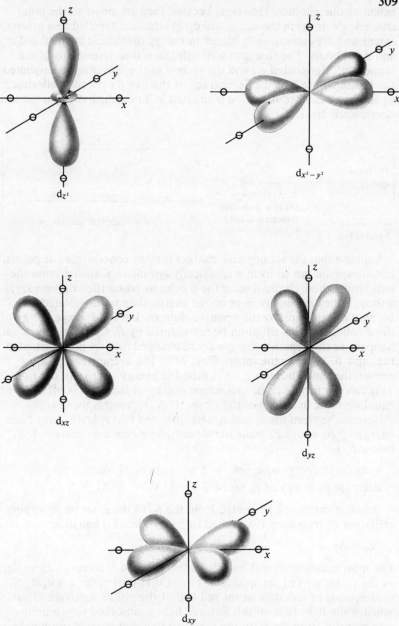

Fig. 14.6 The five 3d orbitals in relation to a set of six octahedrally arranged point charges (ligands). The lobes of the d_{z^2} and $d_{x^2-y^2}$ orbitals point directly at the point charges and hence are repelled to a greater extent than the d_{xz}, d_{yz} and d_{xy} orbitals, whose lobes are not positioned directly towards the point charges.

extent as one another. However, because they are closer to the point charges, electrons in the $d_{x^2-y^2}$ and d_{z^2} orbitals are repelled to a greater extent and are consequently higher in energy than those in the d_{xz}, d_{yz} and d_{xy} orbitals. The first group of orbitals is thus referred to as the 'upper set', designated e_g, and the second as the 'lower set', designated t_{2g}. Hence we see that the degeneracy of the five d orbitals is alleviated whenever an isolated metal ion is situated in an octahedrally symmetrical electrostatic field.

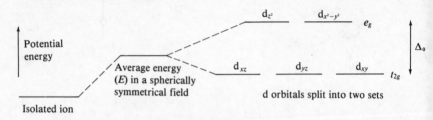

Suppose that the six negative charges are not concentrated at points, but are spread out to form a spherically symmetrical shell around the ion. Under these circumstances the d orbitals retain their degeneracy, although they are higher in potential energy than in the isolated ion because of repulsion by the negative charges. Let the average energy of the d orbitals in this situation be represented by E. Consider now what happens as the negative charges are rearranged into six points situated the same distance as the sphere from M^{n+}. The average energy must remain the same, but the e_g set is raised in energy relative to the t_{2g} set. This can occur only if the increase in energy of the e_g set is offset by an equal decrease in energy of the t_{2g} set. If Δ_0 represents the energy difference between the e_g and t_{2g} sets, then the two e_g levels must have energy $\frac{3}{5}\Delta_0$ above E, while the three t_{2g} levels have an energy $\frac{2}{5}\Delta_0$ below E, i.e.

increase in energy of e_g set $= 2 \times \frac{3}{5}\Delta_0 = \frac{6}{5}\Delta_0$

decrease in energy of t_{2g} set $= 3 \times \frac{2}{5}\Delta_0 = \frac{6}{5}\Delta_0$

An electron can be promoted from the t_{2g} to the e_g set on absorbing radiation of frequency (ν), related to Δ_0 by Planck's equation:

$$\Delta_0 = h\nu$$

For most transition metal complexes this frequency corresponds to light in the visible part of the spectrum. For $[Cu(H_2O)_6]^{2+}$, for example, Δ_0 corresponds to radiation at the red end of the visible spectrum. Thus, when white light falls on this ion, red light is absorbed in promoting one electron from the t_{2g} to the e_g set, so that compounds containing the ion appear blue. (White light minus red gives blue.)

$$\xrightarrow{\text{white light}} [Cu(H_2O)_6]^{2+} \xrightarrow{\text{blue light passes on}}$$

Similar arguments apply to other complex ions, e.g. the hexaaqua-titanium(III) ion, $[Ti(H_2O)_6]^{3+}$. The absorption spectrum of this ion has one peak in the visible region centred at 493 nm (Fig. 14.7). It therefore absorbs some, but not all, light from the blue end of the visible spectrum. The solution thus transmits red light, together with some blue light, and for this reason appears violet.

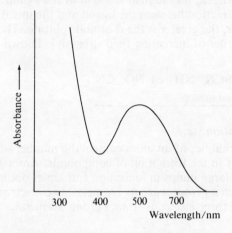

Fig. 14.7 The absorption spectrum of the $[Ti(H_2O)_6]^{2+}$ ion in the visible region.

The Ti^{3+} ion has a $3d^1$ configuration, and in the ground state of the aqua-complex the 3d electron occupies the orbital of lowest possible energy. This is one of the t_{2g} set orbitals. Blue light is absorbed because its wavelength (λ) corresponds to Δ_0, i.e. the energy required to promote the 3d electron from the t_{2g} to the e_g set. From the wavelength, 493 nm, we can readily calculate the value of Δ_0.

For one ion,

$$\Delta_0 = h\nu = \frac{hc}{\lambda} = \frac{6.625\,6 \times 10^{-34} \times 3.0 \times 10^8}{4.93 \times 10^{-7}}\ J$$

$$= 0.040\,29 \times 10^{-17}\ J$$

In this equation, wavelength has been written as 4.93×10^{-7} m for consistency in the units.

For 1 mol,

$$\Delta_0 = 0.040\,29 \times 10^{-17} \times 6.022\,52 \times 10^{23}\ J\ mol^{-1}$$
$$= 0.242\,6 \times 10^6\ J = 2.426 \times 10^2\ kJ\ mol^{-1}$$

For an electronic transition to occur from the t_{2g} to the e_g set, there must be at least one electron in the t_{2g} set and at least one vacancy in

312

the e_g set (to accommodate the electron). Hence, colourless complexes arise from Sc^{3+}, where there is no electron in the t_{2g} set, and from Zn^{2+} and Cu^+, where there is no vacancy in the e_g set.

The value of Δ_0, and hence the colour, varies from one metal to another, and for a particular metal it depends on the charge on the ion and the nature of the ligands. A change of ligand around an ion alters Δ_0 and the colour. Δ_0 is dependent on the *field strength* of the ligand, i.e. the magnitude of the interaction between the ligand and the metal. The greater the field strength, the greater is the d orbital splitting. The following list of ligands in order of increasing field strength is known as the *spectrochemical series*:

I^- Br^- Cl^- F^- HO^- H_2O SCN^- NH_3 en NO_2^- CN^-

$\xrightarrow{\hspace{4cm}}$
increasing field strength

Variable valency state (oxidation state)

The successive ionisation enthalpies of an atom control the number of electrons which can take part in the formation of compounds. Among the non-transition elements, large jumps in ionisation enthalpies occur after the removal of one electron from a group 1A metal, two electrons from a group 2A metal, and three electrons from a group 3B metal.

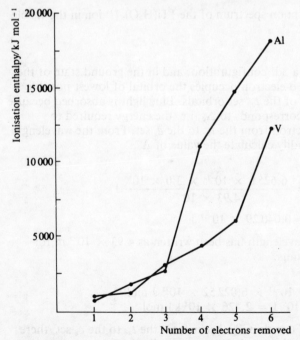

Fig. 14.8 Successive ionisation enthalpies of aluminium and vanadium.

The significant jump after the removal of a third electron from aluminium means that the Al^{4+} ion cannot be obtained by chemical means. Aluminium atoms can use only three electrons (3p and $3s^2$) in the formation of ionic or covalent bonds. However, the ionisation enthalpies of a transition metal atom, such as vanadium (Fig. 14.8), increase gradually as electrons are removed from the energetically similar 3d and 4s orbitals. This close similarity in energy means that both 4s and 3d electrons are available for bond formation (ionic or covalent), and accounts in part for the variability of valency or oxidation state. Therefore, within limits, a transition metal atom can adjust its valency or oxidation state according to its environment, i.e. the presence of ligands, anions, oxidants, reductants, etc.

Table 14.4 Valency states of the first series transition elements. The commonest states are printed in bold type.

Sc	Ti	V	Cr	Mn	Fe	Co	Ni	Cu	(Zn)
3	**4**	**5**	**6**	7	6	4	4	2	2
	3	**4**	**3**	6	**3**	**3**	**3**	**1**	
	2	**3**	**2**	**4**	**2**	**2**	**2**		
		2		**3**					
				2					

The common oxidation states are all positive and numerically equal to the valency states shown in Table 14.4. Notice that, with the exception of cobalt, the highest valency exhibited by a metal is equal to the number of 4s electrons plus the number of unpaired 3d electrons in the neutral atom.

The higher states (above 4) occur in fluorides, oxides, oxoanions and, to a limited extent, in the chlorides of the metals. (Highly electronegative elements stabilise high oxidation states.) The bonding in the higher states (5, 6 and 7) is predominantly covalent, since the production of discrete, highly charged ions is energetically impossible in chemical systems. For the lower states (2 and 3) discrete ions can exist (e.g. in the oxides), but complex ion formation is perhaps the outstanding feature.

The mono-, di- and trivalent states (+1, +2 and +3 oxidation states)

The monovalent state (+1 oxidation state) is important only for copper, and will be discussed later.

The divalent state (+2 oxidation state) involves the two 4s electrons (one 4s and one 3d for chromium and copper), while of necessity 3d electrons are always concerned in the trivalent or +3 oxidation state.

Successive ionisation enthalpies show an overall increase from scandium to copper (Fig. 14.9), in keeping with decreasing atomic

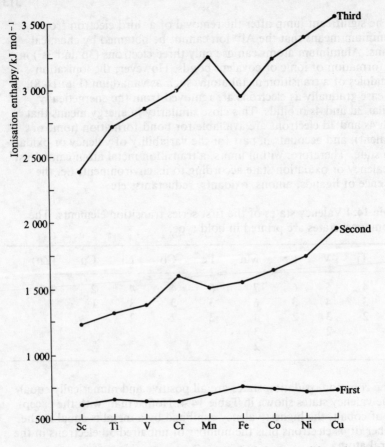

Fig. 14.9 Successive ionisation enthalpies of the transition elements.

radii. The production of M^{3+} ions from elements on the right of the series (Co, Ni, Cu) is energetically expensive, and consequently such elements show a preference for the divalent ($+2$) state. Attainment of the trivalent ($+3$) state by metals on the left (Sc, Ti, V, Cr) is easier, and this state is generally more stable than the divalent ($+2$) one, thus:

	Sc	Ti	V	Cr	Mn	Fe	Co	Ni	Cu
more stable state	3	3	3	3	2	2	2	2	2

The divalent ($+2$) state for those elements preferring the trivalent ($+3$) one is thus a reducing condition, although scandium does not form Sc^{2+} ions. Conversely the trivalent ($+3$) state, for those preferring the divalent ($+2$) one, is an oxidising condition. The stability of a particular valency or oxidation state is influenced by the nature of the ligands attached to the ion (§14.9), but the above pattern is generally followed.

In aqueous solution, in the absence of other ligands, water usually coordinates to metal ions to give *aqua ions* (hydrated ions). The stability of these ions in solution is worth further discussion.

The divalent state (+2 *oxidation state*)   Except for scandium and possibly titanium, all the metals form aqua-complexes (hydrated ions) of general formula $[M(H_2O)_6]^{2+}$, often abbreviated to $M^{2+}(aq)$ or even M^{2+}. Solutions of V^{2+} and Cr^{2+} are strongly reducing, even attacking the solvent water, especially if it is acidified:

$$2[M(H_2O)_6]^{2+} + 2H_2O = 2[M(H_2O)_6]^{3+} + H_2 + 2HO^- \quad \text{(M = V or Cr)}$$

$[Fe(H_2O)_6]^{2+}$ is oxidised by oxygen and many other oxidants, but the ions of manganese, cobalt, nickel and copper are much more stable in this respect.

The trivalent state (+3 *oxidation state*)   Simple $[M(H_2O)_6]^{3+}$ ions, abbreviated to $M^{3+}(aq)$ or M^{3+}, exist for all the metals except copper and nickel. The $[Co(H_2O)_6]^{3+}$ ion oxidises water (see below), while $[Mn(H_2O)_6]^{3+}$ is very unstable. The simple hydrated ions of the remaining metals are stable in solution in the absence of oxidants.

The tetravalent state (+4 oxidation state)

In the presence of air, this is the most stable state of both titanium and vanadium. The only other first series transition element to show stability in this state is manganese, which forms the insoluble compound, manganese(IV) oxide, MnO_2. Because of hydrolysis, simple hydrated Ti^{4+} and V^{4+} ions do not exist (§§14.4 and 14.5). In solution, species such as $[Ti(OH)_2(H_2O)_4]^{2+}$ and $[VO(H_2O)_5]^{2+}$ (often written TiO^{2+} and VO^{2+}) are believed to be present. Manganese(IV) has no aqueous chemistry of note.

The penta-, hexa- and heptavalent states (+5, +6 and +7 oxidation states)

Oxidation states of +5 for vanadium, +6 for chromium and +7 for manganese are common. The compounds are oxidising agents, becoming increasingly powerful as the oxidation number increases, e.g. dichromates $(Cr_2O_7^{2-})$ and permanganates (MnO_4^-).

Aqueous solutions of chromate (CrO_4^{2-}) or dichromate ions (§14.6) are stable, but not solutions of the permanganate ion (§14.7). Aqueous vanadium(V) chemistry is rather complicated; vanadate ions, VO_4^{3-}, exist in solutions of high pH, and $[VO_2(aq)]^+$ ions are present at low pH.

Effect of ligands on oxidation−reduction behaviour

Ligands can affect the stability of a particular valency or oxidation state of a metal, and therefore the oxidation−reduction behaviour of the ion. The standard electrode potentials for two Co^{2+}/Co^{3+} complexes illustrate this point:

$$[Co(H_2O)_6]^{3+} + e^- = [Co(H_2O)_6]^{2+} \qquad E^{\ominus} = +1.82 \text{ V}$$
$$[Co(NH_3)_6]^{3+} + e^- = [Co(NH_3)_6]^{2+} \qquad E^{\ominus} = +0.10 \text{ V}$$

The oxidising nature of $[Co(H_2O)_6]^{3+}$ is reflected by its high $E^{\ominus}$ value. (The trivalent $(+3)$ state changes readily to the divalent $(+2)$ one.) By comparing it with

$$\tfrac{1}{2}O_2 + 2H^+(aq) + 2e^- = H_2O \qquad E^{\ominus} = +1.23 \text{ V}$$

we can see why this ion oxidises water to oxygen. The greater stability of the trivalent $(+3)$ state (relative to the divalent $(+2)$ state) with ammonia ligands is indicated by the much lower $E^{\ominus}$ value. Molecular oxygen, in fact, converts $[Co(NH_3)_6]^{2+}$ to $[Co(NH_3)_6]^{3+}$. Similarly, cobalt(II) complexes of ethylenediamine, cyanide ions and nitrite ions are all easily oxidised to the corresponding cobalt(III) complexes. Thus we see that with some ligands, e.g. H_2O, the divalent $(+2)$ state is the more stable for cobalt, while with others, e.g. NH_3, the trivalent $(+3)$ condition is preferred. (See §14.9 for other examples.)

Catalytic activity

Heterogeneous catalysis is a feature of many transition metals and their compounds, particularly the oxides (see Table 14.5). The multiplicity of orbitals (3d and 4s) for the first series elements no doubt facilitates bond formation between reactant molecules and the catalyst surface, thereby providing an alternative route of lower activation energy.

In solution, the ions may function as homogeneous catalysts by changing their valency or oxidation states. A commonly cited example

Table 14.5 Examples of catalysts taken from the first transition series.

Catalyst	Reaction catalysed	Comment
V_2O_5	$2SO_2 + O_2 \rightleftharpoons 2SO_3$	contact process
Fe	$N_2 + 3H_2 \rightleftharpoons 2NH_3$	Haber process
Cr_2O_3 + ZnO	$CO + 2H_2 = CH_3OH$	
MnO_2	$2KClO_3 = 2KCl + 3O_2$	
Ti compounds	polymerisation of ethene and propene to poly(ethene) and poly(propene)	Ziegler catalyst
Ni	$\underset{\displaystyle }{>}C{=}C\underset{\displaystyle }{<} + H_2 = \begin{matrix} H & H \\ \mid & \mid \\ -C-C- \\ \mid & \mid \end{matrix}$	hydrogenation
Ni	$C_xH_y + xH_2O = xCO + (x + \tfrac{y}{2})H_2$	steam reforming
Co compounds	alkenes + CO + H_2 = aldehydes and ketones	OXO process
Mn^{2+}	$2MnO_4^- + 5(COO)_2^{2-} + 16H^+(aq) = 2Mn^{2+} + 10CO_2 + 8H_2O$	autocatalysis
Co^{2+}	$2ClO^- = 2Cl^- + O_2$	

is the catalysis, by Fe^{3+}, of the reaction:

$$S_2O_8^{2-} + 2I^- = 2SO_4^{2-} + I_2$$

A proposed, possibly oversimplified, mechanism is as follows:

$$2Fe^{3+} + 2I^- = 2Fe^{2+} + I_2$$
$$2Fe^{2+} + S_2O_8^{2-} = 2Fe^{3+} + 2SO_4^{2-}$$

Magnetic properties

Compounds can be classified according to their behaviour in a magnetic field. *Diamagnetic* compounds are weakly repelled, and *paramagnetic* compounds are weakly attracted by the field.

A spinning electron in an orbital produces a magnetic field, as does an electric current flowing in a wire. We should expect the net magnetic moment for two electrons with opposite spins in an orbital to be zero, but an external magnetic field distorts the electron clouds slightly, effectively producing a small magnetic field which opposes the external field. Thus, diamagnetism occurs when all orbitals are doubly occupied.

The condition for paramagnetism is that an atom, ion or molecule must possess one or more unpaired electrons, which cause the species to behave as a magnet with a weak magnetic moment. An external magnetic field aligns and attracts these magnets. (Compare this with the behaviour of a weak magnet placed in the field of a stronger magnet.)

For a transition metal ion which has both full and half filled orbitals the two effects are opposed. However, the paramagnetic effect is about 100 times stronger than the diamagnetic one, and so the former predominates. The more unpaired electrons there are, the greater the paramagnetism and the magnetic moment of the ion. Theoretically, magnetic moment is related to the number of unpaired electrons (n) by the equation

magnetic moment (units are *magneton numbers*) $= \sqrt{n(n+2)}$

Experimental measurement of magnetic moments for the first series transition elements often gives values close to the theoretical (Table 14.6). Paramagnetism is therefore extremely useful for gaining an insight into the number of unpaired electrons in an ion and hence its configuration.

In some cases the experimental data do not correlate precisely with the theoretical magneton numbers. The reason for this is that the motion of an electron in its orbital also contributes to the magnetic moment of the ion, and the calculated magneton numbers in Table 14.6 do not take this orbital contribution into account. They are termed *spin-only values*. Nevertheless, in many instances, we can still use the data to draw some conclusions concerning electronic configurations (Table 14.7). Notice that the t_{2g} set is always filled before the e_g set,

Table 14.6 Magnetic moments of first series transition metal ions.

Ion	3d configuration	Number of unpaired d electrons	Calculated magneton number	Experimental magneton number
Ti^{3+}, V^{4+}	$3d^1$	1	1.73	1.73
V^{3+}	$3d^2$	2	2.83	2.75−2.85
V^{2+}, Cr^{3+}	$3d^3$	3	3.88	3.70−3.90
Cr^{2+}	$3d^4$	4	4.90	4.75−4.90
Mn^{2+}, Fe^{3+}	$3d^5$	5	5.92	5.65−6.10
Fe^{2+}	$3d^6$	4	4.90	5.10−5.70
Co^{2+}	$3d^7$	3	3.88	4.30−5.20
Ni^{2+}	$3d^8$	2	2.83	2.80−3.50
Cu^{2+}	$3d^9$	1	1.73	1.70−2.20

and that the occupation of both sets is in accordance with Hund's rules and Pauli's exclusion principle (§2.4).

Complexes in which the number of unpaired electrons is at a maximum, as listed in Table 14.7, are referred to as either *spin-free* or *high-spin* complexes. In some cases, however, the number of unpaired electrons is less than the theoretical maximum, and it may appear that Hund's rule is not obeyed. Such species, known as either *spin-paired* or *low-spin* complexes, can occur when there are four, five, six or seven 3d electrons. For example, with four 3d electrons, two configurations are conceivable:

e_g ⥮ — ⟱ Δ_0 e_g — — ⟱ Δ_0

t_{2g} ⥮ ⥮ ⥮ t_{2g} ⥮⥮ ⥮ ⥮

high-spin   low-spin
$(t_{2g}^3 e_g^1)$ $(t_{2g}^4 e_g^0)$

If two electrons occupy the same t_{2g} orbital they repel each other. Consequently, if both the other t_{2g} orbitals are singly occupied, one of the paired t_{2g} electrons will tend to move into a vacant e_g orbital. The necessary energy (Δ_0) for this promotion may be available, because two mutually repellent electrons occupying one t_{2g} orbital are higher in energy than two electrons occupying separate t_{2g} orbitals. However, if Δ_0 is greater than the repulsion energy between the paired electrons, promotion will not occur. The paired configuration will be favoured because it represents a state of lower energy than the unpaired arrangement. Thus, for $3d^4$ complexes, if Δ_0 is relatively small the configuration is $t_{2g}^3 e_g^1$, i.e. high-spin, but if Δ_0 is large it is t_{2g}^4, i.e. low-spin.

The value of Δ_0, and hence the type of complex, depends on the nature of the ligand. In general, ligands towards the right-hand side of

Table 14.7 Occupation of the t_{2g} and e_g sets in high-spin complexes.

Configuration	Orbital occupation t_{2g}	e_g	Number of unpaired electrons	Notes
$3d^2$	↑ ↑ —	— —	2	Both electrons occupy the t_{2g} set (t_{2g}^2). In accordance with Hund's rule, the electrons are in different orbitals and possess parallel spins.
$3d^3$	↑ ↑ ↑	— —	3	All three electrons occupy the t_{2g} set (t_{2g}^3) in accordance with Hund's rule.
$3d^4$	↑ ↑ ↑	↑ —	4	All four electrons possess parallel spins with the configuration $t_{2g}^3 e_g^1$.
$3d^5$	↑ ↑ ↑	↑ ↑	5	In the $t_{2g}^3 e_g^2$ arrangement the number of unpaired electrons is at a maximum.
$3d^6$	↑↓ ↑ ↑	↑ ↑	4	Spin pairing occurs in the t_{2g} set before e_g ($t_{2g}^4 e_g^2$).
$3d^7$	↑↓ ↑↓ ↑	↑ ↑	3	Spin pairing again occurs in t_{2g} before e_g ($t_{2g}^5 e_g^2$).
$3d^8$	↑↓ ↑↓ ↑↓	↑ ↑	2	The t_{2g} set is now full ($t_{2g}^6 e_g^2$).
$3d^9$	↑↓ ↑↓ ↑↓	↑↓ ↑	1	Spin pairing now occurs in the e_g set ($t_{2g}^6 e_g^3$).

the spectrochemical series (p. 312), e.g. CN^-, produce low-spin complexes, while those at the left-hand side, e.g. Cl^-, lead to high-spin complexes (Table 14.8).

Ferromagnetism, a rarer but stronger magnetic phenomenon than paramagnetism, is restricted to a few elements, namely iron, cobalt and

Table 14.8 Some examples of high-spin and low-spin complexes.

Configuration	High-spin complexes		Low-spin complexes		Typical experimental magneton numbers for low spin
	Orbital occupation	Examples	Orbital occupation	Examples	
3d⁴	↑ — / ↑ ↑ ↑	$[Cr(H_2O)_6]^{2+}$	— — / ↑↓ ↑ ↑	$[Cr(CN)_6]^{4-}$	3.20–3.30
3d⁵	↑ ↑ / ↑ ↑ ↑	$[Fe(H_2O)_6]^{3+}$, $[Mn(H_2O)_6]^{2+}$	— — / ↑↓ ↑↓ ↑	$[Fe(CN)_6]^{3-}$, $[Fe(phen)_3]^{3+}$, $[Mn(CN)_6]^{4-}$, $[Mn(CN)_5(NO)]^{3-}$	1.80–2.10
3d⁶	↑ ↑ / ↑↓ ↑ ↑	$[Fe(H_2O)_6]^{2+}$, $[CoF_6]^{3-}$	— — / ↑↓ ↑↓ ↑↓	$[Fe(CN)_6]^{4-}$, $[Co(NH_3)_6]^{3+}$	diamagnetic
3d⁷	↑ ↑ / ↑↓ ↑↓ ↑	$[Co(H_2O)_6]^{2+}$	↑ — / ↑↓ ↑↓ ↑↓	$[Co(NO_2)_6]^{4-}$	1.80–2.0

nickel, their alloys and some of their compounds, e.g. Fe_3O_4. In such substances, the magnetic moments of the separate ions or atoms align themselves in a parallel manner and reinforce one another. Above a certain temperature, called the *Curie temperature*, thermal agitation destroys this arrangement and the substance becomes paramagnetic.

Properties of the individual transition elements

The important properties of the first series transition elements and their compounds are discussed in §§14.3–14.12. (Zinc is included for convenience.) The outer electronic configuration and principal valency states of each element are given in the appropriate sections, and some physical properties are shown in Table 14.9.

Table 14.9 Some properties of the first series transition elements.

	Sc	Ti	V	Cr	Mn
atomic number	21	22	23	24	25
relative atomic mass	44.955 9	47.90	50.941 4	51.996	54.938 0
density/g cm⁻³	2.99	4.54	5.96	7.19	7.20
melting temperature/°C	1 540	1 675	1 900	1 890	1 240
boiling temperature/°C	2 730	3 260	3 000	2 482	2 100

	Fe	Co	Ni	Cu	Zn
atomic number	26	27	28	29	30
relative atomic mass	55.847	58.933 2	58.71	63.546	65.37
density/g cm⁻³	7.86	8.90	8.90	8.92	7.14
melting temperature/°C	1 535	1 492	1 453	1 083	420
boiling temperature/°C	3 000	2 900	2 730	2 595	907

14.2 Comparison of the transition elements with s- and p-block elements

s-Block   With the exception of copper and chromium, the transition elements possess a $4s^2$ outer configuration. Copper and chromium have a $4s^1$ outer configuration. We may therefore expect the transition elements to bear resemblances to the s-block elements because they too possess s^2 or s^1 outer configurations. Most of the transition elements do form dipositive ions (cf. group 2A), while copper forms a monopositive ion (cf. group 1A). However, apart from these similarities, there is little resemblance between s-block and transition elements.

The transition elements have much higher ionisation enthalpies than the s-block elements and are therefore much less reactive. This is attributed to the poor screening properties of the 3d electrons, which causes the outer 4s electrons to be strongly attracted by the nucleus and lost only with difficulty. The underlying completed shells of the s-block elements, e.g. $3s^2\,3p^6$ for potassium, are far better at screening the outer s electron(s) from the nuclear charge, with the result that ionisation occurs relatively easily.

The melting temperatures of the transition elements are also much higher than those of the s-block elements, except for beryllium, which melts at 1 277 °C (1 550 K). High melting temperatures are indicative of strong metallic bonding. In transition elements, both 3d and 4s electrons are used to give strong metallic bonding, whereas the s-block elements are limited to using their outer s electrons only.

p-Block   Because they possess no outer p electrons, we should not expect transition elements to resemble those of the p-block. While this is generally true of the transition elements themselves, it is not the case for some of their ions or compounds. Some of the notable similarities which occur are listed below.

(i)   Scandium resembles aluminium (§14.3).
(ii) Titanium(IV) compounds bear some marked resemblances to the corresponding compounds of tin(IV) (§14.4). The same is true, to a limited extent, for vanadium(IV) compounds.
(iii) Some similarities are evident between chromium(VI) compounds and sulphur(VI) compounds. The chromate and dichromate ions, CrO_4^{2-} and $Cr_2O_7^{2-}$, respectively, correspond to the SO_4^{2-} and $S_2O_7^{2-}$ ions. Both the chromate and sulphate ions are tetrahedral, and many resemblances exist between salts containing these ions. For example, the hydrated chromate and sulphate of sodium have similar formulae, namely $Na_2CrO_4 \cdot 10H_2O$ and $Na_2SO_4 \cdot 10H_2O$. Also, the chromates of barium, lead and silver are all sparingly soluble in water, like the corresponding sulphates. However, the chromium ions are coloured and are powerful oxidants, while the corresponding sulphur ions are not.

322

Chromium also forms an oxide, CrO_3 (cf. SO_3), and an acid chloride, CrO_2Cl_2 (cf. SO_2Cl_2).

(iv) Both manganese and chlorine form an unstable oxide of formula X_2O_7.

(v) Some tripositive ions of transition elements, e.g. V^{3+}, Fe^{3+} and Cr^{3+}, form alums (§8.5).

14.3 Scandium

Outer electronic configuration: $3d^1 4s^2$. Principal valency: 3 ($+3$ oxidation state).

Scandium is an uncommon element, which resembles aluminium rather than the other transition elements. It forms halides, ScX_3, salts with acids, and a hydrated ion, $[Sc(H_2O)_6]^{3+}$, which undergoes hydrolysis (cf. $[Al(H_2O)_6]^{3+}$). The oxide of scandium, Sc_2O_3, is more basic than that of aluminium.

14.4 Titanium

Outer electronic configuration: $3d^2 4s^2$. Principal valencies: 2, 3, 4 ($+2$, $+3$, $+4$ oxidation states).

The element

The principal ores of titanium are rutile, TiO_2, and ilmenite, $FeTiO_3$. It is impossible to obtain the metal by reduction of these ores with carbon because titanium forms a very stable carbide. Titanium is isolated by the *Kroll process*, in which titanium(IV) chloride is first prepared by heating the ore with carbon in a stream of chlorine:

$$TiO_2 + C + 2Cl_2 = TiCl_4 + CO_2$$
$$2FeTiO_3 + 3C + 7Cl_2 = 2TiCl_4 + 2FeCl_3 + 3CO_2$$

The titanium(IV) chloride is purified by fractional distillation and then reduced with magnesium or sodium at 800 °C (1 073 K) in an atmosphere of argon:

$$TiCl_4 + 2Mg = 2MgCl_2 + Ti$$
$$TiCl_4 + 4Na = 4NaCl + Ti$$

The atmosphere of argon is necessary because titanium combines readily with oxygen and nitrogen at elevated temperatures.

In its physical properties titanium resembles stainless steel, i.e. it is hard, has a high melting temperature and is resistant to corrosion at ordinary temperatures. It has a low density, 4.54 g cm^{-3}, which is almost half that of steel, and the metal is widely used in the construction of aircraft, space vehicles, nuclear reactors, chemical plants and steam turbines.

Titanium is unreactive at room temperature, but at higher temperatures, approximately 800 °C (1 073 K), it combines readily with most non-metals, particularly oxygen and nitrogen. Many of the products are interstitial (§6.3), especially when the non-metal atom is small, e.g. TiH_2, TiN, TiC, TiB and TiB_2. These interstitial compounds are very stable and hard, and even when present in small amounts they make the metal brittle and useless for constructional purposes.

Titanium dissolves in hot concentrated hydrochloric acid to form hydrated Ti^{3+} ions and hydrogen, but with hot nitric acid hydrated titanium(IV) oxide, $TiO_2(aq)$, and oxides of nitrogen are produced. Hydrofluoric acid or acidic solutions of ionic fluorides readily dissolve titanium to form fluoro-complexes, e.g.

$$Ti + 4H^+(aq) + 6F^- = [TiF_6]^{2-} + 2H_2$$

The divalent state

(+ 2 oxidation state) $3d^2$
Few compounds of divalent titanium are known. The oxide, TiO, and the chloride, $TiCl_2$, are prepared by heating the appropriate titanium(IV) compound with titanium, e.g.

$$TiCl_4 + Ti = 2TiCl_2$$

Titanium(II) compounds are readily oxidised, and rapidly reduce water to hydrogen:

$$2Ti^{2+} + 14H_2O = 2[Ti(H_2O)_6]^{3+} + 2HO^- + H_2$$

The trivalent state

(+ 3 oxidation state) $3d^1$
Titanium(III) compounds display the typical properties of transition element compounds, because the 3d orbitals contain one electron. The violet hydrated titanium(III) ion, $[Ti(H_2O)_6]^{3+}$, is prepared by reducing acidic solutions of titanium(IV) compounds, either with zinc or electrolytically. The hexaaquatitanium(III) ion undergoes hydrolysis in solution:

$$[Ti(H_2O)_6]^{3+} + H_2O \rightleftharpoons [Ti(OH)(H_2O)_5]^{2+} + H_3O^+$$

With alkalis hydrated titanium(III) oxide, $Ti_2O_3(aq)$, is formed.

Titanium(III) compounds are powerful reducing agents, and are rapidly oxidised to titanium(IV) species by reagents such as oxygen or the halogens.

The tetravalent state

(+ 4 oxidation state) $3d^0$
This is the most stable state of titanium in the presence of air, and involves either the loss of the four outer electrons, to form the Ti^{4+} ion,

or the participation of titanium in four covalent bonds. Because there are no electrons in the 3d orbitals, titanium(IV) compounds do not show any of the typical characteristics of transition element compounds. For example, they are colourless, and often bear a strong resemblance to the corresponding compounds of tin(IV).

Titanium(IV) oxide (titanium dioxide)

Like tin(IV) oxide, titanium(IV) oxide is a white ionic solid, i.e. $Ti^{4+}(O^{2-})_2$. It occurs in three crystalline forms, of which the best known is *rutile* (Fig. 14.10). Each titanium(IV) ion in the lattice is surrounded by six oxide ions in an octahedral arrangement, and each oxide ion by three titanium(IV) ions in an equilateral triangle arrangement.

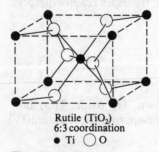

Rutile (TiO₂)
6:3 coordination
● Ti ◯ O

Fig. 14.10 The structure of titanium(IV) oxide.

Titanium(IV) oxide is amphoteric although rather inert to most reagents. It dissolves slowly in concentrated sulphuric acid to form a compound known as 'titanyl sulphate', $(TiO)SO_4 \cdot H_2O$, and with fused alkalis it forms titanates of unknown structure but of empirical formula M_2TiO_3, e.g.

$$2KOH + TiO_2 = K_2TiO_3 + H_2O$$

The hexafluorotitanate(IV) ion, $[TiF_6]^{2-}$, is formed when titanium(IV) oxide is dissolved in hydrofluoric acid:

$$TiO_2 + 4H^+(aq) + 6F^- = [TiF_6]^{2-} + 2H_2O$$

Titanium(IV) oxide is used extensively as a white pigment in paints.

Titanium(IV) chloride (titanium tetrachloride)

Titanium(IV) chloride, $TiCl_4$, the most important halide of titanium, is prepared by heating titanium(IV) oxide with carbon and chlorine, or by direct combination of the heated elements. Like tin(IV) chloride, titanium(IV) chloride is covalent. It is a colourless liquid which fumes in moist air and reacts with water to form a white precipitate of the oxide:

$$TiCl_4 + 2H_2O = TiO_2(aq) + 4HCl$$

Complex ions, such as the hexachlorotitanate(IV) ion, $[TiCl_6]^{2-}$, are

formed when titanium(IV) chloride is dissolved in concentrated hydrochloric acid.

Titanium(IV) chloride is used as a cocatalyst with organometallic
compounds such as pentyllithium in the polymerisation of alkenes.

Aqueous chemistry

Because of its high surface charge density, the Ti^{4+} ion distorts
coordinated water molecules and hydrolysis occurs in aqueous solution
to form hydroxo-species, e.g. $[Ti(OH)_2(H_2O)_4]^{2+}$ (often written TiO^{2+}).
Proton loss occurs on the addition of alkali to form the hydrated
dioxide (cf. tin):

$$[Ti(OH)_2(H_2O)_4]^{2+} + 2HO^- = TiO_2(aq) + 6H_2O$$

'Titanyl sulphate' contains polymeric chains consisting of alternate
titanium and oxygen atoms, with each titanium atom also bonded to
sulphate groups and water molecules through their oxygen atoms.

14.5 Vanadium

Outer electronic configuration: $3d^3\ 4s^2$. Principal valencies: 2, 3, 4, 5
($+2, +3, +4, +5$ oxidation states).

The element

Vanadium resembles titanium in its physical and chemical properties at
room temperature. It is, however, very reactive at elevated temperatures, and on heating in air it forms the oxide, V_2O_5, and an interstitial
nitride, VN. Vanadium combines readily with the halogens at high
temperatures but is unaffected by alkalis and non-oxidising acids, with
the exception of hydrofluoric acid. Nitric acid, concentrated sulphuric
acid and aqua regia dissolve the metal to give vanadium(V) compounds.

Because of its high reactivity at elevated temperatures, vanadium is a
difficult metal to prepare in the pure state. It is usually produced as an
alloy with iron ('ferrovanadium') by reducing a mixture of vanadium(V)
oxide and iron(III) oxide with coke in a furnace. Vanadium is used
principally as a constituent of vanadium steel, a hard metal suitable for
making knives. The alloy is manufactured by adding the appropriate
quantity of ferrovanadium to molten steel.

The divalent state

($+2$ oxidation state) $3d^3$
This is the least stable state of vanadium. The lavender coloured
hydrated vanadium(II) ion, $[V(H_2O)_6]^{2+}$, is formed either by dissolving
the basic vanadium(II) oxide, VO, in acids, or by reducing acidic solutions of other vanadium compounds with zinc. Vanadium(II) compounds
are powerful reducing agents and are slowly oxidised by water:

$$2[V(H_2O)_6]^{2+} + 2H_2O = 2[V(H_2O)_6]^{3+} + 2HO^- + H_2$$

The trivalent state

(+3 oxidation state) $3d^2$

Vanadium(III) oxide, V_2O_3, is basic and dissolves in acids to give the green hydrated vanadium(III) ion, $[V(H_2O)_6]^{3+}$. This ion is also formed by the reduction of compounds of pentavalent or tetravalent vanadium with zinc and hydrochloric acid, or by electrolysis. Alums are known which contain the hexaaquavanadium(III) ion, e.g. $(NH_4)_2SO_4 \cdot V_2(SO_4)_3 \cdot 24H_2O$.

Vanadium(III) compounds are easily oxidised to vanadium(IV) or vanadium(V) compounds.

The tetravalent state

(+4 oxidation state) $3d^1$

Because vanadium(IV) compounds possess no marked oxidising or reducing properties, this is generally considered to be the most stable state for vanadium.

The dark blue amphoteric vanadium(IV) oxide, VO_2, is formed by reducing vanadium(V) oxide with sulphur dioxide, ethanedioic acid or vanadium(III) oxide. It dissolves in acids to form the hydrated vanadium(IV) oxide ion, $VO^{2+}(aq)$. There is evidence to indicate that this ion is $[VO(H_2O)_5]^{2+}$, in which the oxygen atom occupies one coordinate position and water molecules the other five. Complex polymeric vanadate(IV) anions are formed when vanadium(IV) oxide dissolves in alkalis.

Vanadium(IV) forms many five-coordinate complexes, e.g. $[VO(SCN)_4]^{2-}$, although this is a comparatively rare coordination number among the transition elements. Most vanadium(IV) compounds involve the 'VO' grouping, but exceptions include the halides such as VF_4, VCl_4 and VBr_4. Vanadium(IV) chloride, VCl_4, which is prepared by heating vanadium in chlorine, resembles titanium(IV) chloride in its chemical properties.

The pentavalent state

(+5 oxidation state) $3d^0$

The pentavalent state for vanadium corresponds to the formal loss of all five outer electrons. The resemblance between vanadium and the metallic elements of group 5B, however, is much less marked than between titanium(IV) and tin(IV) compounds. Acidic solutions of vanadium(V) compounds are moderately powerful oxidants.

Vanadium(V) oxide, V_2O_5, is prepared by direct combination of the heated elements, or by the action of heat or acids on ammonium vanadate, NH_4VO_3:

$$2NH_4VO_3 = V_2O_5 + 2NH_3 + H_2O$$
$$2NH_4VO_3 + 2H^+(aq) = 2NH_4^+ + V_2O_5 + H_2O$$

The colour of vanadium(V) oxide varies from orange to red depending on its mode of preparation. It is amphoteric, and dissolves readily in alkalis to produce anionic vanadate(V) species. For example, the simple vanadate(V) ion, VO_4^{3-}, exists in strongly alkaline solutions, but if the pH is lowered by the addition of acid condensed anions are formed, such as $V_2O_7^{2-}$, $V_3O_9^{3-}$ and $V_{10}O_{28}^{6-}$. With acids, vanadium(V) oxide forms the yellow vanadium(V) oxide ion, VO_2^+(aq).

The only binary halide of vanadium(V) is the fluoride, VF_5. Covalent halides of vanadium(V) containing oxygen are also known, e.g. vanadium(V) oxide trichloride, $VOCl_3$.

Vanadium(V) compounds are used as catalysts in the manufacture of sulphuric acid (§11.5).

Summary

The colours of vanadium compounds in the four different valency states can conveniently be demonstrated by reducing an acidic solution of ammonium vanadate with zinc. The colour changes observed are as follows:

valency state	5	4	3	2
species present	VO_2^+(aq)	VO^{2+}(aq)	$[V(H_2O)_6]^{3+}$	$[V(H_2O)_6]^{2+}$
colour	yellow†	blue†	green	lavender

the colour changes in this sequence as reduction proceeds ⟶

† A green colour is often observed, due to the combined presence of pentavalent and tetravalent species.

14.6 Chromium

Outer electronic configuration: $3d^5\ 4s^1$. Principal valencies: 2, 3, 6 ($+2$, $+3$, $+6$ oxidation states).

The element

Pure chromium is obtained either by reducing chromium(III) oxide with aluminium at a high temperature:

$$Cr_2O_3 + 2Al = Al_2O_3 + 2Cr$$

or by the electrolysis of an aqueous solution of chromium(VI) oxide, CrO_3, to which a small quantity of sulphuric acid has been added.

It is a bluish white metal, with the highest melting temperature of any first series transition element except vanadium. It dissolves readily in non-oxidising acids, but is passivated by oxidising acids such as nitric acid. At elevated temperatures it combines directly with many non-metals, e.g. the halogens, oxygen and sulphur, to form chromium(III) compounds.

The metal is highly resistant to atmospheric corrosion, which accounts for its extensive use in chromium plating and stainless steels. The latter, which are alloys of iron, chromium and nickel, are manufactured by adding ferrochromium and nickel to molten steel. 'Ferrochromium', an alloy of iron and chromium, is obtained by reducing the principal ore of chromium, namely chromite, $FeCr_2O_4$, with carbon in a furnace.

The divalent state

(+2 oxidation state) $3d^4$

The turquoise-blue hexaaquachromium(II) ion, $[Cr(H_2O)_6]^{2+}$, is prepared either by dissolving chromium in non-oxidising acids, or by reducing acidic solutions of chromium(III) or chromium(VI) compounds with zinc. Like most chromium(II) species, the hydrated chromium(II) ion is easily oxidised, e.g. by oxygen:

$$4[Cr(H_2O)_6]^{2+} + O_2 + 2H_2O = 4[Cr(H_2O)_6]^{3+} + 4HO^-$$

It is slowly oxidised by water, especially if the solution is acidic:

$$2[Cr(H_2O)_6]^{2+} + 2H_2O = 2[Cr(H_2O)_6]^{3+} + 2HO^- + H_2$$

The trivalent state

(+3 oxidation state) $3d^3$

Chromium(III) compounds possess no marked oxidising or reducing properties, and this state is therefore considered to be the most stable for chromium. Perhaps the most distinctive feature of chromium(III) is its strong tendency to form complexes which are noted for their kinetic inertness, i.e. the low rate at which one ligand is substituted by another. Because of this, a large number of chromium(III) complexes have been isolated and studied. Most of them are octahedral, and vary in colour from green to grey-blue depending on the ligands present, e.g. the isomers of $CrCl_3 \cdot 6H_2O$ (§14.1).

In aqueous solution, the hexaaquachromium(III) ion, $[Cr(H_2O)_6]^{3+}$, resembles the hydrated aluminium ion, $[Al(H_2O)_6]^{3+}$, in that the small, highly charged cation (Cr^{3+}) distorts the coordinated water molecules so that hydrolysis occurs:

$$[Cr(H_2O)_6]^{3+} + H_2O \rightleftharpoons [Cr(OH)(H_2O)_5]^{2+} + H_3O^+ \qquad pK_1 = 3.9$$

The addition of bases, e.g. alkalis, ammonia, sulphide ions or carbonate ions, to hydrated chromium(III) ions produces a green precipitate of hydrated chromium(III) oxide, $Cr_2O_3(aq)$, often referred to as 'chromium(III) hydroxide'. Anhydrous chromium(III) oxide, Cr_2O_3, is a green powder which is prepared by heating the hydrated oxide or ammonium dichromate (§10.5).

Both the hydrated oxide and the anhydrous oxide are amphoteric, dissolving in acids to form complex chromium(III) ions, and in alkalis to produce a green solution containing anionic chromate(III) species, believed to be $[Cr(OH)_4(H_2O)_2]^-$, $[Cr(OH)_5(H_2O)]^{2-}$ and $[Cr(OH)_6]^{3-}$.

The hexavalent state

(+6 oxidation state) 3d⁰

Stable compounds of chromium(VI) exist only in combination with oxygen. For example, chromium(VI) oxide, CrO_3, is stable, but chromium(VI) fluoride, CrF_6, is unstable.

Chromium(VI) oxide (chromium trioxide)

Red-brown crystals of chromium(VI) oxide, CrO_3, are precipitated by adding cold concentrated sulphuric acid to a saturated solution of a dichromate:

$$Cr_2O_7^{2-} + H_2SO_4 = 2CrO_3 + SO_4^{2-} + H_2O$$

Chromium(VI) oxide is extremely soluble in water to give an acidic solution which is known as 'chromic acid', although the exact nature of the species present in solution is far from certain. There are two well defined series of salts derived from chromium(VI) oxide, namely the *chromates* and the *dichromates*.

Chromates

The chromate ion, CrO_4^{2-}, is obtained by oxidising chromium(III) salts with the peroxide ion, O_2^{2-}, under alkaline conditions. Sodium peroxide or hydrogen peroxide is a convenient reagent:

$$2Cr^{3+} + 3O_2^{2-} + 4HO^- = 2CrO_4^{2-} + 2H_2O$$

Chromates are also formed by strongly heating chromium(III) compounds with potassium chlorate and 'fusion mixture', i.e. a mixture of Na_2CO_3 and K_2CO_3:

$$2Cr^{3+} + ClO_3^- + 5CO_3^{2-} = 2CrO_4^{2-} + Cl^- + 5CO_2$$

Many yellow crystalline salts containing the tetrahedral CrO_4^{2-} ion are known, e.g. Na_2CrO_4, K_2CrO_4 and $BaCrO_4$. Silver chromate, Ag_2CrO_4, is unusual in having a brick-red colour. Only the chromates of the alkali metals, ammonium, magnesium and calcium are soluble in water.

The chromate ion is stable in neutral or alkaline solution, but in acidic solution immediately changes into the dichromate ion:

$$2CrO_4^{2-} + 2H^+(aq) = Cr_2O_7^{2-} + H_2O$$
yellow   orange

The reaction involves the formation and dimerisation of the hydrogen-chromate ion:

$$CrO_4^{2-} + H^+(aq) = HCrO_4^-$$
$$2HCrO_4^- = Cr_2O_7^{2-} + H_2O$$

If alkali is added to a solution of a dichromate the reverse change occurs:

$$Cr_2O_7^{2-} + 2HO^- = 2CrO_4^{2-} + H_2O$$

The chromate ion is also produced from dichromate solutions by the addition of cations which form soluble dichromates but insoluble chromates:

$$2M^{2+} + Cr_2O_7^{2-} + H_2O = 2MCrO_4(s) + 2H^+(aq) \quad (M^{2+} = Pb^{2+} \text{ or } Ba^{2+})$$
$$\text{yellow precipitate}$$

Dichromates

The dichromate ion consists of two tetrahedral CrO_4 units bonded together by a common oxygen atom, i.e.

In acidic media it possesses powerful oxidising properties, and the sodium and potassium salts are commonly used as oxidising agents in the laboratory.

$$\tfrac{1}{2}Cr_2O_7^{2-} + 7H^+(aq) + 3e^- = Cr^{3+} + \tfrac{7}{2} H_2O \qquad E^{\ominus} = +1.33 \text{ V}$$

Chromates are weaker oxidising agents than dichromates, as evidenced by the more negative $E^{\ominus}$ value:

$$CrO_4^{2-} + \tfrac{5}{2} H_2O + 3e^- = \tfrac{1}{2}Cr_2O_3(aq) + 5HO^- \qquad E^{\ominus} = -0.13 \text{ V}$$

Sodium dichromate is often used as an oxidant in organic preparations. It is deliquescent. Potassium dichromate is not deliquescent and can be obtained in a high state of purity. Consequently, it is used as a primary standard in volumetric analysis, principally for the determination of iron(II) in acidic solution:

$$Cr_2O_7^{2-} + 6Fe^{2+} + 14H^+(aq) = 2Cr^{3+} + 6Fe^{3+} + 7H_2O$$

The dichromate solution is placed in the burette and the acidified iron(II) solution in the flask. A redox indicator, such as barium diphenylaminesulphonate, is necessary to detect the end-point. This is a colourless substance, which is converted to a deep blue compound by oxidants. Thus, the end-point of the titration is observed as a deep blue colour with the first drop of dichromate solution in excess. The hydrated iron(III) ion can interfere, because it, too, is able to oxidise the indicator, turning it deep blue. However, phosphate complexes of iron(III) do not affect the indicator, and for this reason phosphoric acid is added to the iron(II) solution before starting the titration.

Unlike permanganates, dichromates do not oxidise chloride ions, since the $E^{\ominus}$ value ($+1.36$ V) for Cl^-/Cl_2 is more positive than that for $Cr^{3+}/Cr_2O_7^{2-}$. Dichromates can therefore be used for the titration of iron(II) in solutions containing chloride ions.

Besides oxidising iron(II), the dichromate ion readily oxidises sulphur dioxide or sulphite ions to sulphate ions, and iodide ions to iodine.

Chromyl chloride

Chromyl chloride, CrO_2Cl_2, the acid chloride of the acid H_2CrO_4, is formed by warming a mixture of a dichromate and a chloride with concentrated sulphuric acid:

$$Na_2Cr_2O_7 + 4NaCl + 3H_2SO_4 = 2CrO_2Cl_2 + 3Na_2SO_4 + 3H_2O$$

Chromyl chloride vapour distils off and can be condensed to a red-brown liquid. This reaction can be used as a specific test for ionic chlorides, since neither bromides nor iodides form the corresponding chromyl compounds.

Chromyl chloride is hydrolysed by water to chromic acid and hydrochloric acid. With alkalis it reacts to form chromates:

$$CrO_2Cl_2 + 4HO^- = CrO_4^{2-} + 2Cl^- + 2H_2O$$

Potassium chlorochromate

Potassium chlorochromate, $KCrO_3Cl$, is obtained as orange crystals by crystallising a solution of potassium dichromate in hydrochloric acid. The salt is stable in hydrochloric acid, but is hydrolysed by water:

$$2KCrO_3Cl + H_2O = K_2Cr_2O_7 + 2HCl$$

Peroxides of chromium

A number of unstable peroxide compounds of chromium(VI) are known. The blue solution which is obtained when hydrogen peroxide is added to a cold solution of an acidified dichromate contains the peroxide, CrO_5. This compound decomposes rapidly in aqueous solution, but is far more stable in ethoxyethane (ether). Its formation is used as a test for chromium.

Summary

The colours of chromium compounds in the three principal valency states can be demonstrated by reducing an acidified dichromate solution with zinc. The colour changes which are observed are as follows:

valency state	6	3	2
species present	$Cr_2O_7^{2-}$	complexed Cr^{3+} ions	$[Cr(H_2O)_6]^{2+}$
colour	orange	green	turquoise

colour change as reduction proceeds ⟶

The principal compounds of chromium and their inter-relationships are shown in Fig. 14.11.

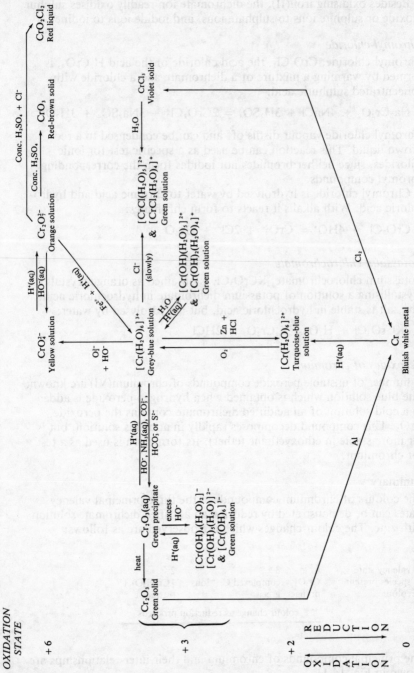

Fig. 14.11 Flow diagram of the principal chemistry of chromium.

14.7 Manganese

Outer electronic configuration: $3d^5 4s^2$. Principal valencies: 2, 4, 6, 7 ($+2$, $+4$, $+6$, $+7$ oxidation states).

The element

Manganese is extracted from its purified ore, pyrolusite, MnO_2, by reduction with aluminium at a high temperature:

$$3MnO_2 + 4Al = 3Mn + 2Al_2O_3$$

The metal can also be obtained by the electrolysis of aqueous manganese(II) salts.

Manganese dissolves readily in non-oxidising acids to produce manganese(II) salts, and reacts with various non-metals on heating. It is used principally as an alloying ingredient in steels. To make these steels, a mixture of manganese(IV) oxide and iron(III) oxide is reduced with coke in an electric furnace.

The divalent state

($+2$ oxidation state) $3d^5$
This is the most stable state of manganese. Neutral or acidic solutions of manganese(II) salts are very pale pink and contain the hexaaqua-manganese(II) ion, $[Mn(H_2O)_6]^{2+}$, which forms salts with all the common anions. The addition of alkali to aqueous manganese(II) salts precipitates white manganese(II) hydroxide, $Mn(OH)_2(aq)$, which is rapidly oxidised by atmospheric oxygen to give brown hydrated manganese(III) oxide, $Mn_2O_3(aq)$. Both the oxide and hydroxide of manganese(II) are basic.

The tetravalent state

($+4$ oxidation state) $3d^3$
The only important compound of tetravalent manganese is manganese(IV) oxide (manganese dioxide), MnO_2. The compound has a stable ionic structure, $Mn^{4+}(O^{2-})_2$, despite the large amount of energy needed for ion formation:

$$Mn(s) = Mn^{4+}(g) + 4e^- \qquad \Delta H^{\ominus} = +10\,945 \text{ kJ mol}^{-1}$$
$$O_2(g) + 4e^- = 2O^{2-}(g) \qquad \Delta H^{\ominus} = +1\,924 \text{ kJ mol}^{-1}$$

The reason is that there is a strong attraction between the highly charged Mn^{4+} cations and the relatively small doubly charged O^{2-} anions:

$$Mn^{4+}(g) + 2O^{2-}(g) = MnO_2(s) \qquad \Delta H^{\ominus} = -13\,390 \text{ kJ mol}^{-1}$$

This very high lattice enthalpy more than compensates for the enthalpy requirement, and the overall enthalpy of formation is negative, i.e.

$$Mn(s) + O_2(g) = MnO_2(s)$$
$$\Delta H_f^{\ominus} = +10\,945 + 1\,924 + (-13\,390) = -521 \text{ kJ mol}^{-1}$$

Anhydrous manganese(IV) oxide is prepared as a black powder by heating the hydrated oxide (see below) or manganese(II) nitrate:

$$Mn(NO_3)_2 = MnO_2 + 2NO_2$$

A brown hydrated form of manganese(IV) oxide, $MnO_2(aq)$, with a variable water content, is obtained by reducing permanganate ions in alkaline solution (p. 335) or by oxidising manganese(II) ions with peroxodisulphate ions, $S_2O_8^{2-}$, or hypochlorite ions, ClO^-:

$$Mn^{2+} + S_2O_8^{2-} + 2H_2O = MnO_2(aq) + 2SO_4^{2-} + 4H^+(aq)$$

Manganese(IV) oxide, because of its high lattice enthalpy, is insoluble in water. It is a powerful oxidising agent, particularly under acidic conditions; e.g. it oxidises warm concentrated hydrochloric acid to chlorine:

$$MnO_2 + 4H^+(aq) + 2Cl^- = Mn^{2+} + Cl_2 + 2H_2O$$

At $0\,°C$ (273 K), however, it dissolves in concentrated hydrochloric acid to form the hexachloromanganate(IV) ion, which decomposes at room temperature:

$$MnO_2 + 4H^+(aq) + 6Cl^- = [MnCl_6]^{2-} + 2H_2O$$
$$[MnCl_6]^{2-} = Mn^{2+} + Cl_2 + 4Cl^-$$

Concentrated solutions of alkali metal hydroxides slowly dissolve manganese(IV) oxide with disproportionation to form blue solutions containing equimolar amounts of manganese(III) and manganese(V) compounds. Manganese(IV) species of uncertain constitution are obtained when manganese(IV) oxide is fused with metal oxides.

Manganese(IV) oxide functions as a catalyst in many reactions (Table 14.5).

The hexavalent state
(+6 oxidation state) 3d^1

The deep green tetrahedral manganate ion, MnO_4^{2-}, is the only known species of manganese(VI). It is prepared by fusing a mixture of manganese(IV) oxide and potassium hydroxide with an oxidant such as potassium chlorate or potassium nitrate:

$$3MnO_2 + 6HO^- + ClO_3^- = 3MnO_4^{2-} + Cl^- + 3H_2O$$

Alternatively, the manganate ion can be obtained by reducing permanganate ions with manganese(IV) oxide in a strongly alkaline solution. The reaction is reversible:

$$2MnO_4^- + MnO_2 + 4HO^- \rightleftharpoons 3MnO_4^{2-} + 2H_2O$$

The manganate ion is stable only in alkaline solution. In neutral or acidic media the equilibrium is displaced to the left by the removal of hydroxide ions, and the manganate ion disproportionates into manganese(IV) oxide and permanganate ions.

The heptavalent state

(+7 oxidation state) $3d^0$

Potassium permanganate, $KMnO_4$, a deep purple compound which contains the tetrahedral permanganate ion, MnO_4^-, is the most familiar compound of heptavalent manganese. The permanganate ion can be prepared from various other species of manganese, including:

(i)   the manganate ion, by disproportionation (see above), by electro-lytic oxidation, or by oxidation with chlorine:

$$2MnO_4^{2-} + Cl_2 = 2MnO_4^- + 2Cl^-$$

(ii) the manganese(II) ion, by oxidation in acidic solution with powerful oxidants such as sodium bismuthate, $NaBiO_3$, or the periodate ion, IO_4^-;

(iii) the element itself, by anodic oxidation. For this purpose, an aqueous alkali metal carbonate is electrolysed using a manganese anode.

Acidic, neutral or weakly alkaline solutions of permanganates are unstable and slowly deposit hydrated manganese(IV) oxide:

$$4MnO_4^- + 4H^+(aq) = 4MnO_2(aq) + 3O_2 + 2H_2O$$

The reaction is accelerated by light, and for this reason standard permanganate solutions are stored in dark bottles.

In strongly alkaline solution the permanganate ion decomposes rapidly by a different reaction to give the manganate ion:

$$4MnO_4^- + 4HO^- = 4MnO_4^{2-} + O_2 + 2H_2O$$

The permanganate ion is a powerful oxidising agent. Its reduction product, and hence its standard electrode potential, depends on the pH of the solution.

(i)   In acidic solution it is reduced to the manganese(II) ion:

$$MnO_4^- + 8H^+(aq) + 5e^- = Mn^{2+} + 4H_2O \qquad E^\ominus = +1.52 \text{ V}$$

If the permanganate is present in excess, hydrated manganese(IV) oxide is formed by the oxidation of manganese(II) ions:

$$2MnO_4^- + 3Mn^{2+} + 2H_2O = 5MnO_2(aq) + 4H^+(aq)$$

(ii) In neutral or alkaline solutions hydrated manganese(IV) oxide is produced:

$$MnO_4^- + 2H_2O + 3e^- = MnO_2(aq) + 4HO^- \qquad E^\ominus = +1.67 \text{ V}$$

(iii) In strongly alkaline solution, and with an excess of permanganate, the manganate ion is formed:

$$MnO_4^- + e^- = MnO_4^{2-} \qquad E^\ominus = +0.56 \text{ V}$$

Aqueous potassium permanganate is widely used as a laboratory oxidant, in both volumetric analysis and preparative chemistry.

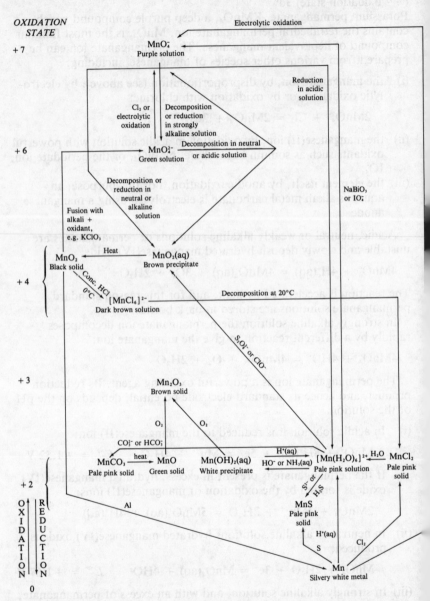

OXIDATION
STATE

Fig. 14.12 Flow diagram of the principal chemistry of manganese.

Redox titrations with potassium permanganate

Acidic solutions of reductants, notably iron(II) salts, ethanedioates, nitrites and hydrogen peroxide, are rapidly and quantitatively oxidised by potassium permanganate. Under these conditions, the manganese(II) ion is the reduction product of the permanganate ion. Solutions of these reductants can therefore be analysed with a standard solution of the permanganate. The acid employed is usually sulphuric acid. Hydrochloric acid is unsuitable for the purpose because it is oxidised to chlorine by permanganate ions, and nitric acid is also unsuitable since it is itself an oxidising agent. The end-point of the titration is recognised by the appearance of the first permanent pink coloration in the solution being titrated. Potassium permanganate is not used as a primary standard because it is difficult to obtain in a high state of purity, and its solutions are not stable over long periods of time.

Preparative reactions of potassium permanganate

Alkaline solutions of potassium permanganate are commonly used as oxidants in organic chemistry. Under these conditions the final reduction product of the permanganate ion is hydrated manganese(IV) oxide, although the green manganate ion is often formed as an intermediate.

Summary   The principal compounds of manganese and their interrelationships are shown in Fig. 14.12.

14.8 Iron

Outer electronic configuration: $3d^6 4s^2$. Principal valencies: 2, 3, 6 ($+2$, $+3$, $+6$ oxidation states).

The element

Pure iron can be obtained by electrolysing an aqueous solution of an iron(II) salt, or by reducing the oxides of iron with hydrogen. It is seldom employed in industry. Steel, which is iron containing between 0.1 and 1.5 per cent of carbon, or alloys of iron with other metals, are used instead.

Crude iron is extracted from its principal ore, iron(III) oxide (haematite), Fe_2O_3, by reduction in a blast furnace, which is essentially a vertical furnace with a temperature gradient ranging from approximately 1 500 °C (1 773 K) at the base to 400 °C (673 K) at the top. A mixture of the ore, coke and limestone, $CaCO_3$, is fed into the top of the furnace and air, preheated to 600 °C (873 K), is forced in at the bottom. Many reactions, some very complex, occur in the blast furnace. The more important, together with the approximate temperatures at which they take place, are outlined in Table 14.10.

The combustion of coke at the bottom of the furnace, equation (h), provides both the energy and the principal reducing agent, namely

Table 14.10 Some blast furnace reactions and the temperatures at which they occur.

Reaction	Temperature/°C (K)
(a) $Fe_2O_3 + 3CO \rightleftharpoons 2Fe + 3CO_2$	400–700 (673–973)
(b) $C + CO_2 = 2CO$	
(c) $CaCO_3 = CaO + CO_2$	
(d) $Fe_2O_3 + CO = 2FeO + CO_2$	700–900 (973–1 173)
(e) $CaO + SiO_2 = CaSiO_3$ (slag formation)	
(f) $FeO + C = Fe + CO$	
(g) $Fe_2O_3 + 3C = 2Fe + 3CO$	1 100 (1 373)
(h) $2C + O_2 = 2CO$	1 500 (1 773)

carbon monoxide, for the production of iron. Reaction (a) is reversible and exothermic in the forward direction, and is therefore favoured by relatively low temperatures and a high ratio of carbon monoxide to carbon dioxide. In the lower, hotter regions of the furnace other iron-forming reactions occur (equations (f) and (g)). Iron is produced in the semi-molten state and sinks to the bottom of the furnace from where it is drawn off periodically. Calcium oxide, formed by the decomposition of limestone, equation (c), combines with the earthy and sandy impurities present in the ore to give a molten slag, represented in simplified form by equation (e). The slag, also, sinks to the base of the furnace but floats on top of the molten iron and is periodically tapped from a separate hole.

Crude iron from the blast furnace contains up to 5 per cent of impurities, chiefly carbon, phosphorus and sulphur, which tend to make the metal hard and rather brittle. While it is satisfactory for use as cast iron, for most applications the crude iron is refined to produce various steels. The steel making process entails the removal of most of the impurities by oxidation at high temperatures. Other metals, e.g. manganese, chromium, nickel, tungsten or vanadium, may be added to the steel to produce alloys with special properties, such as hardness or resistance to corrosion.

Pure iron, in contrast to most steels, is rather soft, malleable and ductile. It is fairly reactive, and rusts in moist air to give, ultimately, hydrated iron(III) oxide, $Fe_2O_3(aq)$. Non-oxidising acids attack the metal to form hydrogen and, in the absence of air, iron(II) salts:

$$Fe + 2H^+(aq) = Fe^{2+} + H_2$$

In the presence of air, some iron(II) is oxidised to iron(III):

$$4Fe^{2+} + O_2 + 4H^+(aq) = 4Fe^{3+} + 2H_2O$$

Warm dilute nitric acid dissolves iron to give iron(II) and iron(III) nitrates and oxides of nitrogen, i.e. reduction products of nitric acid, but concentrated nitric acid renders the metal passive. On heating, iron combines with many non-metals, notably oxygen, sulphur and the halogens.

The divalent state

(+ 2 oxidation state) $3d^6$

Many compounds of iron(II) are known, ranging from simple binary compounds to those containing complexes of iron(II). Most iron(II) compounds are reducing agents, since they are easily oxidised to the corresponding iron(III) compounds.

Binary compounds of iron(II)

Iron(II) oxide, FeO, is a black powder which is prepared by heating iron(II) ethanedioate in the absence of air:

$$(COO)_2Fe = FeO + CO + CO_2$$

The compound is pyrophoric, i.e. it inflames in air to form iron(III) oxide. It has a tendency to be deficient in iron and is often non-stoicheiometric, e.g. its formula may be $Fe_{0.95}O$. At very high temperatures iron(II) oxide decomposes:

$$4FeO = Fe + Fe_3O_4$$

Iron(II) sulphide, FeS, is prepared by heating a mixture of iron filings and sulphur, or by introducing sulphide ions into a neutral iron(II) solution. Like the oxide, iron(II) sulphide is black and tends to be non-stoicheiometric. Naturally occurring pyrites, FeS_2, is also an iron(II) compound; it contains the disulphide ion, S_2^{2-}.

The anhydrous halides of iron(II) are obtained by heating iron in a stream of the appropriate hydrogen halide:

$$Fe + 2HX = FeX_2 + H_2 \qquad \text{(X = F, Cl, Br or I)}$$

Because iron(III) iodide does not exist, iron(II) iodide can also be made by heating iron with iodine. The hydrated halides are prepared by adding water to the anhydrous compounds, or by dissolving iron in the appropriate hydrohalic acid. Iron(II) halides are essentially ionic.

Complexes of iron(II)

Iron(II) forms a large number of complexes, the commonest being the pale green hexaaquairon(II) ion, $[Fe(H_2O)_6]^{2+}$. Several crystalline salts containing this ion are known, e.g. $FeSO_4 \cdot 7H_2O$, $Fe(ClO_4)_2 \cdot 6H_2O$ and $FeSO_4 \cdot (NH_4)_2SO_4 \cdot 6H_2O$. Other examples of six-coordinate iron(II) complexes include the $[Fe(CN)_6]^{4-}$ ion and the complex trans $[FeCl_2(H_2O)_4]$ which is present in $FeCl_2 \cdot 6H_2O$. Haemoglobin is also an iron(II) complex.

The oxidation of iron(II)

All iron(II) compounds are capable of being oxidised to iron(III) species. The ease with which oxidation occurs depends on various factors, such as the pH of the solution and the ligands which are coordinated to the iron(II) ion. Most crystalline iron(II) salts are susceptible, at the very least, to superficial aerial oxidation, and some, e.g. $FeSO_4 \cdot 7H_2O$, are also efflorescent. However, the crystalline double salt, ammonium iron(II) sulphate hexahydrate, $FeSO_4 \cdot (NH_4)_2SO_4 \cdot 6H_2O$, is sufficiently stable in both respects to be used as a primary standard in volumetric analysis.

In acidic solution the hexaaquairon(II) ion is oxidised only slowly by the atmosphere, despite the favourable $E^{\ominus}$ values for the half-reactions:

$$[Fe(H_2O)_6]^{3+} + e^- = [Fe(H_2O)_6]^{2+} \qquad E^{\ominus} = +0.77 \text{ V}$$
$$\tfrac{1}{2}O_2 + 2H^+(aq) + 2e^- = H_2O \qquad E^{\ominus} = +1.23 \text{ V}$$

However, more powerful oxidants, such as permanganate or dichromate ions, or hydrogen peroxide, oxidise iron(II) to iron(III) rapidly in acidic solution.

In alkaline conditions, where the insoluble hydrated hydroxide, $Fe(OH)_2(aq)$, exists, iron(II) is oxidised more readily than in acidic solution. This is indicated by the less positive $E^{\ominus}$ value for the half-reaction:

$$\tfrac{1}{2}Fe_2O_3(aq)(s) + \tfrac{3}{2}H_2O + e^- = Fe(OH)_2(aq)(s) + HO^-$$
$$E^{\ominus} = -0.56 \text{ V}$$

When alkali is added to a solution containing $[Fe(H_2O)_6]^{2+}$ ions, a *white* precipitate of iron(II) hydroxide is obtained in the complete absence of oxygen. On exposure to air iron(II) hydroxide is rapidly oxidised to a dark green insoluble iron(III) compound, formulated as $FeO(OH)(aq)$, and finally to a brown sludge of hydrated iron(III) oxide, $Fe_2O_3(aq)$. It is interesting to note that iron(II) hydroxide is weakly amphoteric, since it dissolves in acids to form iron(II) salts and in concentrated alkalis to yield the ferrate(II) ion, $[Fe(OH)_6]^{4-}$. Iron(II) oxide, in contrast, appears to be exclusively basic.

The iron(II)−iron(III) system provides some excellent examples of the effect of ligands on the relative stability of different valency states. The water ligands of the hexaaquairon(II) ion can easily be substituted by six cyanide ions to form the yellow hexacyanoferrate(II) ion, $[Fe(CN)_6]^{4-}$. The $E^{\ominus}$ values show that the iron(II) cyanide complex is oxidised to the corresponding iron(III) complex, $[Fe(CN)_6]^{3-}$, more readily than the hydrated iron(II) ion is oxidised to the hexaaquairon(III) ion:

$$[Fe(CN)_6]^{3-} + e^- = [Fe(CN)_6]^{4-} \qquad E^{\ominus} = +0.36 \text{ V}$$

Thus, by changing water ligands for cyanide ions, the trivalent state of iron is stabilised relative to the divalent state, i.e. the $[Fe(CN)_6]^{4-}$ ion is a better reducing agent than $[Fe(H_2O)_6]^{2+}$. Despite this, the hexa-cyanoferrate(II) ion, in contrast to the aqua-complex, is not oxidised by the atmosphere. This suggests that a kinetic effect may possibly be operating, i.e. the cyanide complex is *able* to be oxidised by oxygen, but the *rate* of reaction is extremely low. The high stability of the cyanide complex may be one reason for this. The stability of the $[Fe(CN)_6]^{4-}$ ion is illustrated by the fact that, unlike the hexaaqua ion, it gives no precipitate when treated with either sulphide or hydroxide ions.

Another example is provided by the complex $[Fe(phen)_3]^{2+}$, where 'phen' represents the bidentate ligand 1 : 10-phenanthroline. This complex is more stable to oxidation than both hexaaquairon(II) and hexacyanoferrate(II) ions, as shown by the potential:

$$[Fe(phen)_3]^{3+} + e^- = [Fe(phen)_3]^{2+} \qquad E^\ominus = +1.12 \text{ V}$$

The trivalent state

(+3 oxidation state) $3d^5$
Despite the fact that the iron(III) ion is isoelectronic with the manganese(II) ion, there are few similarities between them.

Binary compounds of iron(III)

Trivalent iron does not appear to form a hydroxide. When alkali is added to an aqueous iron(III) salt, a brown precipitate is obtained of hydrated iron(III) oxide, $Fe_2O_3(aq)$:

$$2Fe^{3+} + 6HO^- = Fe_2O_3(aq) + 3H_2O$$

Anhydrous iron(III) oxide is ionic and exists in two forms. The commoner, α-Fe_2O_3, occurs naturally as haematite, and can be prepared as a red-brown powder by dehydrating the hydrated oxide at 200 °C (473 K), or by heating iron(II) sulphate:

$$2FeSO_4 \cdot 7H_2O = Fe_2O_3 + SO_2 + SO_3 + 14H_2O$$

The other form, γ-Fe_2O_3, is produced by heating triiron tetraoxide, Fe_3O_4, in oxygen below 250 °C (523 K):

$$4Fe_3O_4 + O_2 = 6Fe_2O_3$$

Iron(III) oxide is amphoteric. It dissolves in acids to form iron(III) salts, and in *concentrated* alkali solutions to form the ferrate(III) ion, $[Fe(OH)_6]^{3-}$.

The anhydrous fluoride, chloride and bromide of iron(III) are prepared by heating iron in a stream of the appropriate halogen. The iodide does not appear to exist in the pure state. Iron(III) chloride, the most important halide of iron(III), is an almost black hygroscopic solid. It is a covalent compound, with a complex polymeric structure at room temperature. When heated, iron(III) chloride melts and vaporises with the formation of the dimer, Fe_2Cl_6, whose molecules possess a similar structure to that of the Al_2Cl_6 molecule (§8.5). Stronger heating produces trigonal planar molecules of the monomer, $FeCl_3$, and finally, by decomposition, iron(II) chloride and chlorine. Iron(III) chloride dissolves in water to form yellow chloro-complexes (see below).

Hydrated iron(III) species are reduced by sulphide ions:

$$2Fe^{3+}(aq) + S^{2-} = 2Fe^{2+}(aq) + S(s)$$

Thus, when hydrogen sulphide is passed into a neutral solution of an iron(III) salt, a black precipitate of *iron(II)* sulphide and a yellow precipitate of sulphur are formed together. Iron(III) species also oxidise iodide ions, which accounts for the instability of iron(III) iodide:

$$2Fe^{3+} + 2I^- = 2Fe^{2+} + I_2$$

Complexes of iron(III)

Many complexes of iron(III) are known, particularly with ligands which coordinate through an oxygen atom. The pale violet hexaaquairon(III) ion, $[Fe(H_2O)_6]^{3+}$, occurs in certain crystalline salts, e.g. iron alum (§8.5) and the perchlorate, $Fe(ClO_4)_3 \cdot 10H_2O$. In solution, however, hydrolysis occurs to give yellow hydroxo-species:

$$[Fe(H_2O)_6]^{3+} + H_2O \rightleftharpoons [Fe(OH)(H_2O)_5]^{2+} + H_3O^+$$
$$[Fe(OH)(H_2O)_5]^{2+} + H_2O \rightleftharpoons [Fe(OH)_2(H_2O)_4]^+ + H_3O^+ \quad pK_1 = 2.22$$

Only in strongly acidic solutions, therefore, does the hexaaquairon(III) ion exist. Hydrolysis occurs because the small, highly charged iron(III) ion distorts the coordinated water molecules. The addition of hydroxide, carbonate or hydrogencarbonate ions to a solution of hydrated iron(III) ions produces a precipitate of hydrated iron(III) oxide (cf. aluminium and chromium), e.g.

$$2[Fe(OH)_2(H_2O)_4]^+ + CO_3^{2-} = Fe_2O_3(aq) + CO_2 + 10H_2O$$

Iron(III) carbonate is not formed because the carbonate ion simply acts as a base towards the hydrated iron(III) ion. The hexaaquairon(II) complex is far less acidic than the corresponding iron(III) species, because the iron(II) ion distorts the coordinated water molecules to a lesser extent than the iron(III) ion. Consequently, iron(II) salts react with carbonates or hydrogencarbonates to give a white precipitate of hydrated iron(II) carbonate, $FeCO_3(aq)$.

In solutions of hexaaquairon(III) ions that contain chloride ions, the yellow chloro-complexes $[FeCl(H_2O)_5]^{2+}$ and $[FeCl_2(H_2O)_4]^+$ are formed. In the presence of a large excess of chloride ions the orange-yellow tetrahedral tetrachloroferrate(III) ion is produced:

$$Fe^{3+} + 4Cl^- \rightleftharpoons [FeCl_4]^-$$

Other important complexes of iron(III) include the orange coloured hexacyanoferrate(III) ion, $[Fe(CN)_6]^{3-}$, and the deep red thiocyanate complexes, e.g. $[Fe(SCN)(H_2O)_5]^{2+}$, which are formed when thiocyanate ions, SCN^-, are added to hydrated iron(III) ions. This reaction can be used as a test to detect hydrated iron(III) ions in the presence of iron(II) ions, since the latter do not form coloured complexes with the thiocyanate ion.

The hexacyanoferrate ions

Potassium salts containing these ions are used in laboratory tests for iron(II) and iron(III). The appropriate reactions are summarised below.

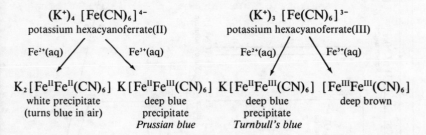

Turnbull's blue and Prussian blue appear to be identical compounds. They have the same basic structure, which consists of a cubic array of iron ions and cyanide ions.

Compounds containing iron in two valency states (oxidation states)

The only important compound in this category, apart from the cyano-complexes discussed above, is triiron tetraoxide, or iron(II) diiron(III) oxide, Fe_3O_4, a black solid which occurs naturally as the mineral magnetite. It can be prepared by heating iron(III) oxide to 1 400 °C (1 673 K), or by passing steam over iron at 800 °C (1 073 K).

$$6Fe_2O_3 = 4Fe_3O_4 + O_2$$
$$3Fe + 4H_2O \rightleftharpoons Fe_3O_4 + 4H_2$$

Triiron tetraoxide is a mixed oxide, which dissolves in acids to form iron(II) and iron(III) salts in a 1 : 2 molar ratio:

$$Fe_3O_4 + 8H^+(aq) = Fe^{2+} + 2Fe^{3+} + 4H_2O$$

The hexavalent state

(+6 oxidation state) $3d^2$

The only species known to contain hexavalent iron is the deep red tetrahedral ferrate(VI) ion, FeO_4^{2-}. It is prepared by oxidising hydrated iron(III) oxide, suspended in concentrated alkali, with hypochlorite ions:

$$Fe_2O_3(aq) + 3ClO^- + 4HO^- = 2FeO_4^{2-} + 3Cl^- + 2H_2O$$

The ferrate(VI) ion is a very powerful oxidant. It is stable in alkaline

344

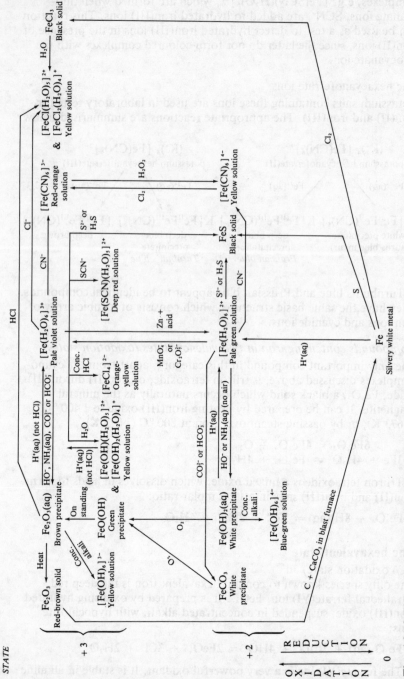

Fig. 14.13 Flow diagram of the principal chemistry of iron.

solution, but decomposition occurs in acidic or neutral solution:

$$4FeO_4^{2-} + 20H^+(aq) = 4Fe^{3+} + 3O_2 + 10H_2O$$

Summary The principal compounds of iron and their inter-relationships are shown in Fig. 14.13.

14.9 Cobalt

Outer electronic configuration: $3d^7 4s^2$. Principal valencies: 2, 3 ($+2$, $+3$ oxidation states).

The element

The isolation of cobalt from its ores is a rather complex process. In the laboratory, cobalt can be obtained by the reduction of cobalt(II) oxide with carbon or hydrogen, or by the electrolysis of an aqueous solution of a cobalt(II) salt.

Cobalt is a hard metal and is used principally for the production of special alloys. Chemically, it resembles iron but is less reactive. It dissolves only slowly in non-oxidising mineral acids, with the liberation of hydrogen and the formation of cobalt(II) salts, and is rendered passive by concentrated nitric acid. Cobalt(II) oxide, CoO, is formed when cobalt is heated in air at 400 °C (673 K), while at higher temperatures the product is Co_3O_4. Cobalt combines directly with the halogens on heating; with fluorine, cobalt(III) fluoride, CoF_3, is formed, but cobalt(II) halides result from the other halogens. Water vapour attacks cobalt only at elevated temperatures.

The divalent state

($+2$ oxidation state) $3d^7$

Cobalt(II) oxide, CoO, is basic and dissolves readily in acids to give cobalt(II) salts. Solutions of the latter, in the absence of complexing ligands such as NH_3 and CN^-, contain the pink octahedral hexaaqua-cobalt(II) ion, $[Co(H_2O)_6]^{2+}$. The ion is also present in hydrated crystalline salts, e.g. $CoSO_4 \cdot 7H_2O$. In contrast to $[Fe(H_2O)_6]^{2+}$, the hexaaquacobalt(II) ion is oxidised only with great difficulty, as indicated by the high $E^\ominus$ value:

$$[Co(H_2O)_6]^{3+} + e^- = [Co(H_2O)_6]^{2+} \qquad E^\ominus = +1.82 \text{ V}$$

The hexaaquacobalt(III) ion, $[Co(H_2O)_6]^{3+}$, is in fact a very powerful oxidant, and cannot exist in aqueous solution because it oxidises water to oxygen:

$$4[Co(H_2O)_6]^{3+} + 2H_2O = 4[Co(H_2O)_6]^{2+} + 4H^+(aq) + O_2$$

The addition of alkali to an aqueous solution of a cobalt(II) salt results in the precipitation of cobalt(II) hydroxide, $Co(OH)_2(aq)$. A blue form is obtained at first, but this changes into a more stable pink modification on standing. Cobalt(II) hydroxide is weakly amphoteric, since it dissolves in acids to give cobalt(II) salts and in *concentrated* alkalis to form the deep blue cobaltate(II) ion, $[Co(OH)_4]^{2-}$. Very little hydrolysis of the $[Co(H_2O)_6]^{2+}$ ion occurs in solution, and consequently a pink precipitate of the carbonate, $CoCO_3 \cdot 6H_2O$, is obtained on the addition of carbonate ions.

Besides forming numerous octahedral complexes, cobalt(II) also forms many that are tetrahedral; in fact, it forms more of this type than any other transition metal ion. The commonest are anionic complexes of general formula $[CoX_4]^{2-}$, where X may be Cl, Br, I, SCN or OH. A solution containing the blue tetrachlorocobaltate(II) ion, $[CoCl_4]^{2-}$, is obtained by adding concentrated hydrochloric acid to an aqueous cobalt(II) salt:

$$[Co(H_2O)_6]^{2+} + 4Cl^- \rightleftharpoons [CoCl_4]^{2-} + 6H_2O$$

The reaction is readily reversed by adding water or by heating.

The trivalent state

(+3 oxidation state) $3d^6$

A hydrated compound of formula $CoO(OH)(aq)$ is obtained by oxidising cobalt(II) hydroxide, suspended in an alkaline solution, with oxygen. Cobalt(III) fluoride, CoF_3, a powerful fluorinating agent, is prepared by direct combination of the elements at 400 °C (673 K). Apart from these and a few other simple compounds, the chemistry of cobalt in the trivalent state is entirely that of complexes.

The relative stability of the divalent and trivalent states of cobalt depends on the coordinated ligands. With water or chloride ions as ligands the divalent state is more stable, but the trivalent state becomes dominant when the ligands are ammonia, cyanide ions or nitrite ions.

H_2O ligands

The hexaaquacobalt(III) ion, $[Co(H_2O)_6]^{3+}$, is a powerful oxidant (see above).

NH_3 ligands

The hexaamminecobalt(II) ion, $[Co(NH_3)_6]^{2+}$, in contrast to the hexa-aquacobalt(II) ion, can be oxidised very easily to a cobalt(III) ammine complex. This can be shown by adding aqueous ammonia to a solution of hydrated cobalt(II) ions. The precipitate of cobalt(II) hydroxide, which is formed initially, dissolves in excess ammonia to give the red-brown hexaamminecobalt(II) ion. The overall equation is:

$$[Co(H_2O)_6]^{2+} + 6NH_3 = [Co(NH_3)_6]^{2+} + 6H_2O$$

The colour slowly darkens on standing in air, as oxidation occurs to a cobalt(III) complex. To obtain the orange-yellow hexaamminecobalt(III) ion, $[Co(NH_3)_6]^{3+}$, the oxidation must be performed in the presence of an activated charcoal catalyst. Without the catalyst other complexes are obtained, e.g. in the presence of chloride ions, the red pentaamminechlorocobalt(III) ion, $[CoCl(NH_3)_5]^{2+}$.

$$[Co(H_2O)_6]^{2+} \xrightarrow{\substack{\text{excess} \\ NH_3(aq)}} [Co(NH_3)_6]^{2+} \begin{array}{c} \xrightarrow{\substack{O_2 \text{ or } H_2O_2 \\ \text{charcoal}}} [Co(NH_3)_6]^{3+} \\ \xrightarrow{\substack{O_2 \text{ or } H_2O_2 \\ \text{no charcoal} \\ Cl^- \text{ present}}} [CoCl(NH_3)_5]^{2+} \end{array}$$

NO_2^- ligands

Oxidation to the trivalent state occurs when ethanoic acid and excess sodium nitrite are added to a cobalt(II) salt. The nitrite ion acts both as an oxidising agent and a ligand:

$$[Co(H_2O)_6]^{2+} + 7NO_2^- + 2H^+(aq) = [Co(NO_2)_6]^{3-} + NO + 7H_2O$$

Sodium hexanitrocobaltate(III), $Na_3[Co(NO_2)_6]$, is water soluble and is used as a qualitative test for potassium ions. When a solution of this compound is added to an aqueous potassium salt, a yellow precipitate of formula $K_2Na[Co(NO_2)_6]$ is obtained.

CN^- ligands

The pentacyanocobaltate(II) ion, $[Co(CN)_5]^{3-}$, is oxidised very readily by oxygen to a peroxocobalt(III) complex. When boiled, a solution of this complex produces the exceedingly stable hexacyanocobaltate(III) ion, $[Co(CN)_6]^{3-}$.

A large number of other six-coordinate complexes of cobalt(III) are known, many of which contain ligands which donate through a nitrogen atom. One particularly important example is vitamin B_{12}. Kinetically, cobalt(III) complexes tend to be inert, i.e. ligand substitution reactions tend to occur slowly, and because of this they have proved extremely useful compounds for studying various aspects of coordination chemistry. Alfred Werner, the pioneer of coordination chemistry, was awarded the Nobel prize for chemistry in 1913 for elucidating the essential structures of various cobalt(III) and platinum(II) complexes.

Compounds containing cobalt in two valency states (oxidation states)

The only important compound in this category is tricobalt tetraoxide, Co_3O_4. Like the corresponding iron compound, it is a mixed oxide; it may be formulated as $Co^{II}Co_2^{III}O_4$ and named cobalt(II) dicobalt(III) oxide. It is prepared by heating cobalt(II) oxide in oxygen at $400-500\,°C$ $(673-773 K)$:

$$6CoO + O_2 = 2Co_3O_4$$

348

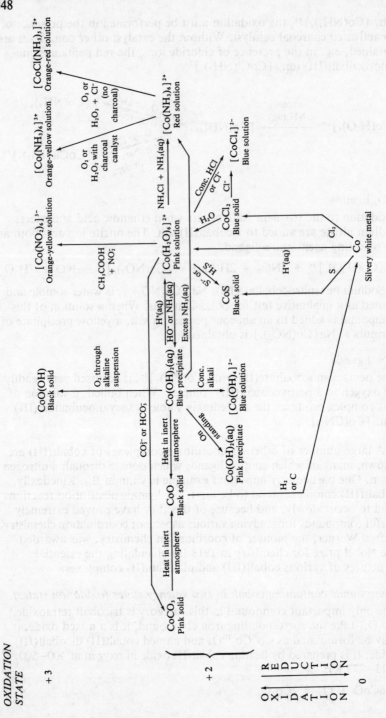

Fig. 14.14 Flow diagram of the principal chemistry of cobalt.

Summary The principal compounds of cobalt and their inter-relationships are shown in Fig. 14.14.

14.10 Nickel

Outer electronic configuration: $3d^8\ 4s^2$. Principal valencies: 2, 3 ($+2$, $+3$ oxidation states).

The element

Like cobalt, nickel is extracted by various complex processes, choice of which depends on the ore being processed. Basically, the ore is converted into nickel(II) oxide, from which the impure metal is obtained by reduction with carbon at a high temperature. Alternatively, nickel is isolated by the electrolysis of a nickel(II) salt, formed by dissolving the oxide in a dilute acid. The *Mond carbonyl process*, operated at Clydach in South Wales, is used to produce some pure nickel, and relies on the fact that carbon monoxide combines directly with the metal at 50 °C (323 K) to give tetracarbonylnickel(0):

$$Ni + 4CO = [Ni(CO)_4]$$

The volatile carbonyl is distilled off from the impurities and subsequently decomposed into pure nickel and carbon monoxide at 200 °C (473 K).

Nickel is a silvery white metal which is resistant to attack by water or air at room temperature, but reacts with non-oxidising mineral acids to yield hydrogen and nickel(II) salts:

$$Ni + 2H^+(aq) = Ni^{2+} + H_2$$

Contrary to popular belief, nickel is not passivated by concentrated nitric acid, but dissolves readily in the acid, particularly if heated, to produce nickel(II) nitrate and nitrogen dioxide. Alkalis have no effect on this metal.

Nickel is used chiefly as an alloying ingredient (e.g. in stainless steels (§14.6) and cupronickel), as an industrial hydrogenation catalyst, and as an electroplated protective coating for steel and brass.

The divalent state

($+2$ oxidation state) $3d^8$

With increasing atomic number, the first series of transition elements displays a marked increase in the stability of the divalent state, relative to the stability of higher states. This is clearly evident with nickel, for the divalent state is the only one that is stable and important.

The principal binary compounds of divalent nickel include the oxide, sulphide and anhydrous halides. Nickel(II) oxide, NiO, is a green solid which is prepared by heating the hydroxide, carbonate or ethanedioate of nickel(II). Black nickel(II) sulphide, NiS, is precipitated from alkaline solutions of nickel(II) ions by the addition of sulphide ions or hydrogen sulphide. Anhydrous nickel(II) halides, NiX_2, are prepared by direct combination of the heated elements.

The most important species of nickel(II) are its complexes. Nickel(II) oxide, which is basic, dissolves in acids to form the green hexaaqua-nickel(II) ion, $[Ni(H_2O)_6]^{2+}$. A number of crystalline hydrated salts are known which contain this ion, e.g. $NiSO_4 \cdot 6H_2O$, $Ni(NO_3)_2 \cdot 6H_2O$, and the double salt $(NH_4)_2SO_4 \cdot NiSO_4 \cdot 6H_2O$. The addition of alkali to a solution of a nickel(II) salt produces a green precipitate of hydrated nickel(II) hydroxide, $Ni(OH)_2$(aq). Like the oxide, nickel(II) hydroxide reacts with acids but not with alkali metal hydroxides. However, it dissolves readily in aqueous ammonia to form the deep blue hexa-amminenickel(II) ion. The overall reaction from a nickel(II) salt is:

$$[Ni(H_2O)_6]^{2+} + 6NH_3 = [Ni(NH_3)_6]^{2+} + 6H_2O$$

In addition to forming a considerable number of six-coordinate complexes, nickel(II) also forms several which are four-coordinate. For example, if potassium cyanide is added to a solution of a nickel(II) salt, a yellow precipitate is obtained of nickel(II) cyanide, $Ni(CN)_2$, which dissolves in excess potassium cyanide to give the stable, orange coloured, square planar tetracyanoniccolate(II) ion, $[Ni(CN)_4]^{2-}$. The overall reaction is:

$$[Ni(H_2O)_6]^{2+} + 4CN^- = [Ni(CN)_4]^{2-} + 6H_2O$$

The red coloured precipitate which is formed when 2,3-butanedione dioxime (dimethylglyoxime) is added to a neutral or slightly alkaline solution of a nickel(II) salt is also a square planar complex:

2,3-butanedione dioxime

bis(2,3-butanedione dioximato)nickel(II)

- - - - - represents hydrogen bonds

This reaction is used as a test for nickel(II) ions.

Some four-coordinate complexes of nickel are tetrahedral, e.g. the blue tetrachloroniccolate(II) ion, $[NiCl_4]^{2-}$, which is formed when chloride ions and nickel(II) ions react together in ethanol. In water hydrolysis occurs:

$$[NiCl_4]^{2-} + 6H_2O = [Ni(H_2O)_6]^{2+} + 4Cl^-$$

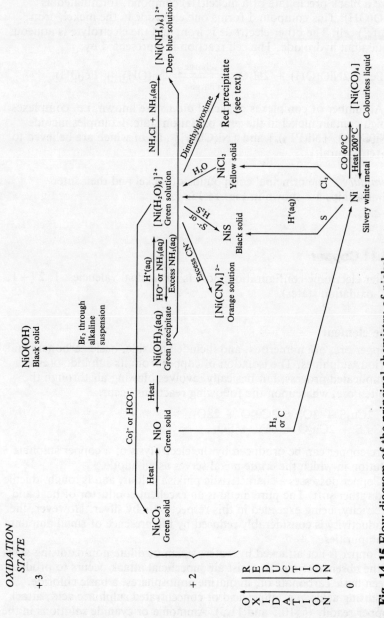

Fig. 14.15 Flow diagram of the principal chemistry of nickel.

The other valency states (oxidation states) of nickel

Bromine oxidises nickel(II) hydroxide suspended in aqueous alkali to give a black precipitate of a nickel(III) compond, formulated as NiO(OH). This compound forms one electrode in the nickel−iron ('nife') cell. The other electrode is iron, and the electrolyte is aqueous potassium hydroxide. The cell reaction is represented by:

$$Fe + 2NiO(OH) + 2H_2O \underset{\text{charge}}{\overset{\text{discharge}}{\rightleftharpoons}} 2Ni(OH)_2 + Fe(OH)_2$$

A number of complexes of nickel *atoms* are known, i.e. complexes which contain nickel in the zero oxidation state. Examples include $[Ni(CO)_4]$, $[Ni(PF_3)_4]$ and $[Ni(CN)_4]^{4-}$, all of which are believed to be tetrahedral.

Summary   The principal compounds of nickel and their inter-relationships are shown in Fig. 14.15.

14.11 Copper

Outer electronic configuration: $3d^{10} 4s^1$. Principal valencies: 1, 2 ($+1$, $+2$ oxidation states).

The element

Copper ores are numerous, and include an oxide, basic carbonate and various sulphides. The isolation of copper from its sulphide ores is a complicated process, but basically involves blowing air through the molten ore, whereupon the following reactions occur:

$$2Cu_2S + 3O_2 = 2Cu_2O + 2SO_2$$
$$Cu_2S + 2Cu_2O = 6Cu + SO_2$$

Pure copper can be produced by the electrolysis of a copper sulphate solution in which the crude metal serves as an anode.

Copper possesses a characteristic pinkish colour, and is tough, ductile and rather soft. The pure metal is an excellent conductor of heat and electricity, being exceeded in this respect only by silver. However, the conductivity is considerably reduced by the presence of small amounts of impurities.

Copper is not attacked by water, steam or dilute non-oxidising acids in the absence of air. In moist air superficial attack occurs to produce a green basic carbonate or, in marine atmospheres, a basic chloride. Oxidising acids, e.g. nitric acid or concentrated sulphuric acid, attack copper readily (§§10.5 and 11.5). Ammonia or cyanide solutions in the presence of either air or hydrogen peroxide also dissolve the metal, with the formation of complexes, e.g.

$$Cu + 2NH_3 \xrightarrow{O_2} [Cu(NH_3)_2]^+ \xrightarrow{O_2} [Cu(NH_3)_4(H_2O)_2]^{2+}$$

$$Cu + 4CN^- \xrightarrow{O_2} [Cu(CN)_4]^{3-}$$

At red heat copper combines with oxygen to form black copper(II) oxide, while at higher temperatures the red-brown copper(I) oxide, Cu_2O, is obtained. Copper reacts with the halogens to give copper(II) halides, and with sulphur on heating to yield copper(I) sulphide, Cu_2S.

Copper is used in plumbing for tanks, pipes, etc, and in electrical equipment. It is a constituent of many alloys, e.g. brass (copper–zinc), bronze (copper–tin) and cupronickel (a copper–nickel alloy used in coinage).

The monovalent state

(+ 1 oxidation state) $3d^{10}$

Because the 3d sub-shell is full, copper(I) compounds are diamagnetic (§14.1) and often colourless. Many copper(I) compounds, especially if they are insoluble, appear to be more stable than the corresponding copper(II) compounds. For example, the addition of iodide ions or cyanide ions to aqueous copper(II) salts produces a white precipitate of a copper(I) compound:

$$2Cu^{2+}(aq) + 4I^- = 2CuI + I_2$$

The oxide, sulphide and chloride of copper(II) all decompose at elevated temperatures into the corresponding copper(I) compounds, e.g.

$$2CuCl_2 = 2CuCl + Cl_2$$
$$4CuO = 2Cu_2O + O_2$$

In aqueous conditions, however, copper(I) compounds are unstable unless:

(i) the compound is insoluble in water, e.g. CuCl, CuCN or CuI;
(ii) the copper(I) ion is complexed with ligands, such as Cl^-, CN^- or NH_3, to give $[CuCl_2]^-$, $[Cu(CN)_4]^{3-}$ or $[Cu(NH_3)_2]^+$ respectively.

If neither of these conditions is satisfied, the simple hydrated copper(I) ion disproportionates:

$$2Cu^+(aq) \rightleftharpoons Cu^{2+}(aq) + Cu(s)$$
$$K = [Cu^{2+}]/[Cu^+]^2 \approx 10^6 \text{ mol}^{-1} \text{ dm}^3$$

The very high value of the equilibrium constant indicates that the disproportionation of copper(I) in aqueous solution may be regarded as complete.

Disproportionation is favoured because the hydration enthalpy of the copper(II) ion ($-2\,284$ kJ mol^{-1}) is higher than that of the copper(I) ion (-482.4 kJ mol^{-1}). This is due to the relatively high surface charge density of the Cu^{2+} ion. The enthalpy of atomisation of copper is $+339$ kJ mol^{-1}, and the first and second ionisation enthalpies are

$+751$ kJ mol^{-1} and $+1\,960$ kJ mol^{-1} respectively,

$\therefore$ for Cu(s) $\rightarrow$ Cu$^+$(aq)
$$\Delta H^{\ominus} = +339 + 751 - 482.4 = +607.6 \text{ kJ mol}^{-1}$$

and for Cu(s) $\rightarrow$ Cu^{2+}(aq)

$$\Delta H^{\ominus} = +339 + 751 + 1\,960 - 2\,248 = +802.0 \text{ kJ mol}^{-1}$$

Therefore, for the reaction

$$2Cu^+(aq) = Cu^{2+}(aq) + Cu(s)$$
$$\Delta H^{\ominus} = -2(607.6) + 802.0 = -413.2 \text{ kJ mol}^{-1}$$

Disproportionation of copper(I) ions is thus exothermic and likely to occur. The same conclusion can be reached by considering standard electrode potentials (§5.2).

Binary compounds of copper(I)

Copper(I) oxide

Copper(I) oxide, Cu_2O, is prepared as a red powder by heating copper(II) oxide above 800 °C (1 073 K), or as an orange-yellow precipitate by reducing an alkaline solution of a copper(II) salt with hydrazine, glucose, sodium sulphite or an aldehyde. The reaction is conveniently represented as

$$2Cu^{2+} + 2HO^- + 2e^- = Cu_2O + H_2O$$

and forms the basis of the Fehling's test for aldehydes and reducing sugars.

Copper(I) oxide dissolves in concentrated hydrochloric acid or aqueous ammonia to form copper(I) complexes, but with oxoacids, such as sulphuric acid, disproportionation occurs on warming:

$$Cu_2O + 4HCl = 2[CuCl_2]^- + H_2O + 2H^+(aq)$$
$$Cu_2O + 4NH_3 + H_2O = 2[Cu(NH_3)_2]^+ + 2HO^-$$
$$Cu_2O + H_2SO_4 = CuSO_4 + Cu + H_2O$$

Copper(I) halides

Copper(I) chloride, CuCl, is the commonest halide of copper(I). A brown solution containing the dichlorocuprate(I) ion is obtained by reducing a solution of a copper(II) salt with copper or sulphur dioxide in the presence of chloride ions:

$$Cu^{2+} + Cu + 4Cl^- = 2[CuCl_2]^-$$
$$2Cu^{2+} + SO_2 + 4Cl^- + 2H_2O = 2[CuCl_2]^- + SO_4^{2-} + 4H^+(aq)$$

A white precipitate of copper(I) chloride is formed when the brown solution is added to oxygen-free water. If the water contains dissolved oxygen, the precipitate rapidly turns green as oxidation occurs to copper(II).

Solid copper(I) chloride possesses a covalent polymeric structure, but the heated vapour contains dimeric and trimeric species, i.e. Cu_2Cl_2 and Cu_3Cl_3. Copper(I) chloride is insoluble in water, but dissolves in solutions of chlorides, cyanides and thiosulphates to form complexes (see below). The dissolution of copper(I) chloride in aqueous ammonia gives the diamminecopper(I) complex, $[Cu(NH_3)_2]^+$, which absorbs carbon monoxide quantitatively to form an addition compound. Ammoniacal copper(I) chloride also reacts with ethyne to give a red precipitate of copper(I) acetylide, Cu_2C_2:

$$2[Cu(NH_3)_2]^+ + C_2H_2 = Cu_2C_2 + 2NH_3 + 2NH_4^+$$

Copper(I) bromide, CuBr, closely resembles the chloride in its preparation and properties. Copper(I) iodide is obtained as a white precipitate by adding excess iodide ions to aqueous copper(II) ions (see above). This reaction is used in the analysis of aqueous copper(II) salts, for the liberated iodine can be titrated with a standard solution of sodium thiosulphate. Copper(I) fluoride is unknown.

Complexes of copper(I)

Low coordination numbers, usually two or four, are a feature of copper(I) complexes. The two-coordinate complexes, e.g. $[Cu(NH_3)_2]^+$ and $[Cu(S_2O_3)_2]^{3-}$, are linear.

Most four-coordinate copper(I) complexes are tetrahedral. A well known example involves cyanide ions. When a soluble cyanide is added slowly to an aqueous copper(II) salt, a toxic gas, cyanogen, $(CN)_2$, is evolved and copper(I) cyanide is precipitated:

$$2Cu^{2+} + 4CN^- = 2CuCN + (CN)_2 \qquad \text{(cf. precipitation of CuI)}$$

The white precipitate, however, dissolves readily in excess cyanide to produce the tetrahedral tetracyanocuprate(I) ion, $[Cu(CN)_4]^{3-}$.

Copper(I) chloride is readily soluble in solutions of chloride ions to form complexes such as $[CuCl_2]^-$, $[CuCl_3]^{2-}$ and $[CuCl_4]^{3-}$, depending on the concentration of chloride ions. For example, in a solution which is 1 M in chloride ions, the dichlorocuprate(I) ion predominates.

The divalent state

(+2 oxidation state) $3d^9$

Because the copper(II) ion has an incomplete 3d sub-shell, copper(II) compounds are paramagnetic and the complexes are coloured.

Binary compounds of copper(II)

Black copper(II) oxide, CuO, is prepared by heating the hydroxide, carbonate or nitrate of copper(II), or by heating the metal in air to temperatures not exceeding 800 °C (1 073 K).

Only three halides of copper(II) exist, namely the fluoride, chloride and bromide. The anhydrous compounds are made by heating copper with the appropriate halogen. The fluoride is ionic and white, while the chloride and bromide are covalent and coloured yellow-brown and black respectively.

chain structure of copper(II) chloride

At high temperatures the chloride and bromide decompose into copper(I) halides and the free halogens, e.g.

$$2CuBr_2 = 2CuBr + Br_2$$

Hydrated halides, e.g. the green $CuCl_2 \cdot 2H_2O$, are obtained by adding the anhydrous halides to water, or by dissolving copper(II) oxide in the appropriate hydrohalic acid.

Copper(II) sulphide, CuS, is obtained as a black precipitate by passing hydrogen sulphide through a solution of a copper(II) salt:

$$Cu^{2+} + H_2S = CuS + 2H^+(aq)$$

Alternatively, it is formed when copper and sulphur are heated together, although if too high a temperature is employed the copper(II) sulphide decomposes into copper(I) sulphide and sulphur.

Complexes of copper(II)

Copper in the divalent state behaves as a typical transition element in forming a large number of coloured complexes. The blue hexaaqua-copper(II) ion, $[Cu(H_2O)_6]^{2+}$, is perhaps the most familiar complex of copper. This ion possesses a tetragonally distorted octahedral structure, in which two of the water molecules are situated further than the other four from the copper(II) ion. The copper ion therefore lies in the centre of a square plane, defined by the four 'near' water molecules, with the 'far' molecules situated one above and one below this plane:

Solutions of the hydrated copper(II) ion are weakly acidic, due to hydrolysis:

$$[Cu(H_2O)_6]^{2+} + H_2O \rightleftharpoons [Cu(OH)(H_2O)_5]^+ + H_3O^+$$

The addition of alkali produces a bright blue precipitate of hydrated copper(II) hydroxide, $Cu(OH)_2(aq)$, which dehydrates at 100 °C (373 K) into copper(II) oxide. Copper(II) hydroxide is weakly amphoteric, and

357

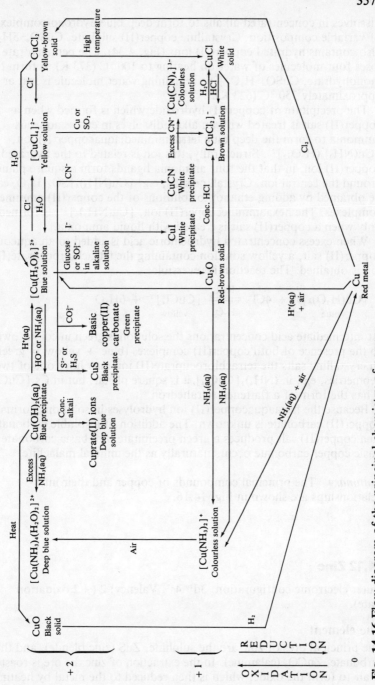

Fig. 14.16 Flow diagram of the principal chemistry of copper.

dissolves in concentrated alkalis to form deep blue hydroxo-complexes of variable composition. Crystalline copper(II) sulphate, $CuSO_4 \cdot 5H_2O$, also contains hydrated copper(II) ions (Fig. 4.34). The pentahydrate loses four molecules of water on heating to 100 °C (373 K) to form the monohydrate, $CuSO_4 \cdot H_2O$. The remaining water molecule is lost at approximately 350 °C (623 K).

The precipitate of copper(II) hydroxide which is formed when a copper(II) salt is treated with an alkali dissolves in excess aqueous ammonia to form the deep blue tetraamminediaquacopper(II) ion, $[Cu(NH_3)_4(H_2O)_2]^{2+}$. Structurally, this ion is related to the hydrated copper(II) ion, in that the four ammonia ligands form a square plane around the central ion. Crystalline salts, e.g. $[Cu(NH_3)_4]SO_4 \cdot H_2O$, can be obtained by adding ethanol to solutions of the copper(II) ammine complexes. The hexaamminecopper(II) ion, $[Cu(NH_3)_6]^{2+}$, is formed only when a copper(II) salt is treated with liquid ammonia.

When excess concentrated hydrochloric acid is added to an aqueous copper(II) salt, a yellow solution containing the tetrachlorocuprate(II) ion is obtained. The reaction is reversible:

$$[Cu(H_2O)_6]^{2+} + 4Cl^- \underset{H_2O}{\overset{HCl}{\rightleftharpoons}} [CuCl_4]^{2-} + 6H_2O$$
blue   yellow

At intermediate acid concentrations the solution is green in colour owing to the presence of both copper(II) complexes (blue + yellow = green). In crystalline salts the tetrachlorocuprate(II) ion may have one of two geometries, e.g. in $(NH_4)_2[CuCl_4]$ it is square planar, but in $Cs_2[CuCl_4]$ it has the form of a flattened tetrahedron.

Because the hexaaquacopper(II) ion hydrolyses in solution, normal copper(II) carbonate is unknown. The addition of a soluble carbonate to a copper(II) salt produces a green precipitate of a basic carbonate. A basic copper carbonate occurs naturally as the mineral malachite.

Summary The principal compounds of copper and their inter-relationships are shown in Fig. 14.16.

14.12 Zinc

Outer electronic configuration: $3d^{10} 4s^2$. Valency: 2 (+ 2 oxidation state).

The element

The principal ores of zinc are the sulphide, ZnS (zinc blende), and the carbonate, $ZnCO_3$ (calamine). In the extraction of zinc the ore is roasted in air to form the oxide, which is then reduced to the metal by heating with coke:

$$2ZnS + 3O_2 = 2ZnO + 2SO_2$$
$$ZnCO_3 = ZnO + CO_2$$
$$ZnO + C = Zn + CO$$

The crude zinc so obtained is separated from impurities, chiefly cadmium, by fractional distillation. An alternative method of isolating zinc involves dissolving the crude oxide in sulphuric acid to form zinc sulphate. Zinc dust is then added to remove cadmium ions:

$$Zn + Cd^{2+} = Zn^{2+} + Cd$$

and the solution is electrolysed.

Zinc, a white metal, is decidedly 'non-transitional' in its properties. For instance, it possesses much lower melting and boiling temperatures than the true transition elements, owing to the lack of 3d electron involvement in metallic bonding. It exhibits only one valency state, and its compounds are colourless (unless the anion is coloured) and dia-magnetic. However, it does form a range of complexes. Although its outer electronic configuration $(4s^2)$ compares with that of the group 2A elements, zinc bears little resemblance to these elements apart from the stoicheiometries of its compounds.

Zinc is fairly reactive. In moist air a film of the oxide and basic carbonate forms on the surface of the metal and protects it from further attack. When heated, it combines with several non-metals, e.g. oxygen, sulphur and the halogens. It dissolves in non-oxidising acids, with the liberation of hydrogen, to give zinc salts. If the zinc is pure the reac-tions are rather slow, but the presence of impurities has a catalytic effect by setting up small, localised electrochemical cells. A similar increase in reaction rate is observed if the zinc is first coated with copper by adding a copper(II) salt:

$$Zn + Cu^{2+} = Zn^{2+} + Cu$$

Metallic zinc reduces nitric acid. The main reduction product may be ions of hydroxylamine, hydrazine or ammonia, depending on the concentration of the acid (§10.5). Hot concentrated sulphuric acid is also reduced by zinc (§11.5). The metal dissolves readily in solutions of alkalis to produce zincate(II) ions, which are anionic hydroxo−zinc complexes, formulated as $[Zn(OH)_4]^{2-}$:

$$Zn + 2HO^- + 2H_2O = [Zn(OH)_4]^{2-} + H_2$$

Zinc is deposited on iron and steel to protect these metals against corrosion. The zinc may be applied by dipping the article into molten zinc ('galvanising'), by heating with zinc dust, or by electrolysis with an aqueous electrolyte of zinc sulphate or a complex zinc cyanide. Zinc is also used in the manufacture of dry batteries and alloys. The principal alloy, brass, contains 20−30 per cent zinc and 70−80 per cent copper.

Compounds of zinc

Zinc oxide, ZnO, a white powder, is prepared by heating the metal in air, or by heating zinc carbonate or zinc hydroxide. It is amphoteric:

$$ZnO + 2H^+(aq) = Zn^{2+}(aq) + H_2O$$
$$ZnO + 2HO^- + H_2O = [Zn(OH)_4]^{2-}$$

When zinc oxide is heated it loses a small amount of oxygen and turns yellow, but on cooling it regains lost oxygen and becomes white again. The yellow colour is not caused by unpaired d electrons, but by a structural defect which occurs in the crystal lattice when oxygen is lost. Zinc oxide is used in paints and as an antiseptic in ointments.

Hydrated zinc hydroxide, $Zn(OH)_2(aq)$, is also amphoteric and is obtained as a white gelatinous precipitate on adding an alkali to an aqueous zinc salt:

$$Zn^{2+}(aq) + 2HO^- = Zn(OH)_2(aq)$$

Zinc sulphide, ZnS, is prepared by heating zinc and sulphur, or as a white precipitate by passing hydrogen sulphide through a neutral or alkaline solution of a zinc salt. The sulphide is decomposed by acids:

$$ZnS + 2H^+(aq) = Zn^{2+}(aq) + H_2S$$

Zinc chloride is the most important halide of zinc. The dihydrate, $ZnCl_2 \cdot 2H_2O$, is prepared by dissolving zinc, or its oxide or carbonate, in hydrochloric acid. Anhydrous zinc chloride cannot be obtained by heating the hydrated salt because, like hydrated magnesium chloride, it undergoes hydrolysis to give a basic chloride:

$$ZnCl_2 \cdot 2H_2O = ZnCl(OH) + HCl + H_2O$$

Anhydrous zinc chloride is prepared by heating zinc in a stream of dry hydrogen chloride or chlorine, and is extremely deliquescent.

Zinc chloride possesses a considerable degree of covalent character: it has a low melting temperature; is soluble in organic solvents, such as alcohols and ketones; and is a poor conductor of electricity in the fused state.

Complexes of zinc

Zinc has less tendency than the transition elements to form complexes. Four-coordinate (tetrahedral) and six-coordinate (octahedral) complexes are known, the former being more common. Solutions of zinc salts are believed to contain the hexaaquazinc(II) ion, $[Zn(H_2O)_6]^{2+}$, and possibly the tetraaquazinc(II) ion, $[Zn(H_2O)_4]^{2+}$. Crystalline salts containing the former are known, e.g. $ZnSO_4 \cdot 7H_2O$. Solutions of zinc salts are acidic because of hydrolysis:

$$[Zn(H_2O)_6]^{2+} + H_2O \rightleftharpoons [Zn(OH)(H_2O)_5]^+ + H_3O^+$$

A hydrated basic carbonate, $ZnCO_3 \cdot 2Zn(OH)_2$ or $Zn_3CO_3(OH)_2$, is obtained if a soluble carbonate is added to an aqueous zinc salt. The normal carbonate, $ZnCO_3$, is obtained if a hydrogencarbonate is used.

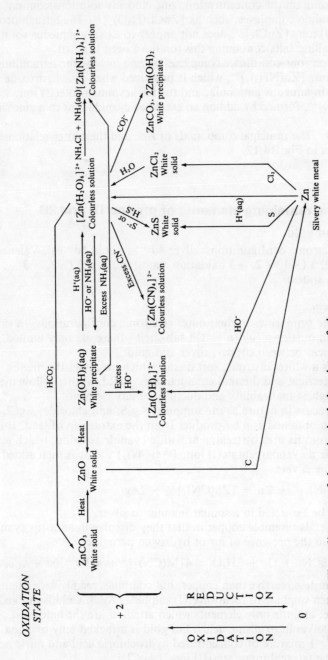

Fig. 14.17 Flow diagram of the principal chemistry of zinc.

Depending on the concentration, zinc chloride solutions contain various halide complexes, such as $[ZnCl_4(H_2O)_2]^{2-}$. The tetrachloro-zincate(II) ion, $[ZnCl_4]^{2-}$, does not appear to exist in aqueous solution, but crystalline salts containing this ion have been isolated.

Common four-coordinate complexes of zinc include the tetraammine-zinc(II) ion, $[Zn(NH_3)_4]^{2+}$, which is produced when zinc hydroxide dissolves in aqueous ammonia, and the tetracyanozincate(II) ion, $[Zn(CN)_4]^{2-}$, formed by adding an excess of cyanide ions to a zinc salt.

Summary The principal compounds of zinc and their inter-relationships are shown in Fig. 14.17.

14.13 The remaining elements of groups 1B and 2B

Silver and gold

Outer electronic configurations: silver $4d^{10} 5s^1$; gold $5d^{10} 6s^1$. Valencies: silver 1, 2, 3 ($+1$, $+2$, $+3$ oxidation states); gold 1, 3 ($+1$, $+3$ oxidation states).

The elements

Despite the similarities in their outer electronic configurations—a single ns electron outside a full $(n - 1)$d sub-shell—there are only limited resemblances between copper, silver and gold.

Silver is a white, lustrous, soft metal, which possesses the highest known electrical and thermal conductivities. Gold, a soft, yellow metal, has the highest malleability and ductility of any element.

Silver occurs in nature as the sulphide, Ag_2S, and chloride, $AgCl$, and is also obtained as a by-product from the extraction of lead. It is isolated from its ores by treatment with a cyanide solution, which gives the soluble dicyanoargentate(I) ion, $[Ag(CN)_2]^-$. Zinc is then added to displace the silver:

$$2[Ag(CN)_2]^- + Zn = [Zn(CN)_4]^{2-} + 2Ag$$

Gold can be extracted in a similar manner to silver.

Both metals resemble copper in that they dissolve in aqueous cyanide solutions in the presence of air or hydrogen peroxide:

$$4M + 8CN^- + O_2 + 2H_2O = 4[M(CN)_2]^- + 4HO^- \quad \text{(M = Ag or Au)}$$

Silver is far less reactive than copper, but combines readily with sulphur or hydrogen sulphide to form silver(I) sulphide, Ag_2S. Gold is markedly unreactive, and the only elements which attack it are the halogens. Silver dissolves in oxidising acids, but gold is attacked only by aqua regia (a 3 : 1 mixture of concentrated hydrochloric acid and nitric acid) to form the tetrachloroaurate(III) ion, $[AuCl_4]^-$.

Compounds of silver

The monovalent state ($+ 1$ oxidation state) $4d^{10}$

The colourless silver(I) ion, Ag^+, is stable in aqueous solution and occurs in many salts of silver, e.g. $AgNO_3$, $AgClO_4$ (both soluble) and Ag_2SO_4 (sparingly soluble). The addition of hydroxide ions to an aqueous solution of a silver(I) salt produces a brown precipitate of silver(I) oxide, Ag_2O, which is insoluble in an excess of the reagent. Aqueous suspensions of the oxide are alkaline due to the formation of hydroxide ions:

$$Ag_2O + H_2O \rightleftharpoons 2Ag^+ + 2HO^- \qquad pK_b \approx 7$$

and they absorb carbon dioxide to give silver carbonate, Ag_2CO_3. At temperatures above 160 °C (433 K) silver oxide decomposes into silver:

$$2Ag_2O = 4Ag + O_2$$

Silver sulphide, Ag_2S, is obtained as a black precipitate by passing hydrogen sulphide through an aqueous solution of a silver salt.

The nitrate, $AgNO_3$, is the most familiar silver(I) salt. It is prepared by dissolving the metal in nitric acid:

$$3Ag + 4HNO_3 = 3AgNO_3 + NO + 2H_2O$$

Like all metal nitrates, it is thermally unstable and decomposes into silver when heated:

$$2AgNO_3 = 2Ag + 2NO_2 + O_2$$

Silver nitrate is used in the laboratory for the qualitative and volumetric estimation of chloride, bromide, iodide and cyanide ions, and for the gravimetric determination of chloride ions.

All the halides of silver(I) are known. The fluoride, AgF, is soluble in water and can be made by dissolving silver oxide in hydrofluoric acid. In contrast, the remaining halides are insoluble in water and can be precipitated from silver nitrate solution by the addition of the appropriate halide ions:

$$Ag^+ + X^- = AgX(s) \qquad (X^- = Cl^-, Br^- \text{ or } I^-)$$

The insoluble silver halides possess an appreciable degree of covalent character, but the fluoride is essentially ionic. The chloride is white, the bromide pale yellow, and the iodide golden yellow. Like all silver(I) compounds, they are *photosensitive*, i.e. they decompose into metallic silver when exposed to light. This property is used in photography, which is based on the photodecomposition of silver bromide or silver chloride on those parts of the film where light has fallen.

Silver chloride is readily soluble in aqueous solutions of ammonia, cyanide ions or thiosulphate ions to form two-coordinate complexes, namely $[Ag(NH_3)_2]^+$, $[Ag(CN)_2]^-$ or $[Ag(S_2O_3)_2]^{3-}$. Silver bromide possesses similar solubility characteristics to the chloride, except that it is less soluble in aqueous ammonia. The iodide is only sparingly soluble in aqueous ammonia, but dissolves readily in cyanide and thiosulphate solutions. The solubility in aqueous ammonia is often used in qualitative tests to distinguish between the three insoluble silver halides. Silver chloride also dissolves in concentrated aqueous solutions of chlorides to produce chloro-complexes, e.g. $[AgCl_2]^-$, $[AgCl_3]^{2-}$ and $[AgCl_4]^{3-}$.

The divalent and trivalent states of silver ($+2$ and $+3$ oxidation states) $4d^9$ and $4d^8$ respectively

The only important compound of divalent silver is the brown fluoride, AgF_2, which is made by the direct combination of the elements. The compound of formula AgO, prepared by the oxidation of a strongly alkaline suspension of Ag_2O with $S_2O_8^{2-}$ ions, is not silver(II) oxide but a mixed oxide, i.e. $Ag^IAg^{III}O_2$. This oxide, and the complex $[AgF_4]^-$, are among the few stable species of silver(III).

Compounds of gold

Because the ionisation enthalpies of gold are high, there is a strong tendency for gold compounds to function as oxidising agents and form elemental gold:

$$Au^+ + e^- = Au \qquad E^{\ominus} = +1.68 \text{ V}$$

The monovalent state ($+1$ oxidation state) $5d^{10}$

Monovalent gold bears a strong resemblance to copper(I). For example, the uncomplexed gold(I) ion, Au^+, disproportionates in solution:

$$3Au^+ \rightleftharpoons Au^{3+} + 2Au \qquad K_c \approx 10^{-10} \text{ mol}^{-2} \text{ dm}^6$$

As a result, the only gold(I) compounds which are stable under aqueous conditions are either insoluble, e.g. the sulphide, Au_2S, and the iodide, AuI, or else complexes, e.g. $[Au(CN)_2]^-$ and $[AuCl_2]^-$.

The trivalent state ($+3$ oxidation state) $5d^8$

This is the most stable state for gold, although many gold(III) compounds are powerful oxidants. The anhydrous chloride and bromide of gold(III) are covalent and exist as dimers, i.e. Au_2Cl_6 and Au_2Br_6 respectively. They are similar in structure to aluminium chloride (§8.5). In aqueous solution most gold(III) compounds tend to form anionic complexes. For example, solutions of gold(III) chloride in water and in concentrated hydrochloric acid contain the ions $[AuCl_3(OH)]^-$ and $[AuCl_4]^-$ respectively. Gold(III) oxide, Au_2O_3, is amphoteric and thermally unstable.

Cadmium and mercury

Outer electronic configurations: cadmium $4d^{10} 5s^2$; mercury $5d^{10} 6s^2$. Valencies: cadmium 2 ($+2$ oxidation state); mercury 1, 2 ($+1$, $+2$ oxidation states).

The elements

Like zinc, these elements have little in common with the elements of group 2A. Cadmium bears some resemblance to zinc, but mercury in many ways is unique.

Cadmium is a soft, white metal. In air it tarnishes slowly to form a protective layer, which defends the metal against prolonged attack. It is used as an electroplated protective coating on steel. Mercury is a bright metallic liquid at room temperature, which is indicative of weak metallic bonding. Because mercury is toxic and has an appreciable vapour pressure at room temperature, it should always be handled in a well ventilated area and stored in closed containers.

Cadmium is obtained during the extraction of zinc (§14.12). Mercury is produced from its only important ore, cinnabar, HgS, by roasting in air at 500 °C (773 K):

$$2HgS + 3O_2 = 2HgO + 2SO_2$$
$$2HgO = 2Hg + O_2$$

Cadmium dissolves in non-oxidising acids to give the colourless hydrated cadmium(II) ion, $Cd^{2+}(aq)$, and hydrogen. Unlike zinc, cadmium is not attacked by alkalis. It forms the dark brown cadmium oxide, CdO, when heated in air, and combines readily with the halogens and sulphur.

Mercury lies below hydrogen in the electrochemical series and therefore does not dissolve in non-oxidising acids. It is, however, attacked by both nitric acid and concentrated sulphuric acid. On heating, mercury combines with several non-metals, including oxygen, the halogens and sulphur. It does not react with alkalis.

Mercury dissolves or combines with many metals to form *amalgams*. Both liquid and solid amalgams are known. Some have a variable composition, while others appear to be compounds or mixtures of compounds of definite composition, e.g. sodium amalgam, $NaHg_2$ and NaHg. Sodium amalgam and zinc amalgam are used as reducing agents in organic chemistry, e.g. for the reduction of alkyl halides, aldehydes and ketones. An amalgam of tin and silver is used for dental fillings. It is pliable when first prepared, but sets to a hard mass after a few hours. Mercury does not volatilise from this amalgam, so there is no danger of poisoning from dental fillings.

Compounds of cadmium

Cadmium hydroxide, $Cd(OH)_2$, is obtained as a white precipitate by adding alkali to an aqueous cadmium salt. Like the oxide, the hydroxide dissolves in acids to form cadmium salts, but it is insoluble in solutions of alkali metal hydroxides. However, both the oxide and the hydroxide dissolve in aqueous ammonia to give the colourless tetraamminecadmium(II) ion, $[Cd(NH_3)_4]^{2+}$, and in cyanide solutions to produce the tetracyanocadmate(II) ion, $[Cd(CN)_4]^{2-}$.

Cadmium fluoride, CdF_2, is ionic and sparingly soluble in water. The remaining halides of cadmium are more covalent in nature than the fluoride (Fig. 14.18). They dissolve in organic solvents, notably alcohols and ketones, and are reasonably soluble in water. Solutions of cadmium halides, like those of zinc halides, contain complexes, e.g. $[CdCl_3(aq)]^-$.

One important physiological difference between compounds of zinc and those of cadmium is that the latter are highly toxic. This can be an environmental problem in the neighbourhood of zinc smelters.

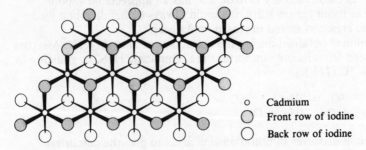

o   Cadmium

◐   Front row of iodine

○   Back row of iodine

Fig. 14.18 The structure of cadmium iodide.

Compounds of mercury

The mercury(I)–mercury(II) equilibrium

The mercury(I) ion is binuclear, i.e. $^+Hg\!\!-\!\!Hg^+$ or Hg_2^{2+}. In the formation of this ion, each mercury atom loses one electron and uses another to form a single covalent bond. In effect, each mercury atom obtains a valency of two, comprising an electrovalency of one and a covalency of one.

The ability of mercury to form the Hg_2^{2+} ion is apparently related to the high electron affinity of the single Hg^+ ion:

$$Hg^+(g) + e^- = Hg(g) \qquad \Delta H = -1\,010 \text{ kJ mol}^{-1}$$

(The enthalpy change for the reverse process, $+1\,010$ kJ mol^{-1}, is the first ionisation enthalpy of mercury.) Because of its strong tendency to gain an electron, the Hg^+ ion forms a single covalent bond with another Hg^+ ion. In this way each Hg^+ ion gains a share in one electron.

Solutions of the mercury(I) ion disproportionate to a small extent:

$$Hg_2^{2+} \rightleftharpoons Hg^{2+} + Hg \qquad K_c = 6 \times 10^{-3}$$

However, reagents which reduce the concentration of mercury(II) ions in solution, by the formation of insoluble or covalent compounds, displace the equilibrium to the right and cause mercury(I) ions to disproportionate. For example, when hydroxide, sulphide or cyanide ions are added to an aqueous mercury(I) salt, mercury(II) species and mercury are formed:

$$Hg_2^{2+} + 2HO^- = HgO(s) + Hg + H_2O$$
$$Hg_2^{2+} + S^{2-} = HgS(s) + Hg$$
$$Hg_2^{2+} + 2CN^- = Hg(CN)_2 + Hg$$

The soluble mercury(II) cyanide is covalent and ionises to a very limited extent.

An excess of mercury favours the mercury(I) ion and reduces mercury(II) compounds to the corresponding mercury(I) species. This effect is also illustrated by the action of nitric acid on mercury. With excess mercury and dilute nitric acid, mercury(I) nitrate is formed:

$$6Hg + 8HNO_3 = 3Hg_2(NO_3)_2 + 2NO + 4H_2O$$

A small amount of mercury, however, dissolves in concentrated nitric acid to produce mercury(II) nitrate:

$$Hg + 4HNO_3 = Hg(NO_3)_2 + 2NO_2 + 2H_2O$$

The monovalent state (+1 oxidation state) $5d^{10}$ $6s^1$

No oxide, hydroxide or sulphide of mercury(I) has yet been isolated. Attempts to prepare these compounds result in the production of either the oxide or sulphide of mercury(II) (see above) and the formation of finely divided mercury as a black precipitate.

Mercury(I) compounds are mostly insoluble in water, except for the nitrate, $Hg_2(NO_3)_2 \cdot 2H_2O$. Crystals of this compound contain the complex ion $[H_2O\text{---}Hg\text{---}Hg\text{---}OH_2]^{2+}$, which hydrolyses in water to give an acidic solution.

The white, insoluble mercury(I) chloride, Hg_2Cl_2, is prepared by heating mercury(II) chloride with mercury, or by adding chloride ions to a mercury(I) nitrate solution:

$$HgCl_2 + Hg = Hg_2Cl_2$$
$$Hg_2^{2+}(aq) + 2Cl^- = Hg_2Cl_2(s)$$

Mercury(I) sulphate, Hg_2SO_4, which is used in the standard Weston cadmium cell, is obtained by warming concentrated sulphuric acid with an excess of mercury:

$$2Hg + 2H_2SO_4 = Hg_2SO_4 + SO_2 + 2H_2O$$

Very few complexes of mercury(I) are known, apart from the hydrated mercury(I) ion, $[Hg_2(H_2O)_2]^{2+}$.

The divalent state (+2 oxidation state) $5d^{10}$

Mercury(II) oxide, HgO, is obtained as a red powder by the thermal decomposition of mercury(II) nitrate or by direct combination of the elements at 350 °C (623 K). It is also produced, as a yellow precipitate, by adding hydroxide ions to a mercury(II) salt. The two colours are due to differences in particle size, and on heating the yellow form turns red. Mercury(II) oxide is basic, and is used as a mild oxidant, e.g. for the conversion of halogens to hypohalous acids (§12.6). Above 350 °C (623 K), it decomposes into mercury and oxygen.

Mercury(II) sulphide, HgS, which occurs naturally as the red mineral, cinnabar, can be obtained in the laboratory as a black precipitate by passing hydrogen sulphide through an aqueous solution of a mercury(II) salt. The black form turns red when heated.

The commonest halide of mercury(II) is the chloride, $HgCl_2$, which is prepared either by direct combination of the elements or by dissolving mercury(II) oxide in hydrochloric acid. Mercury(II) chloride is covalent, and dissolves in organic solvents, such as ethanol. Because of slight hydrolysis, aqueous solutions of mercury(II) chloride are weakly acidic:

$$HgCl_2 + H_2O \rightleftharpoons HgCl(OH) + HCl$$

When solutions of mercury(II) chloride are reduced, e.g. with tin(II) chloride, a white precipitate of mercury(I) chloride is obtained initially, followed by a black precipitate of mercury:

$$2HgCl_2 + SnCl_2 = Hg_2Cl_2 + SnCl_4$$
$$Hg_2Cl_2 + SnCl_2 = 2Hg + SnCl_4$$

Addition of potassium iodide to an aqueous mercury(II) salt gives the iodide, HgI_2, as a yellow precipitate, which rapidly changes into a more stable red form of the same compound.

Mercury(II) salts of oxoacids, notably the nitrate and the sulphate, are essentially ionic. They are acidic in solution because of hydrolysis.

Many complexes of mercury(II) are known. Coordination numbers of two (linear) and four (tetrahedral) are common. In the presence of ammonium chloride, aqueous ammonia reacts with aqueous mercury(II) chloride to form a white precipitate of the complex salt $[Hg(NH_3)_2]Cl_2$, which contains the diamminemercury(II) ion. In the absence of ammonium chloride, the product is a white precipitate of the amide, $HgClNH_2$. Four-coordinate complexes of mercury include the tetra-cyanomercurate(II) ion, $[Hg(CN)_4]^{2-}$, and the tetraiodomercurate(II) ion, $[HgI_4]^{2-}$. The latter is unusual in being more stable than the corresponding chloro-complex. An alkaline solution of potassium tetraiodomercurate(II), $K_2[HgI_4]$, known as *Nessler's reagent*, is used for detecting traces of ammonia in the analysis of water. A yellow or brown colour is produced, depending on the concentration of ammonia.

Index

370